HEAL.. .. .

~ in a ~

HOSPITAL

Scientific evidence that
spiritual healing improves health

SANDY EDWARDS

Cover design
Grateful thanks to Max W Edwards

Dedication

To Roy, Max and Ben

The mention of specific organisations, authorities or individuals does not imply that they endorse this book.

Any person whose full name is given in this book is a real person. Either they have given written permission to do so or their statement or story is already in the public domain and the source is referenced.

Any person referred to only by their first name is a real person, but their name has been changed to protect their identity. In some cases, additional details have been changed to add further anonymity.

Contents

Figures

Acknowledgements

One person cleared the way for me to be a volunteer healer at an NHS hospital. Better still, he allowed me to work in his clinic, which meant that he became personally aware of how healing affected his patients. He also agreed for me to conduct audits so that the healing effects that patients reported could be documented. When I alerted him to the opportunity of gaining research funding from the National Lottery, he brought together the necessary individuals and organisations to make a successful application. Dr Sukhdev Singh, Senior Consultant at Good Hope Hospital and Senior Lecturer at the University of Birmingham Medical School, had the courage, drive and commitment to make all of this happen. Without his willingness to assess the value of healing for his patients, the research programme would not have happened, and this book could not have been written. I am indebted to Dr Singh for his kind and generous support, and for the joy it has brought me to work at his clinic. When I began writing, he gave me valuable advice but he did not read the manuscript. I hope he approves of the book!

My sincere thanks go to all of the healers and individuals who have assisted in my endeavours to bring healing to the public. I would love to acknowledge everyone by name, but one person asked not to be mentioned. Consequently, I have referred only to those people whose involvement is already in the public domain. In particular, I thank David Daniels for his tremendous commitment to our voluntary healing group in Walsall. Despite a full-time profession and extended family commitments, he has kept our dedicated team together for many years. He was also one of the main healers on the research trial.

For help with my two hospital audits, thanks go to Jan Lacy for producing the graphs, and to Marion Willberry for typing up hundreds of patient comments.

I was thrilled and touched when several long-time friends with professional skills in English volunteered to check my manuscript. Sian Davies read through the first draft, and could be objective, since she had no affinity to healing. But I then tinkered with the text and added more while waiting for the research paper to be published. As explained in the book, the latter had to happen before I could go to print. Glynis Alder worked on the second draft—and in record time, because it seemed that the research paper was on the verge of being published. But more months passed, so I continued to add and amend. Then Patricia O'Grady read a proof copy and offered some beneficial ideas. Thank you, my friends, and my apologies for not applying every suggested amendment. Publication of the research paper took longer than imagined, giving me time to add more text, so any errors are mine.

I was a complete stranger to the two people I approached to read my first draft—Dr Michael Dixon and the Duchess of Rutland. I felt honoured when they each readily emailed their agreement, and ecstatic when they provided glowing testimonials. Thank you, both.

My husband has never attempted to discourage me from healing or from embarking on healing-related projects. I am grateful for his continued support during the production of this book.

A note from the author

The assertion that spiritual healing is beneficial may seem unbelievable. You may be eager to read the evidence or you may be approaching these pages with acute cynicism. It is healthy to be sceptical but there may be more to gain by being open-minded while exploring the possibility.

I hope the evidence and testimonials offered will encourage you to incorporate healing sessions within your normal healthcare regime. Healing is not intended as a substitute for any treatment that has been prescribed by a doctor, and medical help should always be sought for a medical problem.

The information also aims to convey to medical professionals how healing supports conventional care; first and foremost in respect of the benefits to patients, but also regarding cost savings.

You do not need to be ill or distressed to benefit from healing. It can be used to maximise and maintain good health and a positive frame of mind.

By reading this book, I hope you will consider the idea that healing sessions could improve your life. I hope that you will feel inspired to put healing to the test and share your findings with others.

Foreword

by Dr Michael Dixon LVO, OBE, FRCGP, FRCC

Chair of Council, College of Medicine
Chair of NHS Alliance
Visiting Professor, University College, London
Visiting Professor, Westminster University, London
Honorary Senior Fellow in Public Policy, Health Services
     Management Centre, University of Birmingham
Honorary Senior Lecturer, Peninsula Medical School

Sandy Edwards' story is one of dogged perseverance on behalf of her patients. Her pioneering work is an example to us all. Having established a hospital healing clinic against all the odds, she then began researching its results, ending with a pragmatic controlled trial of healing, which is about as definitive as it gets. The results of her most recent research are spectacular, though not necessarily surprising for those who have either witnessed or received healing themselves.

It would be as wrong to overestimate the powers of healing as it would be to underestimate them. Some conventional doctors find the whole concept of healing bizarre and scientifically implausible, one example being that of a medical registrar mentioned in the book. Others will dismiss any beneficial effects as placebo. Yet the obvious truth from her research is that healing can provide significant benefit to a substantial number of patients, and she has shown this at a remarkable level of statistical significance.

As stated, the research is pragmatic, and pragmatism would suggest that patients and clinicians should take this work seriously, and especially so if future research also supports its cost-effectiveness.

While Sandy Edwards has taken science just about as far as it can go, her quest is underlaid by deep humanity and compassion. That, after all, is what 'healing' is all about. Yet, ironically, this is the very bit that we normally try to exclude in scientific studies when testing the effectiveness of different tablets and procedures.

Central to her story is the relationship between her and Dr Sukhdev Singh. It reminds me very much of my own relationship with our healer, who first came to my GP surgery well over 20 years ago. My own emotions moved from sceptical fascination to admiration to a deep new learning about patients and my own role as a doctor in healing. Sandy Edwards must be a rather special person to have gained support for healing and for ongoing research in an NHS hospital, against the medical grain and in the way that she did. If my own experience of the work of healers is anything to go by, then I have no doubt that she also healed a number of staff on the way as well.

This is a very impressive book with many important things to tell anyone with open eyes. Some will dismiss the concept of healing and these results on principle. That is not rational. Nor is it rational simply to dismiss everything that cannot be explained. Conversely, Sandy Edwards employs both reason and emotion by applying scientific methodology to a method of healing that is all about feelings and the therapeutic relationship, and which challenges a narrow view of biomedicine. The conclusion of her work is clear. Biomedicine must widen its remit to understand, not reject, the mysteries of healing with the same open-mindedness shown by staff in the hospital where Sandy Edwards has done her work. This is a story that demonstrates the importance of relationships, empathy, commitment and courage. These are the qualities of a great healer, and Sandy Edwards quite clearly has all these in abundance.

Hippocrates (460–370 BC)

the 'father' of modern medicine

'It is believed by experienced doctors that the heat which oozes out of the hand, on being applied to the sick, is highly salutary. It has often appeared while I have been soothing my patients, as if there was a singular property in my hands to pull and draw away from the affected parts, aches and diverse impurities, by laying my hand upon the place and extending my fingers toward it. Thus it is known to some of the learned that health may be implanted in the sick by certain gestures and by contact.' (1)*

*A number in brackets refers to the source of the information, the list of which begins on page 304. Almost all of the citations can be accessed online.

A Healing Expedition

Spiritual   from the Latin 'spiritus', means 'breath of life'

Healing   means 'making well'

Healing is a natural phenomenon. After all these years, it continues to amaze me that moving my hands around someone could possibly make a difference to their health and wellbeing. But there it is. It has been proved to me time and again. The chapters that follow are peppered with patient responses and, despite there being so many, they represent only a fraction of the number of people I have seen. Every other healer will have similar stories to tell and there are many thousands of healers in the UK and around the world, quietly going about their healing work.

If your mind is already teeming with questions about healing, then skip to page 271 for a moment where you will find all the basics. Any other query is bound to be addressed between here and the back cover.

There is nothing out of the ordinary about me. If I can learn to give healing then anyone can, if they are sincere and determined. With me being more at home with logic and order, the strange world of healing opened up a new vista of learning and experiences, leading me to a fresh and wholesome perspective. Discovering healing and developing the skill has been a voyage of awe and wonder that is available to anyone who is prepared to embark.

Every healer I have known talks about sensing energies and seeing colours. They are often surprised to learn that I hardly ever experienced anything extrasensory until many years after I had trained.

1

Healing in a Hospital

Healing has nothing to do with being psychic or being a medium. Though I am not interested in developing either of these skills, I do believe that they are valuable gifts when used wisely. But, even if I were a psychic or a medium, the training I received directed against utilising these senses while giving healing. Our remit is purely and simply to deliver healing. Consequently, when patients eagerly ask if I picked up any information about them, I invariably have to disappoint. Even if someone were psychic in any way, it would be against the rules of a reputable healing organisation for a healer to glean information about a person without their knowledge. It would be like going through someone's handbag without their permission.

People tend to assume that healers must be particularly kindly and goody-two-shoe types, but this is not necessarily so. However, thanks to the principles that underpin healer training, I became aware of the importance of continually working on myself, dissolving fears and limitations, forgiving others and transforming the negative thoughts and emotions that lead to stress and worry. Anyone who has taken this challenge to heart will know that it is truly testing and soul-searching stuff. I had a tremendous amount of work to do on myself and I have achieved a great deal, but it remains a lifelong work in progress. Even now, I can be enraged by the diabolical things that people do, and irritated by irksome things that people say. I often quip that I would be a perfect person if nobody upset me! But even that would not be true, of course. Ask anyone I know and they will confirm that I irk as much as anybody else. But rather than dwell upon where people have room for improvement, the point is that character flaws must be no barrier to becoming effective healers. If we waited until we were perfect or 'good enough', nobody would ever learn to give healing.

If there were anything unusual to mention about me, it would be that I was determined to become a healer despite having no sign of a natural ability. So what made me leap into something for which I had no apparent talent?

It was the outcome of my quest to combat psoriasis, a flaky skin condition that was affecting my scalp, causing itching and embarrassment. Since teens, this had been a constant and tiresome companion. There is no cure for psoriasis, and steroid cream is the only medical method of gaining temporary relief. Not willing to use steroids, I looked to complementary remedies but achieved no success. Psychology books pointed to deep emotional issues, and I attempted various methods of digging up the offending roots. I felt certain that I was on the right track and made some progress, but it was not enough.

To digress for a moment, hypnosis brought a small improvement for the psoriasis, but a major breakthrough for smoking. Exactly as he said, I have not wanted a puff of a cigarette since that one session. If a hypnotist tells you that you need a course of sessions, find someone else.

During those explorations, I was surprised to be advised by a medium that I should take up healer training. The act of giving healing, she said, would balance the energies within me that were causing the psoriasis. At the same time, she recommended the National Federation of Spiritual Healers (NFSH), later to become known as The Healing Trust. I had not heard of the organisation before but I felt inspired to follow it up. My first call was to one of the people with whom I had been meditating every week. To my surprise, she had recently started training with the NFSH.

For me to resolve to be a healer was like someone who had never seen a cooker deciding to be a chef. The prospect of a salaried career in catering might warrant such a choice, but I expected healing to be in my spare time and entirely unpaid. Also, cooking is within everyone's experience and easily justifiable, whereas healing would be awkward to explain to curious family and friends. Despite the negatives, I felt a thrill at the prospect of training to heal, and I immediately made the call to book a place. The most local trainer ran beginner courses a few times a year and, luckily, one was about to commence.

With no sensitivity to the energies that were being talked about on the course, training to be a healer was like being led down a pitch black alley without being able to touch the sides. Everyone else seemed to revel in different sensations that confirmed the validity of what was being taught. Conversely, I seemed impervious to such phenomena and blindly followed instructions. I simply placed my hands in this place or that, precisely as shown, and trusted the process. Although it seemed that I must be way behind the other students, my lack of sensitivity seemed to make no difference to the actual effects. Patients gave as much positive feedback to me as they did to the others. It became evident to me that one could become an effective healer with no prior natural talent and without sensing the energies involved. I supposed that the key to effectiveness must be the amount of passion behind the intent to heal because I had an abundance of that.

My lack of sensitivity to energies could be due to being what is termed 'left-brained'. When the left hemisphere of the brain is dominant, the person is said to be analytical, objective and logical, which I can identify with. 'Right-brained' people, on the other hand, are said to be intuitive, thoughtful and subjective, and these softer qualities certainly seem abundant among the countless healers I know. But, again, my being out of step with most other healers made no difference to the positive outcomes for patients.

Incidentally, a few physical phenomena did eventually develop—described later—but it is still a pleasant surprise if I experience anything extrasensory.

During the training years, a consistent flow of positive feedback from recipients compelled me to believe that the training was effective and that healing works. It was astonishing and exciting to find that, simply by my following the method taught, patients reported feeling better. Occasionally, people told me that they had felt physical movements happening deep within the afflicted part of the body, and that it now felt better. More often, people said that their pain had simply disappeared. Others reported that they had experienced a discomfort or an emotion rise up during the session that had then quickly melted away. Tense patients would leave relaxed and the downcast uplifted.

I would practise my fledgling skills on willing friends and relatives. A colleague at work had been plagued with gout for weeks, and it was getting steadily worse. Walking was excruciatingly painful, but he continued to work full-time. His miserable expression showed that he was unable to find any relief for the agony, and it was getting him down. Although a total sceptic about healing, he was now desperate and prepared to try anything. That Friday lunchtime I gave him a healing session in the office. It was not the ideal setting in which to unwind, but we had no choice.

A Healing Expedition

He was impressed that he was able to relax deeply, despite having so much on his mind. The experience lifted his mood, but the gout problem remained as painful as ever. I suggested that we try weekly sessions and, having enjoyed it, he agreed. But on the Monday morning he strode into work all smiles. With amazement all over his face, he described getting out of bed on the Saturday morning and reaching the bedroom door before realising that his foot was back to normal. And it remained so.

Another surprising success for healing concerned my young son. When flying, he invariably had difficulty getting his ears to pop to counteract the changing air pressure. To minimise the pain, we would travel with menthol crystals so that he could sniff the vapour to open the ear canals. Landing was worse than any other part of the flight, and the prospect of what was to come would spoil any journey for him. During an especially painful descent, I suddenly thought to try healing. There was no time to do the usual whole body circuit so I simply cupped his ears. The pain disappeared within a minute and, for the first time, he was able to happily watch what was happening outside. He never had the problem again.

In the very early training days of discovery and wonder, I would eagerly ask each patient what they had felt or experienced during the session and then listen with incredulity to their account. However, I was soon gently corrected and advised that, as a healer, our only remit is to deliver healing. The extent of any enquiry afterwards should be limited to 'How did that feel?' thereby giving the patient the opportunity to share their experience if they wish to, without feeling pressured.

The range of regular and positive feedback convinced me beyond doubt that healing was making a wonderful difference to people's lives. Further, if I could become an effective healer without the slightest prior ability, and without sensing energies, then surely anyone could. Some healing organisations teach that the ability to heal is a natural part of being human—that everyone is a healer, whether they believe it or not. I must have had the capacity all along; it just needed sparking somehow.

After seeing and experiencing how easily people can be helped by healing, I was passionate about letting the world know that it existed. Surely everyone would want to have a slice of this extraordinary pie? But, no. Scepticism stops most people from giving it a chance, and there are many other reasons, too, explained later. A few people decline healing because they think it is against their religion, which I find perplexing. Bear with me for a few paragraphs while I endeavour to explain why healing must surely be acceptable to the majority of the world's worshippers.

Healing was illegal in the UK until the early 1950s because, historically, the Christian religion stamped out and demonised any spiritual practices that omitted its clergy, which included healing. British law continues to reflect wholesome Christian principles, but the Church's power has diminished in recent decades, partly due to the progress of science, thereby leading to the spiritual liberty that we enjoy today.

Healing was a fundamental part of early Christianity, and remained so for hundreds of years. But when it became an organised religion, many beliefs and practices were modified or rejected. Paradoxically, the resultant Church eschewed healing, even though the most famous healer of all time has to be Jesus. He, of course, was a Jew and is described both in the Bible (John 1:32) and in the Koran (4:171) as being filled with the Spirit of God (2). Muslims, Sikhs, Hindus and some Buddhist sects recognise Jesus as an exceptional prophet so his teachings must be accepted by all those believers.

Any great leader leads by example and, according to scripture, healing was a major aspect of his ministry. In addition to his 12 disciples, the Bible says that Jesus empowered 70 others to give healing (Luke 10) and sent them in pairs to at least 41 different destinations. They were to speak with and heal people of all races and creeds. For their work to continue, they must have been empowered to pass this gift on to others, otherwise their mission would have disintegrated when they died.

To be sent to 41 destinations in an area that was swarming with traders of all nationalities and faiths, the intention must surely have been to spread healing across the world, cascading through the generations to the present day. Indeed, many cultures throughout history are known to have handed down healing knowledge since ancient times (3).

A Healing Expedition

Healing can therefore be celebrated as a common link between religions and nations, as well as a spiritual connection between individuals whether they have a belief system or not. Healers, and people who come for healing, can be from any religion or none. I know healers who are Catholics or other Christian denominations, Jews, Pagans, Hindus, Sikhs and Buddhists—and there are bound to be other religious sects represented within the world's healing fraternity.

Even if healers do not belong to a particular faith, they generally do believe in a higher power. But their patients do not need to believe in anything at all. I have seen confirmed sceptics benefit from healing, despite their stonewall attitude. Once again, this highlights the inclusiveness of healing, providing a universal connection between all people regardless of what they believe.

Regarding the possibility of a higher power, one of the world's leading scientists was prompted by a patient to consider the notion. Dr Francis Collins, head of the world-renowned Human Genome Project, explains in his book *The Language of God* how the sciences convinced him to abandon his atheist beliefs (4).

Whether giving healing or receiving it, both individuals involved often experience a glimmer of what some religions refer to as heaven or nirvana. This state of bliss is possible for anyone, religious or not, and brings about 'biological homeostasis'—the body's natural state of balance and self-repair (5).

Sometimes, stressed people with no religious faith and with no belief in healing have been astounded to experience a profound sense of elation during their first healing session and have left feeling relaxed, buoyant and invigorated. More normally, people gain confidence with each successive healing session and notice gradual improvements over a series of appointments.

Healer training with a reputable organisation is usually spread over a couple of years to ensure that enough supervision and experience is gained before qualifying. The nearest training and support group to me was a handful of motorway junctions away, and I went along every two weeks. Basic training is available to anyone, and this initial course provides enough information and practice for attendees to give healing to willing friends. To go any further, membership of The Healing Trust is necessary, and this calls for character references and qualified healers to provide mentorship during the remaining training period. At the end of the programme, patient testimonials and mentor references form part of the final panel assessment.

At the end of my two years, on the way home from qualifying, the idea struck me to apply for an 'Awards for All' National Lottery grant to set up a voluntary healing centre near my home. Voluntary healing centres are dotted all around the country, but they need to be local enough for people to access them easily. The more, the better, I thought. My husband had previously gained funding for a youth sports project so I felt mildly confident that it was possible.

A committee, a constitution and a bank account were needed to be able to make the application. I placed a free advert in the healing charity's regional newsletter asking for collaborators, then set about the paperwork. News of our successful bid arrived on my birthday, adding an extra sparkle to my celebrations.

The first healer who had agreed to team up was a hairdresser. She could only offer help on her day off, which meant that our sessions would be on Monday mornings. With that decision easily made, the next item on the list was to find patients so I looked for a way to get free advertising. The mayor agreed to pose with us in his parlour, and I sent the photograph to the local newspaper along with information about our group. The printed article must have struck a chord with readers because 27 people booked a session for our opening date in November 2000. Many others kept the cutting and—even years later—people were still making appointments on account of that first coverage.

Our team of eight dedicated healers welcomed patients month after month. Volunteers do not grow on trees, and they have a host of other things that they could be doing with their precious time, but these people made Monday mornings their priority. Some travelled a distance to support our group's infancy, and continued to do so until we were established. Together, we created a friendly and fun atmosphere that our visitors enjoyed being a part of. One new patient stopped mid-stride as he came through the doors, saying that he could feel the vibes already.

Donations covered the cost of our rent, but we needed additional funds to attract newcomers. If we had informative leaflets

A Healing Expedition

displayed in public places, we might reach more people. I applied for another grant and, again, was successful. Subsequent awards supplied us with exhibition equipment, a website, a self-help CD and a DVD that describes and demonstrates healing. Each grant catapulted me into yet another self-inflicted, time-consuming project of which I had no previous experience. But they helped to let more people know that healing existed and that our volunteers were ready to be of service.

The self-help CD is called 'Sleep Easy & Be Well'. It talks the listener into a deeply relaxed state and includes self-healing techniques. Since its production in 2008, regular feedback has confirmed that it achieves what it says on the label. More details appear on pages 91 and 295.

A hospital in Ohio uses a similar recording with great success. Cleveland Clinic is consistently ranked as one of the best hospitals in the USA with patients flying in from all around the world. About 15 years ago, the clinic implemented a seven-year experiment to see if patients benefited from listening to a guided meditation before, during and after surgery. After just two years, the evidence was so convincing that they halted the trial and put the CD into regular service. Their findings agreed with more than 200 previous studies that guided imagery can help people in the following ways (6):

1. Significant reduction of stress and anxiety before and after surgical and medical procedures.

2. Dramatic decrease in pain and less need for pain medication.

3. Reduction of side effects and complications resulting from medical procedures.

4. Faster recovery and shorter hospital stays.

5. Enhanced sleep.

6. Strengthening of the immune system and enhanced ability to heal.

7. Increase of self-confidence and self-control.

Healing in a Hospital

Research shows that patients have been helped by guided imagery whether they are undergoing surgery, chemotherapy, dialysis, in vitro fertilisation and other medical procedures. Given the strength of the evidence over so many years, it would seem obvious to implement this low-cost and effective service throughout the National Health Service (NHS) in the UK. It would be a relatively simple matter to set up and, once installed, the reduced need for medication and ongoing care would more than compensate the NHS coffers. More importantly, patients would benefit from a more positive hospital experience.

Many of the beneficial effects listed above have been commented on by patients who have used the Sleep Easy & Be Well CD and also by patients who have received healing sessions.

No other healing centre had been set up by a Lottery grant before, so I felt duty-bound to make this new knowledge available to other volunteer healers around the country. To encourage people to do the same in their own area, I sent a series of articles to The Healing Trust's national magazine. This is the beauty of belonging to a national organisation—the ideas of its members can be gathered together and benefit everyone.

If those articles in the magazine inspired just one healer to set up a new group, it will have made a difference to many people's lives. At our own healing centre, patients regularly told us about the improvements they noticed. Some wrote a note in our Comments Book, and the following typical examples give a flavour of what they had to say:

1. Better than fantastic! Wild horses will not keep me away.

2. I felt totally rejuvenated, as if I'd slept for a week.

3. I am certainly feeling much better after only a few weeks. I can't wait to see what the future holds.

4. This has helped me to cope with difficult news. Wonderful healing.

5. I always feel low until I get here. After a healing session I feel on top of the world.

6. Healing has made me think and feel positively again. I feel relaxed, happy and ready to start taking control of my life again.

7. Noticeable differences on a wide range of levels.

8. Total peace. What a gift.

9. I have felt much better since last week's session. My shoulder has improved and also my eczema. I feel very positive and relaxed and hope that I continue to feel better each week.

10. A great experience that is relaxing and energising. Next day I feel really great. This is the best experience I ever had.

11. Wonderful healing. Very relaxing. My mum came recently with a nasty strain which is completely resolved now due to healing. She is very happy!

12. What a lovely healing. Relaxing and peaceful. Regular healing has helped me to move on with treatment for obsessive compulsive disorder (OCD) and this has become less of a problem for me over the last 12 months. I feel that healing has played a large part in this improvement. I am now 80/20 in control of my life instead of 20/80 before. What a lovely gift, received with thanks.

13. The doctor said 'no hope' for my painful neck and shoulder and warned that it would get worse. After four healing sessions it has completely healed.

One of the first patients to arrive at our doors was Chris, who had been off work for three years. He had been prevented from taking up a new teaching post by a sudden illness, followed by a succession of different maladies. After a total of 12 healing sessions, this is what he had to say about it:

Healing in a Hospital

'When bad health prevented me from taking up a new job, I felt frustrated yet strongly relieved. A series of illnesses followed, each one seemingly unconnected with the last. It was difficult for my GP to diagnose as the symptoms kept changing.

'I knew something was wrong but felt that conventional medicine was not an effective response. It was around this time that I saw an advertisement in the local press for spiritual healing. I rang the number and spoke to Sandy, who arranged my first appointment.

'I was unsure as to what to expect. I like to think I have an open mind, but I was concerned that it had something to do with the Spiritualist Church and clairvoyance. I needn't have worried; my first session was very upbeat and uncomplicated. The healers were all very friendly and I found the experience pleasant whilst not actually being aware of any unusual sensations.

'Sandy explained that one-off recoveries are rare and that the healing process was generally cumulative. It wasn't until three or four sessions later that I could actually feel the healing process taking place.

'After treatment I always felt lighter and more relaxed, tired later in the day and occasionally emotional. I came to realise that healing is not always comfortable; after all, a high temperature is simply a sign of the body healing itself.

'At times, I was aware of specific improvements, while at others I wondered if I was expecting too much. Like watching your hair to see how quickly it is growing, I was only aware of what a difference the healing had made when I looked back after six months of treatment [12 sessions] and realised that I was, in many ways, a different person. I was physically and mentally stronger, recurrent aches and pains had disappeared, I was sleeping better and, most importantly, feeling optimistic about the future.

A Healing Expedition

'I look upon the healing I have received as a readjustment. I now realise that I was out of balance; I am learning to realign and recover my old sparkle.'

After a total of around four hours' treatment, his life was back on track and he was planning to return to work. In comparison to the three years that he had suffered before coming for healing, this was a very small investment of time to achieve such a change. When Chris came to us, our group met every fortnight so his return to health was achieved within six months. Had we been open every week—as we are now—perhaps he would have been back on his feet in half the time.

If there had been, say, a £6 donation for each of Chris's visits, the total financial outlay would have been £72. This is negligible compared to the cost incurred by the NHS for his repeated visits to the doctor and for prescriptions over the three-year period. Add to that the expense of sick pay and social security payments for those three years. If the NHS had referred him to our healing centre in the initial stages, or had provided a healer at his doctor's surgery, it might have been a different story. Chris could have recovered and returned to work within a few months of becoming ill. With a swift return to work, the national coffers would have made massive savings.

Had Chris not decided to seek healing, he might still be ill now and in a worse condition. The total cost to the taxpayer in healthcare and benefit payments could have been immense. And Chris is only one of many examples.

But healing is about the human story and improving lives. Chris's story highlights the holistic nature of healing in that it helped him physically, mentally and emotionally. The treatments he received from the doctor will have helped some of the symptoms but will not have addressed the cause. Chris enjoyed the healing sessions and positively looked forward to the next one. His recovery was slow and cumulative, which is perfectly normal. Other people report dramatic improvements in fewer sessions. You will find in later chapters that some need only one.

Gwen was another of our first patients. She had suffered from thyroid problems for five years by the time she came to us. Her blood pressure and blood sugar were also problematic and had to be checked every four months. After some regular healing sessions, her thyroid became stable, her blood pressure resumed an acceptable level and her sugar levels improved. Being overweight, she was delighted to find that she had also lost a stone without really trying, and she had this to say:

'Healing has helped with back problems, too, which I had a lot of pain with, and had been housebound for 18 months. It is a lot better now. Healing helps me relax and I know that I've benefited in all kinds of ways, not just medically.'

Like Chris and Gwen, most people who have experienced healing have done so because they actively looked for it, in the hope that it might help them. But others have had healing jumped on them, such as in the following case, where the recipient had no intention of looking for healing and thought it was nonsense.

Steve had a harrowing accident at work with a circular saw. He cut off the ends of his own fingers and they could not be saved. The severed ends on his left hand were conspicuously disfigured and excruciatingly painful. Nine months after being discharged from hospital, his situation was no better, and it was at around this time that I rang his wife for something. Steve answered the telephone so I naturally asked how his hand was and, as expected, he gave a glum reply. I knew from his wife how disparaging he was about healing but, nevertheless, I invited him to try a session. Not for a moment did I think that he would accept— but he did. Perhaps I caught him at a particularly weak moment but I grasped the opportunity and gave him a date and time to come over, before he could change his mind. Normally, I would insist that people go to our healing centre but I made an exception for Steve. It was obvious that he would not countenance having healing in public. Steve's wife and I were agog that he had agreed to a session. Hitherto, his wife had been having healing in secret with me because, had he found out, he would have ridiculed her relentlessly until she stopped coming.

Steve arrived at our house at the appointed time, nursing his hand and looking at the floor in embarrassment. Shaking his head, he apologised that he did not believe in healing one iota and that it was a mistake that he had come. He said that it was a waste of my time and his. Undeterred by his attitude, I cheerily whisked him through the front door and into our conservatory. There, he dutifully sat on a wooden dining chair, with soft music in the background. Twenty minutes later he felt relaxed, and was bewildered that his hand was entirely pain free. He admitted that he had enjoyed the session but was mystified. I suggested that he come again the next week and see what else might happen.

When he arrived for his second appointment, his eyes were like saucers while he told me that there had been absolutely no pain in his hand since we last met. He pointed out, though, that there was now a constant tingling in the ends of his fingers, which he found distracting. Could I get rid of it, he enquired. I explained that I do not ask for a particular outcome; I simply give healing and ask that it be for the highest good of all concerned. At the end of the session, Steve was bemused to find that the tingling had indeed disappeared.

At the next session, he told me that the annoying tingling had not returned but that he now had no sensation at all in the ends of his fingers. With them being totally numb, he did not know what was happening to his fingers unless he looked at them. I conducted the session as normal, again without the intention of a required result.

A week later, he was amazed to report that normal feeling had returned and, with wonderment in his eyes, he demonstrated how he could now pick up a pencil with the ends of his truncated fingers in the usual manner. This had been impossible before, due to the pain.

Steve so enjoyed the deep relaxation of a healing session that he continued coming. Over the weeks, he noticed how much more he was enjoying his life, and each week brought news of another increment. Most surprisingly to both of us, the mushroom-shaped finger ends each became tapered, similar to fingertips, and therefore no longer so noticeably different. Also, although they had been rigid and unbending since the accident, all but one finger had now regained full flexibility and grip. One evening, as Steve was leaving our house, he mentally resigned himself to the fact that he would simply have to live with this last finger remaining in its solid state. But before he reached the end of our drive, it suddenly clicked and it instantly worked normally from then on.

Healing in a Hospital

It was only when a work colleague pointed out how nimbly Steve was handling a tiny nut with his injured hand that he realised just how much progress had been made over the course of treatment.

Some while later, he revealed to me that he used to have a morning ritual after the accident. Every day he would wake up and immediately remember the horror of the accident. In the vain hope that it was a nightmare, he would look at his hand and then feel downhearted at the sight of it. He would swear inwardly and a cloud of despondency would hang over him for the rest of the day. Since having the healing sessions, though, he found that he hardly gave the injury a thought.

Steve told me that he was so full of vim after each healing session that he felt as though he could cartwheel his way back to the car. He also had the revelation that, without having had the accident, he would never have discovered healing and gained all the benefits that it had brought. Before the accident, his life had seemed a daily drudge but now he walked with a spring in his step and was laughing more. Although it was an appalling accident, he felt that it had served an important purpose because, as a result, he was now enjoying life. In stark contrast to his previous disparaging attitude towards healing, Steve now confidently recommends healing to anyone and shrugs off ridicule because he knows that he was once one of those people.

Steve's story reiterates that healing benefits the whole person, not just one aspect. It also shows that people can be helped even if they are totally convinced that healing cannot possibly make a difference. Moreover, his testimony highlights that healing delivered far more than he initially wanted. At the outset, his only concern was to be rid of incessant pain. The by-products meant that his life was now a happier experience than it had been, even before the accident.

Having witnessed Steve's instant recovery from pain and the eventual return of normal use of his hand, I felt that healing could be valuable to others who have lost limbs. I sent his story to a number of organisations and magazines that help amputees, including those that support our injured military personnel. Perhaps the recipients felt that it was too unbelievable, because I had no reply from any of them.

A Healing Expedition

It is rare for me to give the same person a series of regular healing sessions and to also have a leisurely chat about it afterwards. With Steve, I had the opportunity to realise that he had a different experience on every occasion. There was certainly no variation in what I did as I follow the same routine, and Steve sat in the same place every time. One would presume that the healing energy must be constant and, if so, it would seem that any difference could only be caused by something within him or something within me. My training stressed the importance of healers needing to be in good shape to be a clear channel for healing, and I strive to be so. Maybe the difference was within him, in which case a suggestion that I make later may provide part of the answer. Whatever the mystery is that causes variance, Steve marvelled at the range of sensations he experienced and he definitely benefited from every session.

There was another patient I met enough times to discover how far-reaching the effects of healing can be. She was a young mother, whom I shall call Liz. Her baby had a distressing complaint for which there was no cure or effective relief. As she was unable to reach the healing centre, I offered to visit them at home and give healing to both mother and child. During our chats, it came to light that Liz's father had raised her alone and had been devoted to her. But circumstances changed and she had not seen him for several years. After a few healing sessions, Liz found the courage to write a well-crafted letter to him, and ensured that he received it. But weeks passed and she heard nothing. Perhaps he imagined difficult conversations if they met. Her hopes seemed dashed. But then there was an urgent telephone call to say that he had been rushed into hospital. She raced to his bedside, and anything that may have divided them vanished. Thankfully, he recovered and met his son-in-law and grandchildren for the first time. He went on to enjoy being an important part of his daughter's life once more.

Liz's story is another example of the holistic nature of healing. Physically, she and her baby no longer had the medical problems they first came with. Emotionally, her fear of rejection faded enough to allow a positive mental attitude to emerge. She then had the strength to take constructive action and write that letter. Granted, it took a medical emergency for the family to be mended, but sometimes terrible things have to happen for people to realise what is important to them in life.

For me, the unthinkable happened. My sister's first baby was diagnosed with a rare congenital condition and given weeks to live. The tragedy shook me to the core. I gave away my business to be able to focus instead on family and on healing. Of course, my anguish was as nothing compared to that of my sister and her husband. Yet despite their unimaginable grief they had the strength and benevolence to think of others. They made arrangements for Alice's heart valves and corneas to be donated. Unfortunately, the heart valves could not be used, but her corneas restored the gift of sight to a teenage boy who was rapidly going blind.

Being aware of the depths to which people can suffer certainly hones the mind. Nevertheless, remaining totally focused for the entirety of a session must be difficult for any healer. Only determination and practice develop the level of self-discipline necessary to help make every second of a healing session count. In the delightful words of an Anglican priest I once met, my brains can sometimes feel like a tree full of monkeys. If someone like me can learn to get their unruly jumble of thoughts under control, then anybody can. It remains a challenge for me to keep focused for the entire 20 minutes, but I do my best.

I mentioned earlier about not being sensitive to the subtle energies that other healers speak of but, eventually, two unusual phenomena developed that are very physical and can be witnessed by anyone.

While giving healing, either or both of my hands might shake now and again, as though some gentle form of electricity is running through them. Confirmation that this is likely to be an effect of healing energy came later when a married couple came to our healing centre.

Relatives normally stay in the reception area, but this man's wife would sit close and watch me give healing to her husband at every appointment. He had not experienced healing before or anything like it. Nevertheless, whenever he felt my hands quiver he could clearly see 'sheets and sheets of light' behind his closed eyelids. Discussing things with his wife later, they came to realise that when my hands shook but were not touching him, he could still see the sheets of light. I like to think that this involuntary movement in my hands is a sign of particularly strong transformation taking place within the patient and I therefore continue healing in that spot until the vibrating has ceased. Very often, I learn later that the patient had a problem in that area, or they might tell me that they experienced an unusual sensation within that part of the body while I was working on them.

The second phenomenon is a clicking sound from my fingernails. When I take my hands away from an area to move on to the next, my fingernails sometimes give an audible 'click' that sounds and feels like static electricity. I like to think that these clicks are to do with the electromagnetic field that exists throughout and around each one of us that is fundamental for good health (7) (8). Every living thing has such a field, including the Earth. Maybe an interaction is occurring between the patient's field and mine. On rare occasions, a multitude of clicks happen all at once, producing a crackle. I take these clicks and crackles as a sign that I should go back to the area that I was working on and resume healing there. When I can move on without hearing a click, I presume that enough healing has been received. Again, people often confirm afterwards that the particular area concerned had been problematic or was the site of an old injury. Since I am not usually aware of subtle energies, perhaps I need cues like these that are blindingly obvious.

Within three years of setting up our Monday morning healing group, we began opening on Sunday evenings so that patients with office-hour jobs could reach us. Like the patients who came, a number of the healers who volunteered for Sundays also worked full-time. It was an excellent arrangement because the Sunday team could leave the couches and equipment out for the Monday morning group, making less work for everyone.

For a couple of years, I also ran a self-healing meditation group for those who wanted to learn how to help themselves. Anyone could attend, and some had not meditated or had a healing session before. All the same, people who attended these classes experienced the same range of improvements as those who had one-to-one sessions at our voluntary healing centre.

Healing in a Hospital

One woman came along through a chance meeting with an old friend. She had been sitting on a park bench feeling desolate, missing her husband, who had died a few months earlier. Their ensuing chat led to her coming along to my group. After attending for some weeks, she wrote:

'Had it not been for meeting an old friend, whom I had not seen for about 25 years, I would not have attended the self-healing meditation group. I had no idea what to expect as I had never heard of this form of therapy. However, I found it very beneficial. I enjoyed the discussions and the meditation was just so very calming. There were lots of tears in the early weeks but the sessions made everything seem brighter. I still have my moments but I am so much more positive now.'

Going back to our voluntary healing centre, people would naturally stop coming when they felt well, and we therefore needed to continually find more patients to keep our healers fully utilised. I wanted our healers to be assured that it was worth making the effort to come. I called dozens of doctors' surgeries and pharmacies in the area, and all but one agreed to display our leaflets. As well as providing free advertising in an ideal place, this initiative had the added bonus that medical staff became aware that healing existed.

Whenever there was a local exhibition or fete, I would arrange for us to have a stand where we offered sessions and chatted to visitors about healing. I also contacted a range of self-help groups, offering to give a talk and demonstration. Very often, members of our group would accompany me to these so that anyone wanting to sample a session afterwards would not be disappointed.

An initial talk and demo led to our regular attendance at a local motor neurone disease (MND) group. Their meetings were surprisingly enjoyable, considering the terrible disease that it is and knowing there is no cure. Of course, there were tears occasionally, but their meetings were mainly filled with lively banter and joviality. Both the MND members and their volunteer workers were a real inspiration.

Our involvement with the Midlands group led to us being invited to the national organisation's annual weekend conference, where members from all over the UK congregated. I reasoned that if

A Healing Expedition

we gave healing sessions to these representatives, they could take the message of healing back home with them. Their local MND group could then get in touch with healers and voluntary groups in their own area.

Initially, the MND Executive was concerned that the term 'healing' might suggest to their members the possibility of a cure but the Midlands group spoke up for us. They convinced the Executive of the positive impact our healers had made to their members, and we were on board. If we thought that the local meetings were upbeat, these national conferences were positively electric! Our team of three was kept busy for much of the time, and feedback was invariably heartening. The following phrases peppered our Comments Book:

1. Wonderfully relaxing.

2. Calming.

3. Sense of peace.

4. Beautiful feeling throughout.

5. Feeling of freedom.

6. De-stressing.

Others wrote more specific statements, such as:

1. I felt heat and energy in areas that were troubled.

2. Now breathing properly.

3. Headache and shoulder pains gone in five minutes.

4. I no longer feel fear of death. (Written by a young mother.)

Another person told us that he had suffered restless sleep for years until he received a healing session at the previous year's conference. Since then, he had slept like a log. It was rare to learn of longer-term effects, because 50% of sufferers die within 14 months of diagnosis, and the remainder within five years. One famous exception is Professor Stephen Hawking, who has baffled doctors by living with MND for over 40 years.

Comments like the ones above must have reached the ears of the conference organisers because we were invited back every year, and each time they asked us to play a larger part than before.

Tragically, MND affects people of all ages, but at least our efforts helped alleviate some of their symptoms and fears. I was asked to visit a young mother who had reached the stage of being housebound and had only weeks to live. After the first session, her eyes shone while she told me that she no longer feared death and that she now felt at peace about leaving her children without a mother. Until then, she had been utterly distraught.

Although our work with self-help groups was enthusiastically received, one of my main goals was to let the medical world know that healing exists and to have healing made available at NHS venues, such as doctors' surgeries and hospitals.

A Walsall hospital was the home of regular meetings of a thriving support group for breast cancer sufferers. Jo Stackhouse, herself a survivor, had been running the group for decades with her team of volunteers. They organised a range of appealing and varied activities to support the women and their loved ones. Jo welcomed the offer of a talk and demonstration, and a team of healers accompanied me. After my short discourse, we proceeded to give sessions to 20 of their attendees. That was back in 2004, and our volunteers continued to deliver healing at their monthly meetings for at least a decade. Their venue moved out of the hospital, but I hoped that the medical personnel caring for those women continued to learn of our involvement and how their patients had benefited.

While on the subject of support groups, it is worth mentioning their value. A study of women with terminal cancer showed that those who attended a support group survived twice as long as those who did not (9). Another study of patients with skin cancer found that those who attended a structured support group were three times more likely to survive (10).

A chance to work with medical staff came when a Wolverhampton hospital organised an annual Mind, Body & Soul (MBS) event for the parents of children suffering from cystic fibrosis. There is no cure for this condition, and the affected children were too fragile to attend the MBS event. Instead, the idea was to support their distressed and drained parents. Each year, I joined a team of complementary therapists to help bring ease and comfort. Healing was so popular with both mothers and fathers that my appointment sheet was full every time.

Another opportunity to brush with the medical world came in 2005. Nursing in Practice organises national events designed primarily for nurses working in doctors' surgeries. I was asked to provide a healing stand at their upcoming Birmingham show, held annually at the National Exhibition Centre. Besides nurses, their delegates included practice managers and other medical staff. This seemed a perfect opportunity to introduce healing to healthcare professionals.

When I arrived to set up our stand the day before, I learned that one of the organisers had been suffering from severe back pain. Having been troubled with it for some time, she welcomed the opportunity to try healing and was amazed at the result. The pain disappeared and, throughout the show the following day, she was an enthusiastic ambassador for our stand.

It was the first time that the Nursing in Practice organisers had showcased a complementary therapy, and they were delighted with the interest that we generated. Our team of five volunteers hardly sat down as we delivered sessions to over 90 delegates. Almost all of our patients were medical staff who would now be able to take the message of healing back into their workplace. Hardly any of them had experienced healing before and many were surprised at how deeply they managed to relax. Usually, patients might hope for an element of privacy, but this was under the curious gaze of countless delegates as they ambled past. It was also a busy day for our visitors, and they were surrounded by noisy activity. Despite all this, our Comments Book was awash with remarks of how 'relaxing', 'extremely calming', 'pleasurable' and 'energising' their sessions were. Almost every individual wrote 'very relaxing' and 'thank you' so, to avoid repetition, most of these phrases have been omitted from the examples provided. It was difficult to whittle the list down without losing important observations so dozens more are provided on page 282:

Healing in a Hospital

1. A most exhilarating experience. Felt wonderful and so relaxed.

2. Beautiful colours moving around. Very therapeutic.

3. Had a particularly bad night with pain and stress. Much calmer in mind and body now. Ready for the day.

4. Excellent way to escape the rat race. Totally relaxing.

5. Excellent. Felt warmth, then tension in my neck released.

6. Wasn't sure at the start but, by the end, felt relaxed and soothed.

7. Amazing. My pain has gone.

8. Have not experienced this before but would highly recommend it. Have suffered from a headache all morning. It has gone now.

9. I cannot really believe how I felt. It was like a magnet that was pulling [out] my negative energy. I was fully relaxed and will never forget the experience.

10. Absolutely fascinating. I am really surprised how I felt afterwards and will definitely be looking this up on the web.

11. Could feel where the healer was as areas of my body became hot. Felt tired but rejuvenated at the same time.

12. Best part of the day! The anxiety I came with has gone.

13. Interesting departure from my normal logical thinking. The world is full of mysteries and this made me tingle and relax. Will explore further.

14. Wonderful. A real uplifter. Would be great for our patients.

15. I felt as though all my troubles were leaving my body and all happy things entering.

16. I was sceptical and didn't want to have a session but my friend recommended it and I'm glad I did. The experience was definitely calming and relaxing. Instantly, my knee felt better.

17. I felt so relaxed it was unreal. It's like all negative energy left my body.

18. Thank you so much for giving me so much peace in this busy life of ours. It has been a truly special experience.

19. Extremely interesting experience. I would definitely recommend this to my friends and patients.

20. Excellent. Felt lovely and the pain in my right foot went away. I would recommend it to anyone.

These few examples demonstrate that medical professionals report very similar experiences to those related by patients. It should be borne in mind that, unlike our patients at the healing centre, these people did not seek healing. Most did not realise that spiritual healing existed until they passed our stand, and were intrigued but sceptical. Due to the busy conference schedule, their sessions were shorter than usual but they still benefited. They were not unwell yet they noticed improvements.

Many commented that healing could help support their career by acting as an antidote for the pressures involved in their work. Of course, this would apply to anyone in a demanding job or stressful situation, whether at home or at work. Being in the medical profession, some of our visitors recognised the potential benefit for their patients and were keen to recommend healing to them.

Each year we were invited back to the Nursing in Practice exhibition and more healers were eager to join our team. With additional volunteers, we were able to commandeer the odd empty stand for which other exhibitors had paid an enormous sum but had simply not turned up on the day. Even with this extra capacity and additional space, we were still kept extremely busy.

Over the five years that we exhibited at this show, we must have given healing to around 500 nurses and practice managers. If they had each introduced healing into their place of work, a doctor's appointment in the Midlands may have been a different experience by now. Stressed staff and sick patients could both have benefited.

Perhaps the answer lies in the findings of research that shows that nurses are generally open-minded and positive towards healing therapy whereas doctors are not (11) (12) (13). Offering healing at exhibitions aimed at doctors may help change attitudes and begin to open doors.

A further opportunity to bring healing into a medical environment arose in 2005 when Freshwinds—a Birmingham medical charity—set up the Children's Complementary Therapy Network (CCTN). That year, they began holding annual national conferences at Birmingham Children's Hospital. Delegates were mainly medical staff who specialised in children and complementary therapists. The idea was to encourage networking between the two.

When I attended their first conference, I simply took leaflets along and distributed them among the delegates, but at their second conference, there was an opportunity to give a short talk. The theme for that conference was autism, and the presentation had to illustrate how a particular therapy had helped children with this condition. I had recently given healing to an autistic child, and it had gone well so I applied for a slot, thinking that I could find more children to work on if I were accepted. Indeed I was, and within a short time I found two more willing subjects and their results, too, were worthy of an audience.

1. My first patient was a four-year-old girl who had no speech and had a habit of pushing people. She seemed to keep herself fully occupied within her own little world. When I entered the living room where she was playing, she gave no indication that I had arrived or that I existed. As with many children, it would have been inappropriate to ask her to sit quietly or lie down while I gave her a healing session in the way that I was taught. Instead, I simply sat on the sofa while she busied herself with toys, and I conducted the healing session in my head, imagining going through the usual routine. Immediately after I had finished, she came over and gave me a kiss. I presumed that this was normal behaviour for the little girl, but her mother's exclamation and expression left no doubt that this was simply unheard of. Kisses

were extremely rare, she said, and never given to strangers. We left the child playing and went through to the kitchen for a coffee. While we were chatting, her daughter trotted in with her favourite teddy and gave it to me. Again, her mother was bowled over. A few weeks later, I received news that there had been an uplift in the girl's educational abilities and social interaction. The entire family was happier.

2. My second subject was a ten-year-old girl who had a nervous, tickly cough that triggered every few minutes. She was on Ritalin and had no eye contact. Although very tense, she was willing to have a healing session in the normal way, sitting on a chair. During that first session, her persistent cough stopped completely, and she left with a permanent smile. A week later, when she arrived for her second session, I learned that she had been smiling all week. Her concentration had improved, the cough hardly existed and she was better all round. In this second session, she saw a bright light in her head that became more comfortable as the session progressed. When she opened her eyes, she said that everything looked a creamy colour, initially, and when she left, she was still smiling. Soon after her two healing sessions, she took her SATs (national examinations in the UK). Although expected to gain Level 3 passes in all subjects, she achieved 4a for maths and 5b for both English and science. These were far above the grades expected by her teachers and family. Her confidence improved so much that she went on to take part in two school productions before starting senior school.

3. My third and last subject was a delightful junior school lad who was very personable but had difficulty with school work. He was behind in all subjects, especially English, and he was fretting about the approaching SATs. When I arrived at the house, it seemed a little chaotic. His mother seemed to be late for something, the younger children were squabbling and the parrot was having a fit of squawking. The lad and I were ushered into the front room with the parrot and, to top it all, the boy immediately strode up to the television and switched on his

favourite blood and guts movie. Rather than ask him to switch it off, we sat on opposite ends of the settee, him engrossed in carnage and me peacefully conducting healing in my head, the same as with the four-year-old girl. Within a short while, he turned to me and complained that he could not feel anything happening yet. I replied, with a grin, that his attention was probably taken up by the horrors on the screen. Without a further word, he switched the TV off and stretched himself out on the settee in the perfect position to receive healing, eyes closed. I had not made any suggestion for him to do so. Then the whole house became peaceful, including the parrot. It was as though we were the only ones home. Another of the family pets padded in, nestled up against the sofa and fell asleep. Afterwards, the lad announced to his parents that he had enjoyed the session and was happy to have another. When I arrived the next week, his parents told me that he had not worried about the exams since my previous visit. After the second session, he said that he now felt very positive about the SATs, even though they were only a few days away. The following week, he enthusiastically told me how confident he was that his exams had been a success. His parents naturally cautioned him not to be too optimistic, but when his results arrived he was right! His teachers had hoped that he would gain Level 3 for each subject and he did so for English. But he astonished everyone by achieving Level 4 for science and Level 5 for maths. Nobody was more thrilled than he was.

So far as I know, these are the only autistic children that I have given healing to. Considering that the results were so encouraging across all three, healing may be beneficial for other youngsters with this condition. My own limited experience with children is that, whatever their problem, they noticeably benefit from healing.

My initiatives to bring healing into hospitals and to self-help groups were often welcomed. However, if a key decision-maker was not open-minded about healing, then its introduction was blocked. At places where we were well established, we sometimes had a new CEO or group leader arrive who summarily halted our attendance. In these instances, they did not listen to patients or offer an explanation for their decision. It seems unlikely that these situations would occur if it were generally understood that healing is natural and normal. Still greater acceptance could be gained if healing were known to feature in NHS settings.

The conferences at the Children's Hospital and at the Nursing in Practice exhibitions were a step in the right direction towards getting healing noticed by medical personnel, but we needed to bring healing directly into the NHS somehow. If surgeries and hospitals were to offer or recommend healing, the general public might well feel encouraged to give it a try. All of my efforts thus far had not brought us any closer to bringing healing to NHS patients. We needed a senior person within a hospital or a general practice who was willing to champion our cause. It seemed a tall order, but I kept the thought alive in my mind.

Key Points

1. No treatment, whether conventional or complementary, can guarantee a cure, and spiritual healing is no exception.

2. Healing helps the whole of a person, not just the problem that is troubling them the most.

3. Testimonials from patients and medical professionals confirm the efficacy of healing.

4. Babies and children benefit from healing.

5. Healing sessions support people who care for others.

6. In cases where death is inevitable, healing helps the patient gain peace of mind and acceptance.

7. Healing helps relieve emotional issues including bereavement.

8. The patient does not need to tell the healer what the problem is.

9. A healer who belongs to a reputable organisation will not 'pick up' information about the patient.

10. Healing can be effective, even when given in a busy and noisy setting.

11. Healing can be effective, even when the treatment is given in less than the usual time.

12. Healing provides a common link between diverse races and creeds.

13. Healing provides a common link between people who have a religious belief and those who do not.

14. Anyone can learn to give healing.

15. People can learn to self-heal.

A Healing Expedition

16. Healing can act as an antidote for the pressures involved in a demanding job or stressful situation, whether at home or at work.

17. Incorporating healing into conventional healthcare could reduce costs for the NHS, the benefits system and businesses.

Healing at the Hospital

Whenever someone new has an appointment at our voluntary group, I ask how they heard of us. With an eye to future advertising, we might then know which areas to focus on first.

One day in 2006, I gave healing to a woman who had been to our group a few times but whom I had not yet met. I was amazed and thrilled when she told me that her hospital consultant had recommended that she come to us. Apparently, he had picked up some of our leaflets from a display stand somewhere. She said that he had referred a number of his patients to our group and was pleased with the results that he had seen. This was very exciting news. Perhaps he might be open to the idea of making healing available within the hospital.

I wrote to Dr Sukhdev Singh at the Gastroenterology Department of Good Hope Hospital in Birmingham and offered to deliver healing to his patients free of charge. To assure him of professionalism, I detailed the minimum two-year training period, the national standards of training and of accredited tutors, the assessment panels, the professional code of conduct and disciplinary procedures. I supposed that the NHS would stipulate that any practitioner working with patients would need to meet all of these standards whether paid or unpaid. Patients, too, would expect anyone treating them at a surgery or hospital to be subject to such requirements, even if they were only having their toenails cut.

I also gave assurance that we do not manipulate, use needles, diagnose or prescribe and that my training had nothing to do with any religion. For good measure, I detailed members of The Healing Trust who were earning salaries as spiritual healers within the NHS.

Healing in a Hospital

Ruth Kaye's paid employment as a healer at St James's University Hospital, Leeds, began around 1990, and regular articles in local and national media attest to her ongoing success with patients. As well as giving individual healing sessions on the wards, Ruth runs group sessions at the hospital, where she teaches self-empowerment through meditation and music. Searching for 'healing' on the hospital's website brings up some of the media articles about her and explains more about her role. Ruth has also produced a relaxation CD that is free to download from her website (www.ruthkaye.net) and a short film in which she explains healing in more detail.

Angie Buxton-King started work as a salaried healer at University College London Hospital (UCLH) in 1999. After being appointed Manager of the Complementary Therapy Team in 2003, Angie expanded the group from the original five therapists to 14, five of which were healers. A few years later, Angie and her husband set up a charity in memory of her young son who had died of cancer. The Sam Buxton Sunflower Healing Trust has financed the first two years' salary of over 25 healers working in different NHS hospitals and hospices around the country. At the end of the two years, the salary commitment for the majority of these healers has been taken over by the recruiting NHS centre.

Angie wrote a book in 2004 entitled *The NHS Healer.* Its foreword was penned by Stephen Rowley, Clinical Nurse/Manager at University College London Hospital. With Angie's permission, his words are reproduced here:

'University College London Hospital's haematology unit treats patients with leukaemia and other life-threatening diseases. These treatments are highly intensive and carry risks of morbidity and mortality in themselves. For the last five years the unit has developed a complementary therapy team, initially providing conventional therapies such as reflexology and aromatherapy to patients. Introducing a spiritual healer into this pressure cooker environment was considered a risk.

'All of the healing on the unit is provided by Angie Buxton-King, who is now an integral member of the medical and nursing team and I am pleased to say that, over the last four years that Angie has been in the team, the therapy of healing has become not only accepted, but also imperative to many of our patients. Although, clinically, healing remains little understood, the clinical effects are most evident and certainly tangible enough to satisfy the sceptical minds of doctors and nurses. We have seen patients with uncontrolled pain find more relief from healing than intramuscular opiates; we have seen patients in psychological states of utter desperation find, in healing, huge comfort and coping abilities; we have seen patients report significant reductions in chemotherapy related side effects; we have seen the positive effect healing can have on the troubled, dying patient. Working in this field is demanding and many staff have felt the need for healing themselves and have found significant benefit from doing so. Healing is the most popular and well received complementary therapy we provide on the unit.'

In my letter to Dr Singh I could also have referred to Dr Michael Dixon LVO, OBE, Chair of the NHS Alliance and President of NHS Clinical Commissioners. As a General Practitioner, Dr Dixon has made healing available at his surgery for decades. After regularly witnessing positive results, he conducted a study where 57 chronically ill patients each received ten weekly healing sessions (14). The term 'chronic' refers to any illness that has lasted for three months or more, but these patients had suffered for more than six months. They had failed to respond to any other approach, whether conventional or complementary. Two weeks after the healing sessions had been completed, 81% of the treated group thought their symptoms had improved, and nearly half of these thought their improvements were substantial. Gains were still evident three months later.

In 2008, Dr Dixon and his partners created the Culm Valley Integrated Centre for Health, which is widely regarded as a prototype for general practice of the future and includes healing in its provision of care.

If I had thought of it when writing to Dr Singh, I could have quoted a report by the House of Lords Select Committee on Science and Technology (15). In 2000, an inquiry was conducted because so many members of the public were turning to complementary and alternative therapies, and in ever-growing numbers. The Committee was to assess whether this escalating situation should influence public health policy and, if so, how. Although it was completed a while ago, Select Committee investigations are comprehensive and worthy of note. As we shall see, many of the findings of this particular inquiry remain relevant today.

It was chaired by Lord Walton, a retired consultant neurologist who had once been President of the British Medical Association. When the Committee was first formed, it was pointed out that it did not feature a single person who had knowledge and experience of Complementary and Alternative Medicine (CAM). Lord Colwyn and Lord Baldwin were therefore co-opted. At the time of the inquiry, both were patrons of NFSH/The Healing Trust.

As a working dentist, Lord Colwyn used kinesiology every day in his surgery as a diagnostic tool. He says that it worked brilliantly, but he had no idea why (16). Ironically, kinesiology was relegated to Group 3 of their eventual report, the group designated as having no scientific evidence to support its use.

Lord Baldwin had been a dedicated user of CAM for decades, after an experience in his younger years (17). Having damaged both knees in vigorous outdoor pursuits, he was sent to specialists and then to two eminent physicians in Harley Street. The various treatments they administered proved fruitless. Three years later, now hobbling around with knee bandages and a mindset of incurability, he was recommended to a spiritual healer in Cambridge. This healer spent half an hour waving his hands over the injured knees, all the while chatting about his job as a schoolteacher and his thoughts on politics. Lord Baldwin felt nothing, not even the sensation of heat or cold that he had been told to expect. He left in as much pain as when he arrived. But the next morning he was bewildered to find that the pain had vanished, and it was never to completely return. Medical specialists had given him full care and attention over a period of three years, using the latest technology and knowledge. In contrast, the healer saw him in a back bedroom and spent 30 minutes on the job without concentrating on what he was doing. Lord Baldwin makes the pertinent point that his recovery was unlikely to be due to the placebo effect because he fully expected results from the top professionals and had no faith at all in the healer.

Healing at the Hospital

The 'placebo effect' refers to improvements in a patient's condition that are gained simply because the person expects a treatment to be helpful. A later section is devoted to this fascinating subject.

During discussion of the eventual report, it transpired that other peers, who were not on the Select Committee, had experienced complementary therapies (16).

Lord Hodgson had been diagnosed with cancer and underwent surgery followed by six weeks of radiotherapy. Subsequent tests showed warning signs of a recurrence, but no further treatments were possible, only palliative care. Palliative care means that the patient will die slowly, and medical care is limited to reducing unpleasant symptoms. Like many others in this distressing and depressing situation, he was prepared to cast around for unconventional options. He was recommended to a particular reflexologist but was highly sceptical that this could help. However, after a number of sessions he freely admitted that it had been remarkably successful and that he felt better. He had to pay for these treatments himself, and points out that taxpayers benefited by his doing so, because the NHS was consequently saved the expense of providing him with more pills and further appointments with the doctor. Fellow patients also gained, because his appointments were now available for them. By combining conventional treatments with a complementary therapy he achieved a very positive outcome. Lord Hodgson advocated that the various disciplines should work in harmony with each other to relieve the hard-pressed NHS, and to spread the burden of health provision that is currently carried almost solely by orthodox physicians.

The Select Committee's call for papers attracted 180 submissions of evidence from organisations and individuals involved in complementary therapies.

One of them was Dr Craig Brown, representing The Healing Trust. He was a medical doctor whose surgery had offered the services of a healer for many years. At that time, Dr Brown was President of The Healing Trust. During his tenure, he spearheaded the introduction of professional standards designed to smooth the way for healers to work within the NHS. His submission to the Committee reported that there were about 200 healing organisations in the UK, most of which were very small. At that time, The Healing Trust was by far the largest with 6,000 members, and belonged to an umbrella organisation that boasted 14,500 healer members. In addition, an independent survey suggested that healers represented 40% of all CAM practitioners.

A delegation of the Select Committee visited three research establishments where CAM therapies are studied, and also several clinics where therapies are provided to the public. The main ailments being treated at these places included migraine, asthma, irritable bowel syndrome, chronic joint pain, chronic back pain, chronic fatigue syndrome, eczema and allergies. Most GPs find these particular conditions time-consuming and difficult to treat, which is also the case for HIV infection, multiple sclerosis, psoriasis, rheumatological conditions and many others.

During discussions of the final report (16), Lord Rea, a retired GP, asserted that the common factor in all of these problems is stress, which can play a part in the origin or continuation of the physical condition. He stated that some studies have found that those with higher than average anxiety levels are frequent users of complementary medicine, as they often find that it helps them better than mainstream care.

Further discussions revealed that:

'About one third of all patients with chronic symptoms have no organic disease and another third have symptoms that are unrelated to their organic condition.'

This means that a huge number of patients are suffering with long-term problems, and nobody knows why because no physical causes can be found by medical tests and investigations.

Lord Colwyn made the observation that:

'Patients want physicians who are not focused solely on promoting drugs and surgery as the only methods of treatment... They want doctors who will not laugh at them for inquiring about complementary or alternative therapies.'

On the subject of why patients seek complementary therapies, other research revealed the following:

Healing at the Hospital

'Studies show that people who consult complementary practitioners usually have longstanding conditions for which conventional medicine has not provided a satisfactory solution, either because it is insufficiently effective or because it causes adverse effects (18).'

Ultimately, the House of Lords Report on the use of Complementary and Alternative Therapies made the following statement regarding Group 2, which is the group that features healing. Group 2 includes the therapies that are the most often used to complement conventional medicine and that do not purport to embrace diagnostic skills.

'We are satisfied that many therapies listed in Group 2 give help and comfort to many patients when used in a complementary sense to support conventional medical care. In relieving stress, in alleviating side effects (for example of various forms of anti-cancer therapy), in giving succour to the elderly and in palliative care, they often fulfil an important role.'

The full report was duly sent to the Government, whose response included the following statements:

'The Government agrees that there is scope for closer integration of CAM and conventional medicine. This is in the interests of all relevant disciplines and, above all, in the interests of their patients,' and

'The Government recognises the need to develop the research capacity in this field.'

Support for complementary therapies was also stated by the Government in February 2005 when the Parliamentary Under-Secretary for the Department of Health, Melanie Johnson, said in the House of Commons:

'We understand the benefit that many people get from complementary therapies. Local commissioning is a matter for local discretion, but we can see the benefits to local practices of an intermediary pulling together a range of services in the area for alternative medical treatments.'

Support was also forthcoming from the NHS Alliance at its Annual Conference in 2000, when 63% voted in favour of expanding NHS provision of complementary medicine.

The public is equally keen. As a result of the House of Lords Report, the Department of Health issued a document entitled 'Complementary Medicine Information for Primary Care Groups' (19), which states:

'A survey in 1989 showed that 74% of the public surveyed were in favour of complementary medicines being made widely available on the NHS.'

The Lords Report quoted as many as one in four people using CAM, depending on which estimate is used. This same proportion must apply to members of the Government, the scientific community, NHS leaders and to medical professionals. However, bearing in mind that low income people probably cannot afford to pay for CAM treatments, the figure for influential members of society—such as those listed above—must be more than one in four. With so many people in key positions being likely to be proponents of CAM, it is a wonder that more progress has not been made in making complementary therapies available within the NHS.

Sufficient research was seen as a stumbling block, but discussions regarding the Report (16) reveal that:

'Only 8p was spent on CAM research for every £100 spent on researching orthodox methods,' and

'less than 0.1% of the national research budget is spent on CAM treatments.'

Submissions to the inquiry also suggested that conventional medical scientists and practitioners are inherently biased against CAM. Sir Iain Chalmers, Director of the UK Cochrane Centre, had this to say:

'Many in the orthodox medical world remain either sceptical about the desirability of this trend [towards increasing use of CAM] or hostile to it. This scepticism seems to result partly from unwillingness within the orthodox mainstream to apply a single evidential standard when assessing the effects of healthcare.'

The latter sentence means that no matter how many individuals are seen to improve by using CAM therapies, the scientific community will not accept this as evidence. They will only accept placebo-controlled randomised control trials (RCTs). The limitations of RCTs will be discussed later, and also why it is not possible to design a placebo for healing.

However, the Lords Report pointed to encouraging developments within the medical profession, stating that there is increasing support for the view that medics should begin to work with CAM practitioners. The Academy of Medical Royal Colleges confirmed that:

'Pressure is now coming on the medical profession to look around them and see all other practitioners and make sure it all works well for the patient.'

The British Medical Association defines complementary therapies as 'those that can work alongside conventional medicine', and I hoped that Dr Singh would be willing to explore how healing might bring additional support to his patients.

Dr Singh replied to my letter in welcoming terms. He invited me to meet him on the ward where most of his gastroenterology inpatients are cared for. When I arrived, there was no indication as to who might be the senior consultant amongst the staff milling about in the reception area. When a man in a white coat and matching turban stepped forward to shake my hand, my first impression was of his down-to-earth kindliness and I felt that we liked each other from the first moment. In retrospect, he may also have been relieved that I looked and dressed like a hospital administrator and would not look out of place in his clinic. If people imagine that healers wear odd clothes and behave flamboyantly they would most often be wrong.

At that first meeting, Dr Singh introduced me to key members of the nursing and administrative staff on the ward, and we discussed the practicalities of how best to deliver healing to his patients there. An additional suggestion was that I could also give healing to outpatients at his Wednesday morning clinic.

Healing in a Hospital

Now that we had met each other and had agreed upon what was possible, it was for Dr Singh to gain approval from the hospital's management. Even though it was not a paid position, it took over 18 months for a decision to be reached by those on high. Perhaps it was because the proposal was so unusual that caused the inordinate delay but, finally, we were able to get started.

Volunteers at the hospital fall under the responsibility of the Patient Advice Liaison Service (PALS) so the first step was to be interviewed by its Coordinator. She was fascinated by the concept of healing and was curious to know what the patients might experience. I offered to demonstrate on her so that she would have first-hand knowledge of what is involved. Unbeknown to me, her back had been painful for weeks. She was astounded that the discomfort disappeared completely within just a few minutes. As a result, she became a marvellous exponent for healing and, partly due to her enthusiastic support, we subsequently managed to introduce additional healers into other departments on the site.

One might expect a senior consultant physician to only be involved in mainstream medicine, but I learned that Dr Singh led meditation and mindfulness classes for his patients. He provided courses at the hospital, free of charge and in his own time. It was refreshing and uplifting to meet a medical expert who was proactively encompassing a complementary therapy within his provision of care. His patients must have been impressed and touched that he should take such a personal interest in their wellbeing.

I began work with Dr Singh's patients in August 2007. If he felt that he could not help a patient sufficiently with conventional medicine, Dr Singh would suggest that they might benefit from a healing session with me. If they took up the offer, he would introduce me and I would lead the patient to my room next door.

It is often said that a complementary therapy session helps patients to feel better because they are in nurturing surroundings. Conversely, the room I use at the hospital is a standard, sterile consultation room with no soft music or potted palms. The examination couch in the centre is surrounded by the usual array of medical equipment, and the view through the first floor window is of the local cemetery.

Healing at the Hospital

Another common assertion is that patients feel better only because a complementary therapist takes an interest in them as a person and provides a kindly listening ear. In contrast, I exchange maybe a couple of sentences with a new patient, simply to put them at their ease. There is no need for a healer to know anything about the patient, which must be a relief to some people and saves a great deal of time.

In the early days at the hospital, I painstakingly explained healing to every patient, thinking it necessary because they usually had not heard of it before. But there soon came a time when there was a queue and no time to discuss a single thing, other than the bare essentials. I found that the patients were just as content without the long preamble, and their responses were equally good, so it made sense to save my breath.

Most patients are happy to lie down on the couch but if they prefer to be seated, I fetch a comfortable armchair from a nearby office. Either way, they remain fully clothed, even keeping their shoes on, if they wish.

Training with The Healing Trust means learning to heal without touching the patient, except for the shoulders and feet. Personally, I prefer to work with touch, which involves additional contact points on the joints of the arms and legs. We have to gain permission before making any physical contact, and it is perfectly fine if someone does not want to be touched at all. So far as I can recall, nobody has refused, but it would not concern me if they did because it is their comfort and preference that matters, and it makes no difference to the outcome.

A healing session begins with a light touch on the shoulders and then, with hands about ten inches away from the body, we work downwards, starting around the head and finishing at the feet. We then work in line with the skeleton, firstly along the spine, then along the shoulders and down the arms and legs. Touching or getting near to the head was cautioned against during my training, but qualified healers can use their discretion once the full body circuit has been completed. If I feel inclined, I cradle the patient's head in my hands, and people remark how comforting and calming this feels.

43

Healing in a Hospital

Knowing that the people I see at the hospital have gastric problems, I sometimes lay my hands on their abdomen, and feedback from this, too, is very positive. When people are in a hospital they anticipate unpleasant invasive treatment so, by comparison, being asked if it is okay to lightly touch inoffensive areas is probably a welcome departure and they invariably agree.

In accordance with my training, I let patients know that they might become aware of different sensations during the session. Most commonly people feel heat, cold, tingling or involuntary muscle jumps, and they might see colours. If they did not know of these possibilities in advance, they might feel alarmed to experience something out of the ordinary. Whether they sense anything or not has no bearing on the healing outcome; it is simply that some people are more sensitive than others.

Occasionally, a pain or an emotion can develop during the healing session that rises to the surface and then, just as quickly, gently dissipates. It could be likened to a bubble that forms at the bottom of a fizzy drink that floats up and softly pops at the surface. Before a patient leaves me, I check that any sensation that has manifested during the session has completely gone. On the rare occasion that some discomfort remains, we then conduct a simple technique together that dissolves it. This method (see page 294) has worked every time, so far as I recall, and usually with total success.

In line with the training mentioned earlier, I do not ask for a particular outcome for any patient. When I am working at the healing centre, I usually have no inkling as to what they are suffering from because I do not ask. It is therefore impossible to envisage a specific remedy or required outcome. Instead, I simply intend for the strongest appropriate healing for the highest good of all concerned.

It did not feature in the training, but I believe that the greater a sense of elation and bliss that the healer can generate and maintain during the session, the better the outcome for the patient. Even if it were not true, it feels brilliant for the healer. Occasionally, I feel intense waves of euphoria and at others a sudden upwelling of deep emotion that passes through and goes. When this happens to me, the patient often remarks afterwards that they felt something similar happening to them, and how light and bright they now feel. If someone volunteers this type of feedback, I might then admit to having felt the same thing, if I did. Others have described the most amazing experience while I was aware of nothing at all. Equally, there have been times when I felt incredible sensations yet the patient seemed completely oblivious and passed no comment.

I also believe that it is helpful for the healer to remain positive, even in the face of seemingly insurmountable odds. Physical problems certainly appear impossible to change. It consequently pleases me to think of different ways in which improvements may not be as difficult to achieve as we imagine.

For instance, as easily as cells have moved out of their perfect place for health, why should they not return just as easily? After all, each cell is made up of millions of atoms, and each atom is mostly empty space. The nucleus of an atom is equivalent to the size of a football in the middle of a pitch, with the nearest electron orbiting way outside of the stadium. With such a vast amount of space inside atoms, and with atoms being the building blocks of everything in our world, even the most solid piece of rock is, in fact, mostly empty space. It seems bizarre, but without all of this space—as is the case in a neutron star—material the size of a sugar cube would weigh as much as Mount Everest (20). So perhaps there really is more room for the cells of our body to manoeuvre than first seems possible.

Added to this, astrophysicists know that mysterious elements exist that affect the world we can perceive. Named 'dark energy' and 'dark matter', they sound sinister, but the term 'dark' simply means they are not visible. They are known to exist only because of the effect they have on the discernible world. About 68% of the universe is dark energy and about 27% is dark matter. Less than 5% of all that exists is therefore observable, even when using the most advanced instruments. NASA's website confirms that more than 95% of our world is a complete mystery to scientists. This 95% is only known about because it has an effect on the physical world around us (21). It does not seem so far removed, then, for healers to say that there must be an unknown force called 'healing energy' because it has a positive effect on living things.

All in all, it seems possible to me that the physical positioning of atoms, and therefore cells, may be more fluid than we think. Even if it were not actually true, the concept gives me a more limitless mindset when giving healing. But in many cases there seems no other explanation.

Probably the best documented example is that of Anita Moorjani (22). Anita had already suffered from cancer for over three years when she was suddenly rushed into hospital one morning, unable to move. Scans showed that the lymphoma had spread throughout her entire body. The oncologist then announced that her organs had shut down and gave her just hours to live. While unconscious, Anita slipped into a different level of awareness where she experienced great clarity of how life works, as well as an understanding of her own life and its purpose. She came to understand that 'heaven' is a state of mind, not a place, and that her mission was to inspire others with this knowledge. The next morning, Anita regained normal consciousness. In three days, the tumours that had been the size of lemons reduced by 70%. Over the next two weeks, every test came back clear. Her oncologist was baffled. Other doctors who were not involved in her care examined the medical evidence and confirmed that she had returned from certain death. At least one medical expert travelled half way around the world to investigate, and he reached the same conclusion. Anita's motivational story, which is designed to help others, is related in her book *Dying to Be Me*.

Dannion Brinkley (23) was hit by a bolt of lightning and pronounced dead. On regaining consciousness, he found that he was paralysed and in intense pain. It was only by blowing on the sheet that had been pulled up over his face that he was able to alert someone nearby that he was not dead. It took two years to recover from the appalling burns and impact injuries. Before this freak incident, Dannion had been a self-centred hellraiser but during his 'death' he had an intense spiritual experience. When he recovered, he devoted his life to healing and to the care of those approaching death. For more than 20 years he has been actively involved in educating policymakers in the USA about the value of complementary therapies and the need for research. His bestselling book *Saved by the Light* was made into a popular film of the same name.

Healing at the Hospital

Denise Linn (24) was out cycling in the countryside, aged 17, when an unknown gunman drove past and shot her at close range. A great deal of her abdomen was blown away and she was left for dead on the roadside. It was not thought possible that she could survive such horrific injuries and loss of blood. But while unconscious, she received spiritual revelations and her wounds subsequently healed at an amazing rate. She has since devoted her life to healing.

Another person who returned to vibrant health despite the odds is Martin Brofman (25). Martin had a high-powered Wall Street career when he was diagnosed with a cancerous tumour on his spine and given weeks to live. Surgical removal of the tumour would be so risky that there was hardly a chance of survival. With little alternative, he determined to investigate complementary therapies instead and he made a total recovery. As a result of his experience, he became a healer and spiritual teacher.

Donna Eden (26) developed multiple sclerosis (MS) during her teens. MS is a disorder of the central nervous system and, since the nervous system links everything that the body does, many different symptoms can appear. It can affect the mind, the body and the emotions and there is no cure for it. Despite how severely the condition affected her, Donna overcame MS completely by using what she terms 'energy medicine'. Since that time, she has been teaching others how to heal themselves.

Byron Katie (27) experienced a ten-year downward spiral into depression, rage and self-loathing. One in four British adults experience at least one diagnosable mental health problem in any one year, and one in six people are suffering with this at any given time (28). Normally, it would be unimaginable to recover quickly or completely from the depths of Byron's state. However, she simply woke up one morning in a state of joy that has never left her. In her enlightened state of mind, she realised that questioning her stressful thoughts was the key to her recovery. She went on to teach others how to utilise this technique and called it The Work.

Eckhart Tolle (29) was an intellectual who had spent his life in an almost constant state of anxiety, interspersed with periods of suicidal depression. At the age of 29, he woke up in the early hours with a feeling of absolute dread, and the repeating thought that he could not live with himself any longer. When he stopped to think who the 'I' was that the 'self' could no longer live with, his intellect kicked in and he pondered the problem. By the morning, he was filled with a deep peace and sense of bliss that has remained with him. His bestselling book *The Power of Now* describes his transformation, and guides readers towards the same realisations.

Norman Cousins (30) was diagnosed with heart disease and told that he had little chance of survival. To take his mind off the constant pain, he watched comedy films. He discovered that ten minutes of genuine belly laughter had an anaesthetic effect that lasted for at least two hours. When the pain-killing effect of the laughter wore off, he would watch more of the film. He believes that laughter cured him and he wrote of his experience in his book *Anatomy of an Illness*, which was later made into a movie. Subsequent research studies have revealed that episodes of laughter help to reduce pain, decrease stress-related hormones and boost the immune system (31).

Louise Haye (32) was brought up in poverty and had a violent step-father. Raped at the age of five and pregnant at 15, it was no wonder that she later changed her name and moved to New York. Eventually finding success and happiness, she was devastated when her husband left her after 14 years of marriage. She turned to religion where she discovered the transformational power of positive thought and became a popular workshop leader. When she was diagnosed with an incurable cancer, she declined conventional treatment and began a regime that she believes rid her body of the disease. She describes her techniques and philosophies in her bestselling book *You Can Heal Your Life*.

Despite the harrowing situations that these individuals endured, each one of them discovered a key to transformation and went on to lead a healthy and fulfilling life. Further, they had the courage to tell the world their personal stories so that others may be helped and inspired. Although they each propose a different method, they all have the same objective.

If just one person can make a physical, mental or emotional recovery, then anyone can. The Institute of Noetic Sciences has compiled a database of thousands of medically reported cases where clinical remission has mysteriously occurred (33). Not one of these recoveries can happen outside of the natural laws of physics, chemistry and biology. It must be that we simply do not yet know all of the laws.

Another way that I buoy myself in spite of the apparent odds against a patient's improvement, is to deem that the person I am giving healing to is ready to take a quantum leap into wellness and joy. I imagine that they have an internal guidance system that has brought them to this particular place at this precise time so that they can take advantage of this unique healing opportunity. Considering the vastness of space and time, it is easy to envisage that an invisible force could have created this serendipitous 'coincidence'. Whatever the truth is, generating a positive mindset has to be helpful.

When I first started at the hospital, in August 2007, I worked a full day every Wednesday. I would spend the morning at Dr Singh's outpatients clinic and then grab a quick bite to eat before dashing across the campus to the ward where most of his inpatients were. At both departments, the nurses and the administrative staff were most welcoming and helpful towards me. On the ward, I was to work only with Dr Singh's patients, and a notice board in the reception area confirmed which patients these were.

Many of the inpatients were glad of a visitor of any description and a good number took up the offer of a healing session. In a shared ward, the only chance of privacy was to pull the curtain around but some patients were perfectly happy to be in full view while I worked. When others could see what was going on, they would sometimes gain the confidence to call me over and ask questions or request a session.

But no session was without interruption. At any time, the patient could be visited by a team of doctors, a nurse, the tea lady or visitors. One young man already had a visitor when I arrived so I told them both that healing was available and offered to come back later if he was interested. He was keen to try it straight away and his mother was agreeable, so she looked on while I worked on her son. Afterwards, he felt that he had benefited from the healing and was more relaxed, but his mother remarked with surprise that her own aches and pains had all disappeared. This is a very common feature of healing. Years later, this same youngster decided to enter the medical profession, and I hope that the memory of this healing experience goes with him.

A very frail woman, who seemed to be a permanent fixture on the ward, told me that she had enjoyed consistently good health until her husband died some years before. She blamed herself for his premature death, even though it was clear that the cause could not have been her fault. Since that traumatic time, her grief and self-abjuration had accompanied a downward spiral into ill-health and now she was bed-bound. On the rare occasion like this that I learn the details of someone's background, there is often a story of great loss or anguish that predates the beginning of their illness. Therefore, when giving healing I imagine encompassing the person's invisible past, not just their current physical problems. Medication can be excellent for painful symptoms but it cannot treat a painful past.

Another patient had a similar health pattern except that her loss was the home she adored. Bereavement can be in many forms.

One colourful pensioner so enjoyed his first healing session at the hospital that he would get a message to me each week to tell me which ward he was now on, and I would go find him. Upon first sight of me, he would bellow his welcome across the ward and herald 'the arrival of the healer'. During each session he had strange and wonderful experiences that made his eyes sparkle in the recounting. On my departure, he would call out behind me how wonderful he now felt and, thanks to his hearty announcements, a number of patients, staff and visitors came to hear about healing. Sadly, his condition was terminal but healing lifted his spirits no end and he always commented on feeling more physically comfortable.

After several months, I passed this ward work on to other volunteer healers whom I had introduced to the hospital, and I then only attended the outpatients clinic.

The window of my first-floor hospital room is usually open, so my work is often accompanied by the sound of traffic and conversations from the pavement below. Noise rarely distracts me from healing and very few patients complain that it is a problem for them. However, at nine o'clock every Wednesday morning, the fire alarm is tested, and a sounding device is on the wall of my room. If

Healing at the Hospital

I have a patient that early, I warn them in advance. In preparation for when it begins, I ask them to imagine that the blaring din is a wake-up call to every unhelpful cell, thought and emotion, rousing each of them into a state of readiness for their healing. If we cannot avoid a situation, we may as well attempt to use it to our advantage, and this technique seems to work well.

In the initial months, Dr Singh would make a point of seeing every patient again immediately after their healing session to discover how they had fared. Feedback was consistently positive, giving him the confidence to progressively reduce how many patients he called back in.

Usually, I see each of his patients only once. If they return at a later date for a follow-up appointment with Dr Singh, I might see them a second time but that could be many months later. Ideally, they would benefit from a series of weekly sessions but there is no time for this on Wednesday mornings. Instead, I give each patient a leaflet about our voluntary healing group and encourage them to go along. Although our group is reasonably local to the hospital, Dr Singh's patients can live much further afield. However, our leaflet gives details of similar groups throughout the Midlands, so anyone who is keen to have further sessions should be able to find something local enough to them, and affordable. Unfortunately, very few patients follow this up, a point that I shall come to later.

It must seem extraordinary to a patient, to have their specialist offer them the opportunity of a healing session. Nevertheless, many of those who do not have to rush back to work do take up the opportunity and, as you will see from my two audits, they most often benefit from just one 20-minute session.

Having been a healer for some years, the patient responses seemed perfectly normal to me, but to many of them the experience was astonishing. At the outpatients clinic, it was delightful to see Dr Singh sometimes beckon other consultants over to hear what patients had to say. On one such occasion, he asked the gathered consultants, 'How many patients leave our consultations saying, 'That was fantastic!'?'

Almost all of the patients I have seen at the hospital were referred to me by Dr Singh. The nursing staff and administrative personnel began actively encouraging patients to see me after they witnessed the difference in some of the patients. Very few other consultants at Dr Singh's clinic sent their patients to me. One registrar was initially hesitant but after seeing the difference it made to one of his patients, he then referred several more to me. Soon afterwards he took up a promotion at a different hospital but, before he left, he told me that he intended to introduce healing at his new post as soon as he was established enough. At the other end of the spectrum, another registrar never referred a patient to me and told me point blank that medication is the only answer. He said that he could not see a place for healing in any medical setting. In between these two poles, the other consultants seem cautiously open-minded, and they would send me the occasional patient. Judging from the few that they sent, it did not dampen the patient's experience of healing if they were referred to me by a sceptical consultant.

To my knowledge, I am the only healer to have had the privilege of working so closely with a senior consultant physician. It is immensely valuable that Dr Singh has witnessed the effects of healing on his own patients, some of whom he has been treating for a long time. The medical file for just one patient can sometimes be several inches thick, giving evidence of the length of time they have been suffering and the number of procedures they must have endured.

Knowing that scientists and medics often ridicule colleagues who dare to use unconventional methods, one has to marvel at the risk that Dr Singh was prepared to take by openly introducing healing to his clinic. However, I came to learn from others that Dr Singh's reputation is sufficient to withstand such criticism, should any exist, and that he steadfastly puts his patients' interests first. His empathy with patients is sincere and unwavering, and every patient who has mentioned Dr Singh in my presence has done so with deep appreciation, even reverence.

Patients are usually only referred to a specialist when their GP has exhausted all of the standard medical remedies for their condition. It follows that Dr Singh's patients will typically have suffered for quite a time before they are referred to his clinic. With his specialist knowledge and experience, he naturally has certain expectations of what a patient's prognosis might be and, against this backdrop, he was intrigued that healing seemed to be making a

Healing at the Hospital

difference. Improvements were often evident immediately after a session. If patients returned months later for a follow-up appointment, Dr Singh sometimes learned of positive effects that had remained in the longer term.

Especially when patients arrive at the clinic in severe pain, and in cases where medication has been unable to give relief, Dr Singh suggests to them that healing may help.

One morning, a young man arrived for his appointment in a hospital wheelchair because he was in too much agony to stand or walk. His wife carried their baby. There was no immediate remedy to alleviate his condition so Dr Singh suggested a healing session. Although the man opted to lie on the couch rather than stay in the wheelchair, his body was stiffly contorted in an attempt to reduce the pain. Within seconds of beginning my work, his body began to slowly unwind from its torment, and he melted into a relaxed position, free of pain, for the rest of the session. He walked out of the unit carrying his baby and left the wheelchair behind. A year later, he was back for a check-up. In the interim, he had been diagnosed with three different conditions and was in far less pain than at our initial meeting. His wife confirmed that, after the healing session a year before, he had been well for four days. It mystified me that he had made no attempt to access healing near to where he lived. Furthermore, he turned down the invitation to have another session with me after this check-up appointment.

It does seem puzzling to avoid a chance of improving or getting well, but there must be a reason why people make such a decision. I tend to think that the answer is fear, in one guise or another.

One example of this concerned someone I knew whose long-term back pain disappeared after one healing session. Despite the success, she refused a further session some months later when she had another ailment. Eventually, she divulged to me that it had bothered her that healing had solved her back problem, because it challenged her understanding of how the physical world works. If healing is effective, she reasoned, there must be more to life than we can physically see, hear and touch. This prospect seemed like a Pandora's box to her and she was afraid to contemplate the matter further or to have healing again. Years later, though, she did return for additional healing when she was in dire need, and those worries

53

evaporated, along with many others. After that, she was glad to return for healing on a number of occasions. When she was bereaved, she felt that healing supported her immensely. Later on, a whiplash accident left her with recurring shooting pains in her neck and head. She was taking medication and waiting for tests, but the pains disappeared after a few sessions. Then she had a painful growth on her foot that was getting bigger and affecting her gait. After three healing sessions, the lump melted away and she cancelled the operation to remove it.

Another example of someone avoiding healing because of fear is one of Dr Singh's elderly patients. She told me that, in her youth, she had seen a healer about a troublesome ailment and had an immediate and full recovery in one session. She was so impressed and overjoyed that she told all her family and friends about it. But they ridiculed her to such an extent that she vowed that she would never go to see a healer again, no matter how ill she was. It seems strange that, despite the fact that her family and friends must have seen the evidence with their own eyes, they refused to acknowledge it. Stranger still that she would rather be ill than be taunted for using an unorthodox therapy that she knew worked. However, when Dr Singh recommended healing to her, she did overcome her lifelong stance and agreed to have a session with me. Constant abdominal pain had made her housebound for some time, but this disappeared during the session and she left the hospital walking normally. The next time I saw her, she told me that, after the previous session, she had caught the bus into town and spent several happy hours shopping, as though she had been let out of prison. By the evening, though, she was back to square one. On that particular occasion, the escape from pain could only be counted in hours, but it proved the principle that healing was effective. A second session gave longer-lasting results but, again, the pain returned. Knowing that it was impossible for her to reach any of our voluntary groups, I offered to see her weekly at the hospital. Unfortunately, she felt that the pain was too great for her to travel by public transport and that taxis would be too expensive.

A man once initially shied away from having healing because he thought that I might psychically discover secrets about him and his past. Even if people have nothing to be ashamed of, they naturally expect their privacy to be respected. As regards 'picking up' information of any sort, no ethical healer would attempt to do so, even if it were possible. It would be prying.

Some people refuse healing because their spouse has influenced them against it. Occasionally, I ask patients in the waiting area if they would like a healing session before their appointment with Dr Singh. Female patients often turn to their husband or partner for a decision, rather than make up their own mind. In this situation, the husband almost always dismisses the idea, and his wife then declines the offer. I have not seen this happen the other way about, where a man asks his wife for advice or permission.

On the other hand, some women know full well that their husband will be against them having healing, and they are prepared to resort to subterfuge. A woman with Parkinson's disease found that healing eased her symptoms tremendously, but she had to come secretly for sessions because her husband was set against it. He controlled her every move so it was inevitable that he would eventually discover what she was doing. Sure enough, he found out and stopped her from having healing again.

It is not only husbands who stop wives from having healing. An attractive young woman had an abusive ex-partner, and his persistent calls were unwelcome and frightening. After two healing sessions, she found the courage to demand that he stop contacting her. He must have recognised a new tone in her voice, because his calls dwindled and stopped. When she told her priest about it, he advised against having healing again and she complied. Other priests welcome healing, even at orthodox Catholic and Anglican churches, but it depends on the attitude of the particular priest in charge.

Additional reasons for refusing healing are more to do with not truly wanting to get well. This category is as much an obstacle for medics as it is for healers. However, healing helps melt away the underlying fears that cause resistance to positive change, and this is another way in which healing can support conventional treatment.

For some, illness brings compassionate care and attention that would otherwise be missing from their lives. Many people appreciate and welcome the kindly interest of medical professionals. Some have little human contact in any other way. Even people with family around them sometimes feel neglected. More than one person has told me that they did not know they were loved by their families until they were diagnosed with a terminal condition.

Others are afraid of the responsibilities that accompany a return to health. While a person is ill, he or she might not be expected to contribute as much as others, whether in the workplace or at home. Some might not be able to work at all, and the longer that someone remains in this demoralising situation, the more daunting it must be for them to return to the world of work and independent living.

Another reason can be financial. One patient told me that she fell ill and temporarily had to be on Sickness Benefit but as soon as she felt capable of work again, she found a job. She felt that a menial position would help rebuild the confidence necessary to return to her own line of work. However, on pay day, she was shocked to find that her take-home pay was not enough to cover the bills. She was keen to work but could not afford to. Believing that she had no choice, she feigned a relapse of her previous illness and went back on Sickness Benefit.

Another patient confided that she wanted to be well enough to do what she wanted but at the same time remain disabled enough to continue having a new Mobility car every three years. She had not been able to afford a new car when she worked for a living and did not want to lose this valuable asset.

Someone else told me that she did not want a healing session because she would feel a fraud if the pain disappeared. She was concerned that people would think that the pain had not been real. Furthermore, she had an imminent appointment with a specialist and did not want to waste his time by arriving with nothing to complain of.

Others refuse healing because they believe that they are not sick enough to warrant it. They feel that others are in greater need and should take their place. In reality, it is better to tackle a problem while it is small, rather than wait for it to get out of hand. All of us can benefit from healing, even if we appear to be happy and healthy to the outside world. Not one person is physically perfect throughout and totally free of stress and worry. Having regular healing sessions is an easy and pleasant method of gaining and maintaining the inner equilibrium that leads to good health.

Healing at the Hospital

Most people dismiss the idea of healing because they think it is preposterous, which is entirely understandable. After all these years, I sometimes have the same thought myself, even part way through a healing session. How on earth can placing my hands near to someone's body make a difference to their health or wellbeing? Yet the feedback from patients continues to corroborate the hundreds of positive comments and reactions that have gone before.

As well as being a hospital specialist, Dr Singh was also a Senior Lecturer at the University of Birmingham's Medical School. He therefore knew of a forum where first-year students are introduced to a complementary therapy, and he suggested that I apply to be a tutor for it. Having given talks to numerous self-help groups, this was well within my capacity and I applied. At the forum, the students are split into groups of around 18 strong and each therapist gives their group a one-hour lecture on their particular modality. Immediately afterwards, another cohort of students replaces the first and the lecture is repeated.

After the talk, I give each student a leaflet about healing and a free copy of the 'Sleep Easy & Be Well' CD. I invite them to copy the CD for their student colleagues as it should help them during their years of study, especially at exam times and prior to job interviews. Another plus is that when they eventually enter the medical profession they may have already experienced a form of healing.

Within the first few years of being involved in this forum, I was able to recommend other healers to the organisers. Between us, we currently introduce healing to around 100 future medical professionals each year. A one-hour talk might be a small beginning but who knows where these seeds might take root.

Another spin-off from Dr Singh being a tutor at the Medical School is that he sometimes has students in attendance at his Wednesday morning clinics. Again, I give each of them a leaflet and a copy of the CD, inviting them to copy the disk for their fellow students.

Some of these students accept a healing session for themselves to see what happens and how it feels. Amidst their heavily pressured academic life, a chance to lie down and relax for 20 minutes must be a welcome oasis for them. Their responses mirror those of the patients, and it is gratifying that they will take this personal experience forward with them into their medical careers.

Other medical students choose to sit and watch a session in progress, and afterwards discuss with the patient how it felt to them. Some learn that pain or discomfort has receded or disappeared, while others are intrigued by the sensations that patients describe.

Constantly looking for ways to spread the word about healing, I thought that an explanatory DVD could be helpful. I applied for another Lottery grant to provide the funding, which sent me into another whirl of activity. The full DVD can be viewed on our healing group's website, where the individual interviews with doctors, healers and patients are also showcased separately.

One of these interviews is with Marie Withers, an accountant and business owner. We first became friends when our boys started school together. On the DVD, she says:

'I was diagnosed with breast cancer in May 2000. I had a mastectomy in June and I started a radical course of chemotherapy. It was the year end at work and I had an awful lot of things going on and to be organising. I set off doing quite well but then, one day, I seemed to hit a wall and I recalled [that Sandy] was involved in healing and had told me that if I ever needed any help to get in touch with her. I saw her regularly but had never asked about the healing. One day I got up to go to work and decided I couldn't go. I was a mess. I phoned her up and she was available, which was brilliant. I went straight round to her house and began a course of healing, which saved my life, I think.

'I sat in a chair and had healing that first time, and felt a complete sense of relaxation. I cried but I didn't sob, I didn't move my shoulders and I didn't cry out. My eyes just dripped water for about half an hour, and I felt so good afterwards that I did go to work.

'Physically, the chemotherapy started knocking me about an awful lot. I reacted very badly and spent about two weeks of each month in hospital and [Sandy] came along to give me healing in hospital, which proved fantastic. It was beneficial, it cheered me up, it made me feel better and I could look more positively at life instead of negatively because, having cancer, everything becomes negative. You question your future. You question your life. Your friends and family find it hard to cope so you find yourself supporting them as much as some of them support you. But when I had the healing I was the one being supported and helped—just me. It was fantastic.

'I still go back [to the healing centre]. Every now and again, with the pressures of everyday life you get stressed out. You don't give yourself enough time, 'me' time, relaxation time, and when I go to the [healing centre] it's like an oasis of calm. I can walk in there and start feeling better already. When I've had the healing I feel wonderful.'

Marie mentions how her eyes continually watered during her first session, and I remember us laughing afterwards because her ears were completely full! Streaming tears, without actually crying, is a sign of deep emotional release and is often commented on by patients. Sixteen years later, Marie continues to live life with enthusiasm.

People who survive a nightmare experience usually want to forget that it ever happened. Marie was different. She had the fortitude to offer support to others who found themselves reeling after a devastating diagnosis. She would point them in my direction, and one of these was another mother of young children. She was suffering too badly from the side effects of chemotherapy to travel to the healing centre, so I went to her house. In addition to the primary tumours, she was worried about some in her neck and shoulders that had newly developed. We could easily feel them. She was highly sceptical that healing could help but during that first session, she thought that she could feel the lumps in her neck physically shrinking. Certainly, within a few visits there was no trace of them. Once she began having healing sessions, the side effects of the chemotherapy treatment reduced substantially. Ultimately, she made a full recovery but the episode had been so traumatising that she avoided any mention of it, even years later.

Healing in a Hospital

David Daniels explains on the DVD how he became a healer after receiving healing for an injury. He had been recommended to me by a mutual friend whose teenage daughter had suffered a serious problem with her spine. The young girl's pain and distress were substantially alleviated in just one session, but I continued giving her healing for several weeks. She improved to such a remarkable degree that several members of her family subsequently asked for a session with me for different things.

When David first called me, our voluntary group only offered sessions on a Monday morning, and David worked full-time. It would be impossible for him to attend during the working week so I made an exception and invited him to my home. This was most convenient for him, because it transpired that he lived just around the corner. In his interview, he says:

'I had been involved in an accident where I suffered physical injury to my knee joint. I was off work for a long time. I was under pressure at work and quite depressed. I was in quite a bad way, really, and found that healing helped on all those levels at once. It eased my depression and made me feel stronger inside. The pain subsided and it gave me inner strength to cope. I thought that if I could give that to someone else, it would be a fantastic thing to do, and that's why I became a healer.'

While David was training, we opened up our Sunday evening sessions where he was able to practise his new skills alongside qualified healers. Despite having a full-time job and extended family to care for, David volunteered to take over organising the Sunday evening sessions when we sorely needed someone, and he continues to do so. He was also one of the main healers on the research trial.

Both Marie's account and David's attest to the fact that healing helped them in a range of ways. Pain and discomfort had been eased, they were now thinking more positively, and their mood was more buoyant.

Coral Gardiner PhD is another person who relates her healing story on the DVD. Unknown to me, Coral had a long-standing medical condition for which she needed to have regular blood checks at the Haematology Clinic. After a number of healing sessions, she had a memorable appointment at the clinic and recounts the occasion in her DVD interview:

'The consultant said to me, 'I'd like you to take a second blood test'. I was a bit curious about this and asked if he was sure because I was the first one in the queue [meaning that the blood sample could not have been mixed up with anyone else's]. The consultant agreed and said he would re-run the test on the same blood instead of taking another sample. When he returned he said that they had checked my blood a second time because it was normal. I looked at him and thought, 'My blood hasn't been normal for 12 years!' The consultant confirmed that my blood was just the same as anyone else's and that they couldn't believe it. I was just through the roof, skipping through the clouds. I could not believe it.'

As a result of her experience, Coral trained to be a healer and became a devoted volunteer at our centre.

Dr Singh agreed to be interviewed for the DVD and stated the following:

'I have been a gastroenterology consultant since 1997, seeing patients with abdominal pain, chest pain, anaemia, lack of energy, weight loss, etc. We do the best we can for patients in terms of investigation and assurance, offering medication or surgery, where appropriate.

'Many of our patients still have symptoms despite our best efforts so, in that situation, I ask patients if they are interested in seeing the healer and, if so, they see the healer following seeing me. We have had this healing service in my clinic for over two years and in that time more than 200 patients have had healing treatment. The responses have been, on the whole, very positive, and for some people very dramatically beneficial.'

Remembering that Dr Singh's patients had only one 20-minute treatment, it must have been astounding for him to witness 'very dramatic benefits', especially in the early days.

In the main, the healers that I introduced to the hospital worked in the Oncology Department, most often seeing patients but

61

occasionally members of staff. Dr John Glaholm, a specialist consultant oncologist, agreed to appear on our DVD and described his own encounter with healing thus:

'I first heard about the [voluntary] healing service [in the Oncology Department] from chemo staff. I have allergy problems myself and one of my colleagues suggested that healing could help.

'I had a number of sessions lasting 20–30 minutes after the end of my clinic, usually very stressful days, that I found tremendously valuable. It provided a tremendous feeling of deep relaxation and wellbeing that continued. I have found this service particularly beneficial and I know that a lot of our patients use this healing service to great effect. The service is provided by volunteer healers, but it is something that the NHS has to consider taking on board as part of a total package for people with cancer because I think that the benefits are certainly significant. If the healing service were funded by the NHS, it could be expanded so that all of the patients could be cared for this way.

'Before having healing I was open-minded about whether it would be of benefit or not. In conventional medicine, we often don't have full answers to problems. You can't just dismiss something because you don't have a scientific understanding of how it might work.

'I would certainly recommend it to all patients and would like to see a totally comprehensive service available.

'Given the pressures that front-line staff in the health service are under—those who are actively caring for patients in clinics and wards—the stress levels can be extremely high. The psychological burden of dealing with people who are ill is quite considerable and this kind of service would be absolutely invaluable.'

Key Points

1. Members of a reputable healing organisation are subject to:

   a. national standards of training taught by accredited tutors,

   b. a minimum training period of two years,

   c. a final assessment,

   d. a professional code of conduct, and

   e. disciplinary procedures.

2. Healing Trust members do not diagnose, prescribe or manipulate.

3. Healing is non-invasive and suitable for all patients no matter how immobile or fragile.

4. Unconscious patients can be given healing.

5. Pregnant mothers and babies can be given healing.

6. Dying people can be given healing to ease their passing.

7. There is no limit as to when and where healing can be administered.

8. Spiritual healing complements conventional treatment.

9. Healing helps dissolve underlying fears that often accompany and/or maintain illness, thereby supporting conventional treatment.

10. Healing sessions can be incorporated into any NHS setting.

11. Consultants and hospital staff have witnessed the benefit to patients.

12. Thousands of medically reported cases exist where clinical remission has occurred that could not be attributed to medical intervention. Recovery is therefore possible.

Effects on Hospital Patients

Within a few weeks of beginning work at the hospital, I asked Dr Singh if I could conduct an audit of the responses that patients were having. From the outset, it was clear that people were benefiting from their 20-minute healing session and I wanted to record their comments, otherwise valuable feedback would be lost into the ether. Dr Singh was agreeable to the idea so I set about researching how to devise an appropriate questionnaire.

It needed to be short enough to be completed in the time available yet comprehensive enough to harvest useful and sufficient data. Anyone could expect to feel better immediately after relaxing for 20 minutes, so it was important to include other indicators of improvement.

My first set of questions asked how the patient had been over the past week. This included how much pain they had been in, how well they had slept and how good their relationships had been. The second set focused on how the patient felt after seeing the consultant but immediately before the healing session. The third and last section recorded any differences directly after the healing session. A separate sheet of identical questions asked how they were faring one week later.

Although all of the participants would obviously have gastroenterological complaints, I did not want the questionnaire to focus on that particular aspect. Another disorder might be their worst problem, with digestive issues being a relatively secondary concern for them.

For instance, I had learned that alcohol and drug addictions lead to gastrointestinal problems, so some of Dr Singh's patients would clearly be suffering deep emotional problems with far-reaching consequences. Rather than the effect on specific symptoms, I wanted to find out whether healing improved their experience of life. Pain relief, feeling positive, sleeping better and improved relationships seemed the most important elements.

The forms had to be easy to understand and straightforward to complete. After each question, I gave a scale of one to six so that the participant could circle the number that most represented the severity of an issue. An even number of options meant that people could not sit on the fence and simply plump for the middle one. They would have no option but to circle either a 3 or a 4, each being either side of the mid-way point.

With '1' clearly labelled as 'Excellent' and '6' as 'Terrible', it was surprising that people could be confused by which end of the scale was which. Some people would start off correctly but then suddenly switch part way down the questions. It was easy to notice when someone went wrong and I would correct them but, occasionally, they would switch back again further down. This confusion happened only on the first two sections of the questionnaire—the ones completed before the healing session. Nobody got muddled completing the section that came after the healing session, and I suspect that their new clarity of mind was due to being so relaxed. Nor did they get mixed up when filling in their 'one week later' form in the privacy of their own homes. Again, perhaps it was because they were feeling calmer, as indicated by their feedback, and therefore better able to concentrate.

When I came to formulate the second audit, I attempted to overcome this confusion by adding visual aids, so that the word 'Terrible' was now accompanied by a sad face and 'Excellent' by a smiley face, but this new arrangement made no discernible difference.

Dr Singh also suggested switching the columns around, putting the 'Terrible' end to the left, and the 'Excellent' end to the right. He explained that, because we write from left to right across the page, this particular direction of movement suggests progress. The alteration meant that the numbers on my graphs now count backwards from left to right. For future use, I have reversed the order on the forms so that they count upwards from left to right in the normal way and the resultant graphs follow suit.

One of the questions asked patients to give a score for their wellbeing. Though commonplace, the term 'wellbeing' seemed vague to me, so when I completed the form with patients I verbally explained the meaning before asking for a score. When patients completed their 'one week later' sheet at home they must have remembered my explanation because their scores were in keeping with the rest of the feedback. This point becomes important later regarding the research results.

The questionnaires can be copied from the following pages and used for official audits or by individuals who wish to plot their own progress. In any event, I ask that the results be forwarded to me (via my website) to enable wider analysis of the expanded data set.

The two forms for my first audit were approved by the hospital, and I was able to press ahead with my initial survey of 75 patients. Figures 1 and 2 present the particular questions posed. As explained, the scoring method on these has been updated, so they do not correlate with the bar charts that follow.

Healing in a Hospital

Healing Questionnaire - Form 1

To be completed <u>before</u> receiving your healing session –

	☹ Terrible				Excellent ☺	
Physical comfort over the past week	1	2	3	4	5	6
Relaxation level over the past week	1	2	3	4	5	6
Sleep pattern over the past week	1	2	3	4	5	6
Energy level over the past week	1	2	3	4	5	6
Relationships over the past week	1	2	3	4	5	6
Sense of wellbeing over the past week	1	2	3	4	5	6

(wellbeing = buoyancy, hope, happiness)

	☹ Terrible				Excellent ☺	
Physical comfort today	1	2	3	4	5	6
Relaxation level today	1	2	3	4	5	6
Energy level today	1	2	3	4	5	6
Sense of wellbeing today	1	2	3	4	5	6

To be completed <u>after</u> receiving your healing session –

	☹ Terrible				Excellent ☺	
Physical comfort now	1	2	3	4	5	6
Relaxation level now	1	2	3	4	5	6
Sense of wellbeing now	1	2	3	4	5	6

Figure 1: Questionnaire, Form 1 (updated)

68

Effects on Hospital Patients

Healing Questionnaire - Form 2

To be completed one week after your healing session

	☹ Terrible				Excellent ☺	
Physical comfort over the past week	1	2	3	4	5	6
Relaxation level over the past week	1	2	3	4	5	6
Sleep pattern over the past week	1	2	3	4	5	6
Energy level over the past week	1	2	3	4	5	6
Relationships over the past week	1	2	3	4	5	6
Sense of wellbeing over the past week	1	2	3	4	5	6

(wellbeing = buoyancy, hope, happiness)

A single healing session can be highly effective. However, a series of 6 weekly sessions is often suggested to establish without doubt that improvements have taken place. If such a programme were on offer, would you be interested in participating?

	Not likely				Very likely	
	1	2	3	4	5	6

Any additional comments _____

_____

Figure 2: Questionnaire, Form 2 (updated)

Healing in a Hospital

By the time I began my first audit, I had introduced a few other healers to Dr Singh's Wednesday morning clinic. To speed the process up, I hoped that my colleagues would help by completing these audit forms with their patients. Working alone, I might have hoped to find three patients per morning who were prepared to be included in the audit and, since I was aiming for 100 patients, it would take at least 33 weeks to complete. With help from the other healers, this period of time could be cut by half and they were very willing to assist. However, the paperwork procedure had to be meticulously adhered to for the results to be reliable, and using multiple healers added complications. An administrative assistant would have solved the problems, but we had no such luxury. Consequently, the other healers were relieved of this extra task within the first few weeks, and only my own patients were included in the audit.

Incidentally, once introduced to the hospital environment, these other healers were soon drafted into other departments, where their skills were thoroughly appreciated by patients and staff alike. Unfortunately, over a handful of years, each one of them left without finding a volunteer to take their place. Similarly, my life eventually changed direction, and after seven years of working at the hospital, I moved away from the area. My extensive search for someone to replace me proved fruitless. Not many people have the luxury of being able to offer their time on a voluntary basis during normal working hours. If the position were to become salaried, perhaps it would be a different matter. In the meantime, I attend whenever I visit the Midlands.

Returning to my audit, not one of the patients at the hospital was looking for healing, so they are in a completely different category from those who come to our healing centre. People who actively seek healing are willing to make an effort to attend, are prepared to make a donation and are hopeful of a positive outcome. The people at the hospital, on the other hand, probably agreed to have a session only because Dr Singh suggested it to them in positive terms and they did not like to refuse. In addition, it was available immediately, free of charge and in the next room. It could not have been easier for them.

Effects on Hospital Patients

Whilst walking with them for the few steps between Dr Singh's room and mine, I would usually break the ice by asking whether they had ever had healing before. Almost nobody had. Surprisingly, out of these 75 patients, only the tiniest proportion had ever accessed a complementary therapy of any description. The same picture emerged during my subsequent audit of 192 patients. Yet the Department of Health's document 'Complementary Medicine Information for Primary Care Groups' (19) paints quite a different picture. It states:

'In any year it is estimated that 11% of the population visited a complementary therapist for one of...six named therapies.'

The 'six named therapies' are acupuncture, aromatherapy, chiropractic, homeopathy, hypnotherapy and osteopathy. If healing and popular treatments such as aromatherapy, reflexology and reiki were added to the list, the quoted percentage of 11% would be very much higher. But even the quoted 11% level was in no way reflected amongst the hundreds of patients I treated at the hospital.

It occurred to me that perhaps people who do embrace complementary therapies are less likely to need a consultant. This might help explain why the national figures are so wildly different from my findings with Dr Singh's patients.

As mentioned before, Dr Singh was also a senior lecturer at the University of Birmingham's Medical School. Knowing that I needed to transfer all the audit data into a computer programme, he introduced me to a medical student who was interested in my work. She kindly created a spreadsheet and entered the information, which she then used for a project that formed part of her university degree. We were both gratified because her work saved me many hours, and the audit gave her a unique topic to write about.

The following series of graphs reflect the figures entered. In each of the charts, the height of the columns represents the number of patients. The further they are to the left of the graph, the worse those patients felt.

The first two sections of the questionnaire were completed directly after the patient had seen Dr Singh. It asked how the patient had been over the past week—the week leading up to their consultation. Black columns in the graphs reflect this information.

71

Healing in a Hospital

The second section asked how they felt after their consultation, and grey columns convey the results. Then they had a healing session. The third and final section refers to how patients felt immediately afterwards, and is represented by white columns.

For ease of reference, the discussion regarding each respective graph is presented on the same opening page.

Looking at Figure 3, the black columns illustrate how much pain the patients said they had experienced over the past week. The closer these columns are to the left-hand side of the graph, the more severe their pain was. The column hugging the left-hand side of the graph (position 6) shows that eight people had such terrible pain over the past week that it could not have been worse. Moving to the next black column along (position 5), ten people had terrible pain over the past week but not quite as bad as the people in 6. The next black column is the tallest (position 4), showing that 28 people had very bad pain over the past week but not as bad as the ones in 5. Severity is progressively less as we move towards the right of the graph, until we reach the 'Excellent' end. Here we find four people in the last black column (position 1) who said they had been totally free of pain all week.

Alongside each black column, the grey ones show how much pain the patient was in straight after their consultation with Dr Singh. They had not yet received a healing session but it is nevertheless clear that the whole set of grey columns has moved towards the right-hand side of the graph, compared to the black ones. This means that the patients were in less pain immediately after seeing the consultant than they had been during the past week. We can see that fewer people are in the 6 position, where the pain was the worst possible, and a couple more have joined those in position 1, where they had no pain at all. Instead of peaking at position 4, where the highest black column is, the majority of patients in the grey columns are now in position 3, one step closer towards the 'Excellent' end. An explanation for this shift is offered in a later section.

Immediately after their healing session, respondents were asked the same question again, and the white columns reveal the difference. Now, nobody is in either of the 'Terrible' 6 or 5 positions and only one person is in the 4 column. The two tall white

Effects on Hospital Patients

columns dominating the right-hand side of the graph give evidence of a spectacular reduction of physical suffering. We see that 30 people were entirely pain-free by the end of the session (position 1), and a further 33 had hardly any discomfort (position 2). This means that, in addition to the upshift seen after the consultation, a further 47 people jumped into the top two positions, simply by having a 20-minute healing treatment.

For some, the pain relief was immediate as well as total. One man had endured incessant pain for over a decade, but almost as soon as I started work, it completely vanished. Understandably, he was overwhelmed with relief. He wept.

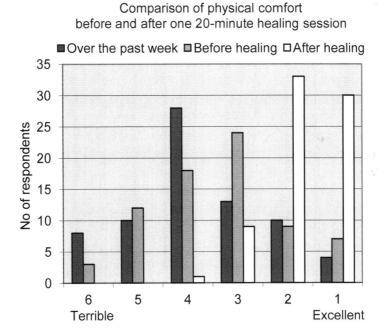

Figure 3: Physical Comfort

When pain is relieved, we can expect people to feel better within themselves.

The term 'sense of wellbeing' describes how positive a person feels and encompasses such aspects as buoyancy, hope and happiness. Figure 4 shows that four people in position 6 could not imagine feeling more miserable and despondent than they had been over the past week. Another 15 (position 5) had suffered almost as badly. A further 44 people in columns 4 and 3 had endured respective levels of dejection.

Again, after the consultation with Dr Singh, we see an improvement because the grey columns have nudged towards the right-hand side of the graph, mainly in columns 4 and 3, but especially in 3.

When asked the same question after their healing session, it was a different picture. The white columns show that nobody at all was in the extremely gloomy position of 6 and only a few appear in positions 5, 4 and 3. The dramatic leap towards the right of the graph demonstrates a massive uplift for these patients during the healing session. The two tall white columns show that 35 people felt brilliant (position 1), and another 30 felt almost as good (position 2).

On top of the gains achieved after their consultation, a further 50 people had moved into the two top positions, simply by spending 20 minutes having a healing session.

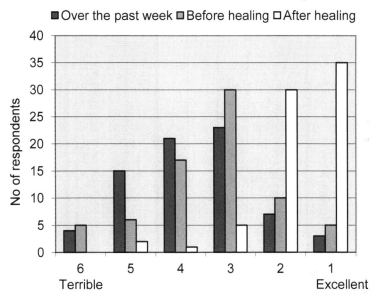

Comparison of Sense of Wellbeing
before and after one 20-minute healing session

Figure 4: Sense of Wellbeing

Figure 5 measures relaxation, and the black column in position 6 indicates that ten people could not imagine feeling more stressed than over the past week. Another 25 people in position 5 had been almost as bad. At the other end of the scale (position 1), only two people had felt relaxed and calm all week

Again, after their consultation with Dr Singh, the grey columns slide across the graph towards the right-hand side, signifying an improvement.

As before, the white columns reveal how people responded to the healing session. Not one person remained highly stressed or worried (positions 6 and 5), and only a couple of people appear in the midway points of 4 and 3. Again, the white columns are highly stacked at the right-hand side of the graph. They represent almost every patient; 46 people could not imagine feeling more relaxed, and a further 27 felt almost as good. The majority of all 75 were now in the 'could not be better' category instead of only two.

In addition to the gains registered after their consultation, a further 58 people were now in the two top positions, as a direct result of having a healing treatment.

Effects on Hospital Patients

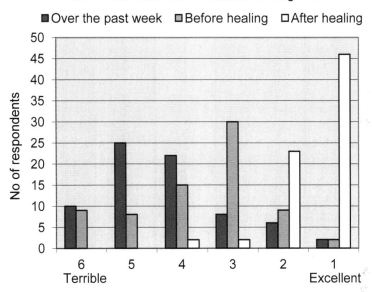

Comparison of Relaxation
before and after one 20-minute healing session

■ Over the past week ▨ Before healing □ After healing

Figure 5: Relaxation

Healing in a Hospital

When plotting the graphs, I was surprised to find the noticeable shift of the grey columns towards the right-hand side of every graph (Figures 3, 4 and 5). This illustrates the improvements experienced by patients on that particular day in comparison to the whole of the previous week.

The grey columns show how patients were feeling after seeing Dr Singh but before having a healing session. Perhaps patients had been keyed up during the week at the prospect of having to visit the hospital and were now relieved that their consultation was over. Maybe some had not yet met Dr Singh and felt uneasy at the prospect of discussing highly personal matters with someone new. And there might be embarrassing examinations to undergo. Others may have worried about getting to the appointment on time and could now relax. Alternatively, having to focus on getting to the appointment may have diverted their attention from their troubles. Some may have been waiting for test results and, now that they knew the outcome, the stress of uncertainty was gone. Of these, some will have been informed that there was nothing more that the medical world could offer them.

The evident improvements—shown by the grey columns, across all three graphs—could also be due to Dr Singh's natural empathy with patients. Compassion from a doctor is known to elicit a positive effect in the patient and could be due to the Hawthorne effect (34). The Hawthorne Works in Chicago had commissioned a study to see if their workers would be more productive in higher or lower levels of light. But productivity seemed to temporarily improve no matter what changes were made, and slumped when the study ended. It was concluded that their increased productivity was simply as a result of the interest being shown in them. Likewise, Dr Singh's patients had received no medical intervention during the consultation yet, directly after receiving his attention, reported feeling better than they had been over the previous week.

An interesting point that emerges from the graphs is the obvious link between wellbeing, relaxation and pain relief. They show that all three aspects improved simultaneously. This phenomenon is made evident to a degree by the grey columns, which register concurrent improvements after the consultation, with all of them shifting a notch towards the 'Excellent' end. But after the healing session, it is made entirely obvious by the towering white columns at the right-hand side of every graph.

Everyone knows from personal experience that it is difficult to relax if something is worrying them. When their mind has been put at ease, they physically relax more. It would seem, then, that peace of mind promotes relaxation, and sufficient relaxation brings about pain relief. Scientific evidence to support this idea is presented later.

It could be said that anyone would expect to feel more at peace and relaxed after lying down for 20 minutes. However, of the 75 patients in this audit, 53 chose to add their personal observations and these give a fuller picture of their experience. The following describe the sensations they encountered during the healing session:

10 felt heat or cold

7 felt heaviness or lightness

6 felt tingling

5 saw light of various colours

3 had involuntary muscle movements

Patients made the following comments after the healing session while they were completing the questionnaire:

21 felt more positive

18 felt relaxed or peaceful

9 stated that pain or discomfort had completely disappeared

6 stated that pain or discomfort had substantially reduced

4 stated that pain or discomfort developed during the session but quickly disappeared

Before any healing session, I let the patient know that they may feel tingling, heat or cold, see colours or experience muscle jumps. Without this forewarning, they may be alarmed if unusual sensations were to occur. Equally, I tell them that they may not see or feel anything out of the ordinary. Although hardly any of my patients knew exactly what to expect, a number of their comments mirrored each other.

Regarding the ones that are reproduced below, I have omitted any that simply repeat the observations listed above and have retained those that give some interesting detail. The unabridged list can be viewed on our healing group's website.

1. Before the session, it felt urgent to leave to visit my husband in hospital but now I feel as though I could just sit here!

2. Wonderful! I feel good for the first time in over 30 years.

3. I felt warmth in the torso, especially in the stomach and colon. Trembling started in right arm during the session but this stopped when the healer touched that shoulder.

4. My left side felt empty. Extra healing was given there and I felt complete.

5. I was aware of lavender light throughout. This has been worthwhile.

6. A tremor that I have had constantly for a year disappeared now and again during session. I was aware of heat in the solar plexus although the healer's hands were cold.

7. I have never sat still and peacefully for so long.

8. I did not expect to be comfortable in the chair, due to my back, but it was. I am very impressed.

9. I felt warmth during the healing sessions and can still feel it now. Also tingling in my hands. I felt physical movements in my knees and a tingling. There is no pain in my left knee now.

10. It is a revelation to me that I have allowed myself to be open to a new approach. My back and shoulder feel eased.

Effects on Hospital Patients

11. I feel that I could sleep for a week! My shoulders feel better now.

12. I felt heavy & tingling during the healing session. I felt a pressure on my shoulders, even when healer took her hands away.

13. I am feeling similar to waking up after a long sleep. It felt as though energy was coming in and going out of the base of my feet.

14. This was a strange but nice experience. I felt tingling and numb all over. Feeling chilled out now.

15. Involuntary muscle movements set up and also various aches and pains arose but they all disappeared during the session. My eyes watered, too.

16. I was most relaxed for what seemed like a long time. It was as though I had been lifted.

17. I have enjoyed the session very much. It felt like lying in the sun. I felt totally at peace.

18. I was aware of coloured circles that gave the impression that something was leaving me, in a positive way.

19. I feel ecstatic! I feel like I could run a marathon. I felt tingling throughout my body, which is happening even now. It was especially strong during the session when the healer's hand was on the part of my body that had been problematic.

20. Before the session, I was dubious and a little cynical. These feelings have all been washed way now and I feel lighter.

21. I had thought that the session would do me no good at all but I definitely feel better.

22. This is the most relaxing technique I have ever experienced! My hands had been sweaty when I arrived but they became dry during the session.

23. I was aware of a purple colour throughout the healing. I found it very relaxing.

24. Wow, marvellous! This has really helped me. My back pain has disappeared!

25. It was as though a huge lamp was switched on above my head. I felt its heat and saw its light.

After concluding the questionnaire, I physically handed them their 'one week later' sheet to complete seven days later. To maximise returns, they were also given a stamped, addressed envelope in which to post it back to Dr Singh.

Of the 75 people in this first audit, 32 returned their feedback sheet. In the following series of graphs you will see that the black bars, as before, reflect how this group of patients had felt during the week prior to having healing. Alongside them, the white bars show the difference they noticed over the following week. As before, where the white bars have shifted to the right-hand side of the graph, this indicates improvement.

For ease of reference, the discussion about a particular chart appears on the same page.

Effects on Hospital Patients

It was delightful to see in graph form (Figure 6) that so many patients had continued to benefit from reduced pain and less discomfort. Improvement for these people had lasted for at least a week and could have remained longer.

If there was a weekly pill that was pleasant to take, had no side effects and achieved as much as this, it would surely be popular. Travelling to somewhere for a healing session each week takes up more time than taking a pill, but the visits could be looked forward to and regarded as a luxurious health pursuit.

In addition to the improvements shown in these graphs, there will also be people who benefited for a short time after the healing session but not to the extent of a week.

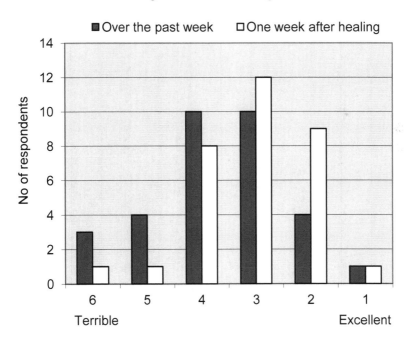

Figure 6: Physical Comfort one week later

83

Healing in a Hospital

Figure 7 shows that improvements gained regarding wellbeing were maintained for at least a week.

The black bars in positions 6 and 5 convey the depth of gloominess and bleak outlook experienced by patients during the week before having healing. This state of mind is usually accompanied by a lack of motivation and pessimism.

At the other end of the scale, a sense of wellbeing incorporates peace of mind, buoyancy and hope. Any shift towards the 'Excellent' end of the graph conveys an upliftment to people's lives.

The evident move of the white bars towards the right-hand side of the graph shows that people continued to feel substantially more upbeat for at least a week after their healing session.

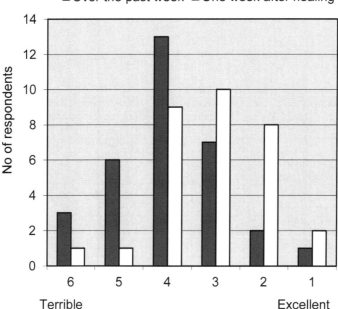

Figure 7: Sense of Wellbeing one week later

Effects on Hospital Patients

With the black columns in Figure 8 mainly being grouped to the left of the graph, we can appreciate the severity of stress suffered by these patients. A week after the healing session, we see that gains achieved had been maintained. The white columns show that people continued to feel far more relaxed than they had before.

An alarming number of people in our society are on medication to overcome anxiety in its different guises, and many more struggle along without medical support. If healing were made available, this natural remedy could help to reduce the NHS pharmaceutical bill and bring an improved quality of life to the countless number of people who suffer with stress and anxiety.

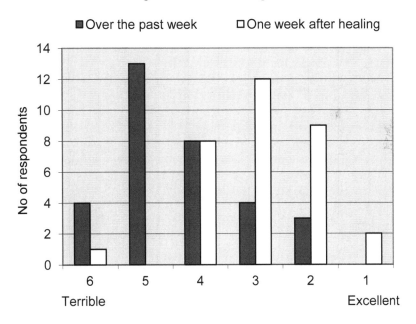

Figure 8: Relaxation one week later

Healing in a Hospital

It takes a great deal of energy to worry or to be stressed, which must be why we find these states of mind so draining. Stress causes muscle groups to bunch up, most notably in the shoulders or stomach. People often comment after a healing session that they did not realise how tense they had previously been. With so much energy being expended keeping muscles taut, less energy must be available for day-to-day activities. Also, one would think that tense muscles must restrict the ability of bodily fluids to flow as easily as they should, and perhaps this contributes to medical issues.

With patients feeling more relaxed, Figure 9 graphically reveals the marked improvement to people's energy levels, one week after their healing session. Again, this benefit may well have lasted longer.

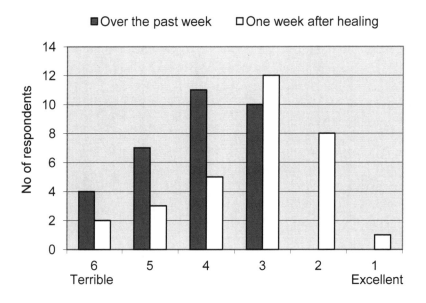

Comparison of energy levels
'before' and 'one week after'
a single 20-minute healing session

Figure 9: Energy Levels one week later

Effects on Hospital Patients

With less anxiety, it should be no surprise that these patients perceived that it was easier to get along with others. Figure 10 displays a noticeable improvement in their personal relationships. Enhanced interaction with family members, friends, neighbours and work colleagues is bound to trigger an upward spiral of harmony and vitality. If there were a cheap and legal pill that improved how we all felt about each other, it ought to be a bestseller!

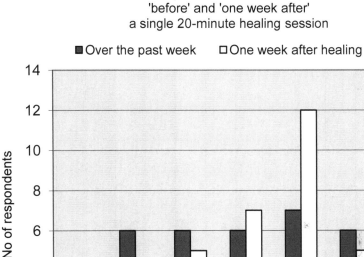

Figure 10: Relationships one week later

Healing in a Hospital

Figure 11 displays the striking improvement that patients experienced regarding their sleep patterns after just one healing session. The white bars, representing results one week later, have moved considerably towards the right-hand side of the graph, signifying a massive improvement. Again, this uplift may have continued for longer than a week.

Comparison of Sleep Pattern
'before' and 'one week after'
a single 20-minute healing session

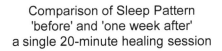

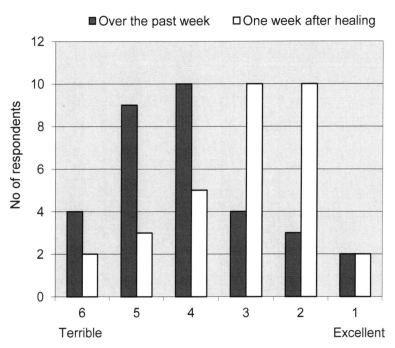

Figure 11: Sleep Pattern one week later

Effects on Hospital Patients

Nobody feels at their best after a restless night but research shows that lack of sleep can be detrimental in a host of ways (35):

1. A study of 56 teenagers over a period of 16 weeks showed that bouts of illness declined when pupils had a longer night's sleep. This reduced school absences, particularly among boys.

2. Sleeping poorly may result in a type of brain abnormality that is associated with Alzheimer's disease. Brain images of adults found that those who said they slept poorly had an increased build-up of beta-amyloid plaques, one of the hallmarks of Alzheimer's.

3. Regularly getting too little sleep could increase the risk of aggressive breast cancer. Getting six hours or less each night also seems to increase the risk of cancer recurring among post-menopausal breast cancer patients.

4. People who regularly sleep for less than six hours a night are 25% more likely to be overweight. The less that women sleep, the more abdominal fat they have, especially those under the age of 50. People who slept less than five hours a night were shown to have belly bulk that often exceeded the medical limit, beyond which coronary diseases become far more likely. Too little sleep affects the production of cortisol and growth hormones in a way that contributes to increased fat storage in the abdomen.

5. Those who sleep less than six hours a night are at greater risk of having a stroke compared with those who sleep seven to eight hours a night. It seems that chronic lack of sleep causes inflammation, elevates blood pressure, raises the heart rate and affects glucose levels, leading to a higher risk of having a stroke.

6. Severe sleep deprivation affects the body's immune system in the same way that physical stress does.

7. A ten-year study found that sleep deprivation raises average daily blood pressure and increases the heart rate. Analysing data from 4,800 people, it was found that those who slept less than

six hours a night were twice as likely to have high blood pressure than those getting quality sleep.

8. Too little sleep leads to lacklustre and wrinkle-prone skin. Those who had poor quality sleep for at least a month had more fine lines, uneven pigmentation and less elastic skin than good sleepers. Bad sleepers also made slower recovery from sunburn, which suggests that sleep is needed to rectify skin damage. Their skin lost water 30% faster than that of good sleepers, making them more susceptible to wrinkling and environmental damage.

9. Quality, unbroken sleep is essential for night-time production of muscle tissue and growth hormones.

10. Workers deprived of sleep costs the UK economy an estimated £1.6bn a year or £280 for each worker.

11. Lack of sleep may fuel a junk food habit. It hinders the ability to make healthy choices about food by changing the way our brains function regarding impulse control and decision-making.

It would seem that some patients sink into a particularly deep state of sleep during a healing session because they exhibit rapid eye movement (REM). During REM sleep, the brain consolidates and processes the information learned during the day and forms neural connections that strengthen memory. It also replenishes the brain's supply of feel-good chemicals like serotonin and dopamine that boost a person's mood during the day. When a person does not get sufficient REM, the brain significantly increases its number of attempts to go into the REM stage while asleep, which suggests that this type of sleep must be crucial (36).

Not one person whose comments are recorded in this book has mentioned noticing that their eyelids flickered during the session. Although I have seen this occur many times, the patients themselves must be oblivious to it. Behind their closed eyelids, I can also see that their eyeballs are very active during these phases. For some patients these movements occur in short flurries but, occasionally, they can last for the entirety of a session. Whenever I witness someone exhibiting these eye movements during a healing session, they usually report feeling markedly better afterwards. They often mention having had pleasant sensations and sometimes lucid dreams of happy times in their childhood.

According to the Mental Health Foundation (November 2012), more than 30% of the UK population has sleeping difficulties. With insomnia being so common, I felt that our 'Sleep Easy & Be Well' CD should be useful to many people. It is a spoken word recording with tranquil music in the background that helps people get to sleep and have healing in the process. Not only is it substantially cheaper than sleeping tablets, but it is also a natural solution with no side effects.

Dr Singh gave a copy to one of his patients who had not slept since her husband died, two years previously. She reported sleeping well from the first time she listened to it.

A man who came to our healing centre had been on sleeping tablets for three years but came straight off them when he started listening to the CD.

Someone I knew listened to it while doing the ironing. She wanted to check it out before offering it to her wakeful teenage daughter. Despite not using the CD in the manner intended, this mother was bemused to find that she was no longer afraid of going to the dentist.

One of the hospital staff listened to the CD so many times that she became a little bored with it and asked if I would please produce another. But despite the drawback of now finding the CD so predictable, she continued to find it more effective than the many others that she owned, and I was flattered to hear that her collection included some famous names. Different styles appeal to different people so if one CD does not help, it is well worth trying another.

Many patients say that they sleep like a log the first night after a healing session. The graph in Figure 11 shows that this welcome effect lasts for at least a week for many people. It may be permanent for some.

Returning to my audit of 75 patients, the 'one week later' sheet invited additional feedback of any sort and, of the 32 patients who returned their form, the following are some of the comments that go beyond simply saying that they felt better.

1. I think that my appreciation of my relationships has increased.

2. My physical problems did not cease after the session but I felt calmer and more able to cope with them. I would definitely be interested in more healing sessions as I felt so much better after just one.

3. I felt relieved in a way. I am hoping that more sessions will make a magnificent change. I am eager to see how I would be after a number of sessions.

4. I am very grateful for my extra energy levels. I felt better after one session but would be grateful for more.

5. I am really impressed and wish that this was available where I live.

6. I had a couple of good days during the week and they were good and relaxed.

7. I have felt calmer about things.

8. I slept really well the first night and I feel very positive now.

9. Today I find out my results and, considering that this has been on my mind, I have been sleeping well and waking up feeling okay.

10. Although my physical condition persists, my feeling of wellbeing has improved.

11. I was really good for a few days but then went downhill.

12. I am feeling relatively good.

13. After my healing session, my relationship with my boyfriend was (and still is) good as the healing got rid of my stress and anxiety levels.

14. I felt irritable after the session but this lifted the next day and I felt very good.

15. I am finding that I can do more things in the day than I could before.

A couple of months after completing this first audit, I bumped into a young man at a Drugs Awareness event. He recognised me and came over to introduce himself as one of the patients I had seen at Good Hope Hospital. Beaming with confidence, he told me that he had been free of all symptoms since that session and that he was now working. I asked if he had sent in his 'one week later' sheet with this splendid news, but he confessed that he had not. Presumably, there will be other patients who had positive responses but overlooked sending in their forms. Had they done so, my graphs may have looked even better.

Another of the audit patients was a woman who had experienced a range of severe problems for over 30 years. A short while after I had seen her, she returned for an appointment with Dr Singh and told me that her extreme addiction to coffee had disappeared after the healing session. I also learned that a hospital letter to her doctor reported 'unexplained anaemia resolved', 'blood count up' and 'stomach and colon normal'.

A woman returned to see Dr Singh for a follow-up appointment and took up the invitation to have a second healing session. With a radiant smile, she confided that, after the previous session several months earlier, she found the courage to sign up for a literacy course. She had not been able to read or write and had been too self-conscious to do anything about it before.

A young woman who had been one of Dr Singh's patients for three years was included in this audit. She told me nothing of her condition and was secretly convinced that healing could not make a difference. This is the letter that she subsequently wrote:

'Three years ago I was diagnosed with an auto-immune disease. I began a heavy dose of steroids, along with other forms of medication to bring the illness under control. I had ups and downs and every so often I felt so ill that I would have to stay in bed. But with the loving support of my family I always pulled through, stronger in spirit than before.

Healing in a Hospital

'Recently, one of my symptoms was what I can only describe as 'heavy legs'. I was unable to walk with the heavy weight of each leg. I collapsed at work and I was off work for a week. There was no explanation as to why my legs were failing to work properly and blood test results came back normal. I believed that I would just have to grin and bear it. That is, until my consultant suggested that I have a healing session. I have to admit that I was very sceptical as I had never been treated by a healer and had no faith in them.

'Sandy Edwards was pleasant, warm and welcoming but I was still wary and decided not to tell her of my ailments or give her any information—just to see the true outcome of the healing session.

'I felt what can only be described as lighter. In fact, I went home and took my two crazy dogs for a walk! This was something I had not managed to do for the past two weeks. When I returned home from the walk, my legs were shaky and had returned to the heavy feeling. But the next day my legs began to return to normal. The weight left my legs, and the soreness on the balls of my feet vanished. The following day was as if nothing had been wrong with me and I returned to work.

'I did not believe that an alternative method would convert me from a very poorly, non-walking girl to my old healthy self within days. I was sceptical and believed that only a tablet could help me get better but now I am more flexible in my thinking.'

It is important to note that the 'one week later' responses and the detailed written accounts, such as the one above, offer more powerful evidence than the questionnaires that I filled in with the patient on the day of the session. People generally like to please and, being face to face with me, some patients may have felt inclined to respond more favourably than they actually experienced. By contrast, the 'one week later' information was completed anonymously, in the privacy of their homes, free of external influence, and is therefore dependable. Statements confessing that

Effects on Hospital Patients

their prior disbelief in healing had now been shattered could only be genuine. In addition, the detailed written statements brim with authenticity.

Subsequent to completing the audits, a young man arrived at Dr Singh's clinic who had to walk in a peculiar way because one of his legs was lifeless. It had been so since birth yet he managed to walk without the aid of crutches. He was a complementary therapist himself and had enthusiastically accessed different natural remedies for any ailments. After his session with me, he was in awe that he had been able to feel his leg for the first time in his life. It had always been dead to him, but throughout the session he could tell it was there, just like the other one. The sensation disappeared when he got up off the couch, but the experience proved that it was possible. It would have been fascinating to see whether further developments might occur with additional sessions. Unfortunately, although he was keen to make the arrangements, he found that he was unable to attend.

No patient that I have ever seen, whether at the hospital or anywhere else, has reported a detrimental effect as a result of healing. There were two hospital patients I should mention, though, who seemed gripped with fear at the thought of healing, and I therefore did not give any.

The first was a man who had suffered a traumatic event when he was a child and had been troubled with a range of medical problems ever since. He did not remember anything of the actual incident, even though he was totally conscious throughout. People who were present at the time told him afterwards what had happened, giving details of what he had said and done. Although he recalled nothing of the incident, every small thing had caused him acute anxiety since that time. He told me that the thought of completing a form would literally make him faint so he was not included in my audit. Simply being asked to close his eyes and relax made his head spin. I suggested that he keep his eyes open, but this made no difference.

The second person was a woman who seemed rigid with stress. She told me that she constantly fretted about her family and that she was determined to carry on doing so. Perhaps she felt that worrying was about all she could do for her loved ones, because she was physically incapacitated. Personally, I believe that incessant anxiety like this is a contributory factor towards physical problems but, whether or not this is true, her family would surely have benefited if she had tried to be a happier person. I attempted to help her relax but, as soon as she closed her eyes, she became extremely dizzy and asked me to stop.

It was interesting to note that both of these people suffered extreme dizziness when distressed. Perhaps it is coincidental but I know someone else who loses her sense of balance every time she meets a situation that seems threatening. Although it may be considered as being vertigo, fear seems to be the underlying cause for all three of these people. As regards the two hospital patients, I had been unable to give healing to either so, instead, I sent each of them what is termed 'distant healing', which is explained later.

As a consultant gastroenterologist, Dr Singh has many patients suffering from irritable bowel syndrome (IBS). IBS patients know that their symptoms get worse when they are stressed or worried.

The first scientific evidence that the way we think and feel affects the digestive system was discovered in the 1820s (37). A young American soldier was accidentally shot at close range, blasting off the front part of his chest and abdomen. Alexis St Martin was not expected to survive such horrific injuries, but a US army surgeon, William Beaumont, fixed up what was possible and took the young soldier under his wing. Alexis was tough and recovered but, despite all Beaumont's efforts, a hole remained that was directly into his stomach. A fold, like a lid, eventually grew over it that could be opened and shut at will. This curious lid made it possible for Beaumont to conduct digestion experiments by putting in different foodstuffs attached to a string that he pulled out at intervals. It was in this manner that he discovered that digestion was affected whenever Alexis was under stress, or worried about something.

If a chemical reaction is known to occur in the stomach due to stress and worry, it seems likely that it is happening throughout the entire body. Different people may have different weak points through which their inner turmoil makes itself manifest. For IBS sufferers, the weak point is clearly their digestive system, whereas others might suffer with something else. Fibromyalgia is a very painful condition that, like IBS, has no physical causes yet flares up with anxiety (38). Other disorders known to be affected by stress are psoriasis, eczema and hair loss. There may be many illnesses that have not yet been scientifically linked to underlying stress. Low-level but ongoing anxiety probably has subtle effects that overspill in the longer term, like a reservoir that slowly fills until the dam can no longer withstand the pressure.

The Stress Management Society explains the mechanics of stress in detail and offers a range of remedies to try (39). In a nutshell, anxiety triggers an instinctive reaction known as the 'fight or flight' response, which we experience as stress. This 'fight or flight' is a survival necessity for when situations truly are dangerous. Hormones are instantly produced to help us to run faster and fight harder, and they also focus our mind solely on the immediate hazard so that we decide swiftly whether to stand and fight or to run away.

Originally, this reaction was designed for early humans who lived in caves and could have been eaten by wild animals. Few life-threatening events occur in modern-day living, but the same physical reactions continue to occur in response to situations that simply appear to threaten us in some way. Pressure of work, moving house, divorce, children, relationships, traffic jams, unexpected events and financial worries are all contenders. Even a pleasurable event, such as going on holiday, can cause anxiety if the person worries about catching the aeroplane or whether the house might be burgled in their absence.

The more often the 'fight or flight' response is stimulated, the more overactive the hormone production becomes, leading to high blood pressure and heart problems. In addition, these hormones make us sensitive, aggressive, excitable, anxious and jumpy, which are all potentially life-saving qualities in an emergency. In the absence of a real crisis, though, these attitudes and emotions remain in play and make life unpleasant. Vigorous exercise would help burn up these energies, but few people are sufficiently active.

Also, while focused on our own survival, we view the world as a hostile place and we make decisions for our own good instead of considering others.

Clearly, it is well worth finding ways to combat stress and, as can be seen by the audit responses, healing is experienced as a highly effective antidote. The opposite of the 'flight or flight' response is the 'rest and digest' state, and patients regularly comment on feeling more relaxed during and after healing. In addition, they often report feeling more alert and energised, and this makes sense. In light of the above, it seems clear that the massive amount of energy expended on feeling stressed had now been freed up for productive and pleasurable activity.

As regards Dr Singh's gastroenterology patients, the 'digest' part of the 'rest and digest' state of being should be particularly relevant and helpful.

Over the years, I have witnessed a few occasions where a convict has been brought to Dr Singh, handcuffed to prison officers. It is impracticable to offer healing in these circumstances, though I had long wanted to bring healing into prisons. When I mentioned this intention to Dr Singh, it transpired that he had been giving meditation classes at a local prison on a voluntary basis. He offered to enquire on my behalf about the possibility of introducing healing.

I had in mind the idea of conducting an audit, on similar lines to that of the hospital study, but only with offenders due to be released in six weeks' time. Each one would have weekly healing sessions until their release, and subsequent data would ascertain whether reoffending rates for this group were reduced.

Generally, the public does not approve of criminals being treated to enjoyable activities, but this study could potentially benefit everyone in various ways. Just one incident can cause severe detriment to a victim's life, livelihood and family, so even a minimal improvement in reoffending rates would make a massive difference to the lives of numerous innocent individuals. Add to that the financial burden of prosecuting and jailing the offender as well as the expense of a victim's medical treatment, lost income, sick pay and insurance claims. If six healing sessions helped just one inmate to lead a productive life thereafter, subsequent crimes might be avoided, and the public purse could make some worthwhile savings.

But the initial step towards this goal was to gain approval from the prison. Dr Singh put me in touch with the appropriate person within the jail and, as one might expect, it took a very long while to get the idea sanctioned. By that time, I was no longer able to make the commitment but perhaps someone will read this and be inspired to take the idea up.

Working with young offenders could be even more rewarding for society in the longer term. They have a longer—and potentially criminal—life ahead of them and if young people benefit from healing, they are more likely to guide their children towards a more positive future.

With the intention of helping youngsters, I offered to give ten-minute taster sessions to pupils and staff at a local secondary school during lunchtime. However, before any child can have healing, their parents must give written permission. To avoid this encumbrance, it was decided that I could talk students through a self-relaxation process instead. I attended each term, once a week, for the next three years on a voluntary basis. The breezeblock room that I was allocated had no windows, and was piled high with stock. Although appearing to be the furthest removed from being a haven of tranquility, the space successfully served its dual purpose as a healing sanctuary for staff and relaxation room for pupils.

A particularly diligent and stressed sixth-former was so impressed by how calm and clearheaded she now felt that she wanted these relaxation sessions to be a regular activity for all A-level students. One of the first-year boys seemed beset with silent troubles each time he arrived, and rarely uttered a word. But he would leave walking more upright and with the hint of a smile.

Sadly, not enough people attended the sessions to make it worthwhile continuing, probably because the room was too tucked away. In addition, the staff and pupils were not keen on bumping into each other during break times. But there was no choice of location, and the staff members who came gave positive feedback. One in particular reported that her long-term palpitations disappeared.

The value of positive relaxation for children has been reported by two schools in Baltimore, USA, since replacing detention with meditation (40). Located in an area of deprivation, home life for many of these young pupils is chaotic and fraught. Since adopting the new strategy, there have been no suspensions of pupils, and referrals to the head for disciplinary issues have been rare. The general atmosphere has improved in the schools, creating a better learning environment and increased productivity. Furthermore, students have described how they can now respond in a more positive way to the difficult situations they face at home.

The primary data of my first audit were scrutinised by academics and medical practitioners. No queries were raised, which confirms its integrity.

I sent a copy of the audit results to as many people and places as might be interested and placed it on our voluntary group's website. The Healing Trust published an article in their national magazine and added it to the research section of their website.

Originally, I had aimed for 100 patients but, due to the amount of work involved, I stopped at 75. I cannot recall what possessed me to begin another audit almost immediately. Perhaps I felt that there was more power in bigger numbers.

My second audit of 192 patients, added to the first, makes a grand total of 267 hospital patients whose responses to healing have been recorded. Hoping to harvest more detailed information from the second audit, I altered the style of the questions, but the feedback was essentially the same.

The graphs are almost identical to those of the first audit, so there is little point in reproducing them here. The full details appear on our healing group's website. Out of the 192 patients included in this audit:

55 experienced the sensation of heat or cold

52 stated that they now felt more positive

49 people stated that pain or discomfort had disappeared or substantially reduced

30 experienced tingling or rippling sensations

29 experienced involuntary muscle movements

28 experienced seeing light

22 experienced heaviness or lightness

Effects on Hospital Patients

Many of the individual remarks made after the healing session echo those in the first audit, but the personal descriptions are often unique. The comments reproduced below only include those that go beyond repeating the list of observations above.

1. I felt great comfort when the healer's hands were on my lower belly. Also on the shoulders. I feel marvellous.

2. I saw purple light and some dark clouds moved away. Cramps developed but they then disappeared.

3. When the healer touched my abdomen, I could feel bloating and a 'letting go' of it. My left wrist and elbow area went very warm. I started coughing during the healing and my eyes were watering.

4. I had tingling around my right thumb and, at the same time, my left hip and side. My shoulders had been tense but they are fine now.

5. I felt benefit immediately. A ripple moved through my body from my pelvis right up through my body.

6. I now have total peace of mind. I was very stressed and agitated beforehand.

7. An existing ache disappeared. I experienced floating.

8. I feel 100 times better than I did when I came in. I felt my muscles jump and also tingling. My shoulder went very hot and the pain eased.

9. I felt that I could have floated away.

10. I could not believe how good it felt. I experienced reduced pain and felt as though my kidney was floating.

11. I felt things unknotting.

12. It was very relaxing and I feel energised and wide awake now.

13. I felt totally blessed. I had three jerking experiences. I feel completely de-stressed now.

14. The healing made me concentrate on having a positive attitude. I wanted to feel well again.

15. Excellent relaxation. This was the first time for me. It gives you a wonderful feeling.

16. I feel relaxed and glowing. I was aware of a pulsating purple that changed to a golden glow.

17. I feel mentally more stable now. Nice and floaty.

18. This was my first healing session. A big weight has lifted and I felt little stars from top to bottom leaving me. I arrived with a cough, which has now settled. The pain in my stomach has gone.

19. I felt relaxed, warm and floating. Wonderful! I feel more human. It is like having all your Christmas and birthday presents all in one go.

20. It is like feeling a bit 'high'.

21. It was a very good session; very enjoyable. I felt slightly sick afterwards, as I usually do when meditating. Existing headache became worse but then better during the session.

22. I feel refreshed and peaceful.

23. I felt comfortable sensations whenever my attention was brought to particular parts of my body.

24. I had been suffering with a tugging pain in my left rib cage but this disappeared during the session. Also, my neck and shoulders are easier to move and I have no pain now.

25. The session helped me think about the good in my life.

26. Brilliant! Amazing! I have never felt so relaxed in all my life. I feel tingly all over—it is wonderful.

27. Wonderful! I feel lighter and brighter. I tingled during the session and felt warmth. I feel as though I have had a full night's sleep.

28. My chest has always felt tight but it doesn't now.

29. I have not been so relaxed in months. I had the sensation of a knot in the solar plexus appear during healing that then melted away. Blue and red balls of colour in a grid form appeared in my lower right leg (where an injury had been) which then disappeared. Existing pain in my right side disappeared during the session. I felt very heavy. Emotion surfaced but passed quickly. It was fantastic.

30. I honestly feel more alert. Lovely.

31. My legs had been cold when I arrived but now they feel warm. During the session, I recalled myself as a small child in a black dress, and with a handkerchief in my right-hand feeling pleased with myself.

32. I felt intense heat across my shoulders and back when the healer's hands were on my abdomen. I felt heat down my left leg, which had been a problem area. It was a very relaxing and positive experience.

33. I felt lots of warmth, especially in my back. Also a numbness and a wave of something passing through. It was excellent.

34. It felt really good. There was a warmth, like a warm drink, in my lower belly—just like the Ready Brek advert! Really enjoyable, like being in a different world. Really relaxed. I thought I was peaceful when I arrived but, during the session, I realised that I was releasing tensions.

35. I felt as though I had been in a deep sleep. I feel warmth everywhere now. I twitched at the beginning.

36. I felt warmth throughout, especially where the healer's hands were in contact. It was particularly hot in my shoulders, abdomen and knees. I had tingles throughout my arms and legs that were different from normal tingles.

37. My ankle had been throbbing but that has stopped now and I am not half as aware of my ankle as before. The healer's hands felt as though they were cold—refreshingly cold—but, in reality, the actual temperature of her hands was normal. It was wonderful and revitalising.

38. This healing session exceeded my expectations and was a very positive experience.

39. An ache appeared in my shoulder during the session that then disappeared, accompanied by a sensation of heat. My stomach had bloating and tightness before the session, which significantly released. I was cynical about healing before but now I want to have healing again.

40. I have come back for healing as it was so fantastic. For a full five days afterwards, my energy levels were high, I had clarity of thought and I felt peaceful. During this healing session, I felt heat in my tummy and right knee. The tension in my shoulders disappeared.

41. Normally, I want to constantly fidget but I stayed very still during the entire session. I felt very peaceful and calm. I felt heat from the healer, though her hands were actually cold.

42. I felt heat in my stomach and left shoulder, both of which had been aching. I also felt heat in the heart area. Previously, I had almost always been aware of the sensation of a 'lump' in my chest, as though I had swallowed a hard sweet, but that is not so severe now.

Effects on Hospital Patients

43. I felt as thought I was asleep but, at the same time, I was aware that some part of my mind was picking up the words that the healer said. I had been troubled with a burning sensation in my stomach but this disappeared. My right shoulder developed an ache during the session but it then disappeared. I had been sceptical that healing could work.

44. I had unpleasant visions during the session but the situations I saw resolved and ended in a purple light. I shed tears and wept during the session. I feel much better now.

45. I was aware of heat in my neck and head and the discomfort that had been there reduced. I did not want to get off the couch afterwards. I saw lots of blue light. My heart was pounding at the beginning but that has gone now.

46. Marvellous! I felt relaxed enough to sleep during the session. Some discomfort developed during the session but it passed and I now feel warm throughout.

47. I enjoyed the session. With my inner vision, certain areas of my body looked as though they were 'blocked' somehow but they improved during the session.

48. It feels as though a ton weight has been lifted from me. I could not feel the healer's hands on my body. Instead, I was only aware of heat in the areas where there had been pain, which felt like a very hot water bottle. I feel great now.

49. I feel wonderful now. There was a great shiver of cold from my neck all the way down. I also felt a tickling sensation or pressure in the head, mostly on the right-hand side.

50. I was aware of heat in the pelvic area on the right-hand side. I was aware of red, yellow and orange. (Note: This patient's husband was present during the session and his back pain disappeared.)

51. During the session, I felt waves of feeling perturbed but this seems to have lessened quite a bit. It went really dark and cold at one point but this passed. Involuntary tears flowed and I had twitching in the knees. The left side of my body did not seem as relaxed as the right side. Fine now, though.

52. Brilliant! I was aware of a sudden release of tension in the pelvic area.

53. The pain in my right shoulder and right hip both disappeared and I felt 'pins and needles' down the right-hand side.

54. It felt as though pain was being drawn out of me. At the end, I had tingling all over, along with an emotional release. I am so relaxed now!

55. I released emotion during the healing session. It felt icy cold where discomfort had been but warmth around the head area.

56. I feel lighter now. I felt heat during the session and my eyes watered. A muscle was jumping in my right leg and also in both arms. It was amazing. It felt as though something like anger had been lifted out of me.

57. The problem area felt clogged up before but now it seems more 'spread out' and feels very positive.

58. I was aware of greenery and the feeling of it inviting me, or making me, confident of making changes in my life. Purple came in later and also blue.

59. It was very warm wherever the healer was working. The stomach ache that I came with has gone and I feel relaxed.

60. I felt real warmth—hot, even! I couldn't believe it. Everything seemed black but I could see glowing hands that were made of light moving around my body.

Effects on Hospital Patients

61. I felt as though I were floating and had a sense of freedom. I felt as though I was running through a field of knee-high flowers.

62. I arrived with a pain in the right side of my neck and light-headedness but these have now gone. The pain in my abdomen has also reduced to an ache.

63. Initially, I found it difficult to relax but at one point I was so relaxed that I was completely unaware of my body—only my head.

64. I was aware of little lights and tingling, especially around my legs. I had a weird sensation—as though a weight had lifted from my pelvic area and went right up through my body and gone.

65. I feel energised, positive and relaxed. The healer's hand vibrated when it was on my left shoulder, which I had not told her had been painful recently. I was aware of purple, bubbly clouds around my head.

66. During the session, I experienced tingling, pain and heat in my shoulders and heaviness in the solar plexus. It felt as though I had sunk through my own body and into the couch and then as though I had floated up and out of my body. I saw a dark tunnel, showing my white body fitted into a dark outline that transformed into light. The pain left and I felt tingling. I feel weird but great!

67. During the session my feet, tops of arms and my fingers became really cold, yet I felt heat in other parts of my body. I feel as though I have just woken up from a sleep but I was aware of everything so I know that I was not actually asleep. I saw orange and white. I feel weird now but in a good way. I feel happy and energised, like I could run a marathon.

68. I feel as though I have had a deep sleep but I was aware of everything. There is warmth throughout my body now.

69. The healing session felt calming. The benefits of healing stayed with me for a long time after the session that I had a year ago [with Sandy].

70. I feel tired now and could easily go to sleep. My stomach improved during the session and I felt heat in that area.

71. The pains throughout my legs and feet disappeared for a time during the session but returned afterwards.

72. Mind blowing! I felt tingling sensations, as though negativity was being brought out. I feel a bit stronger now.

73. I felt as though I had been in a deep sleep although I could hear people and traffic outside. I feel a lot calmer now. I felt fluttering in the area where the IBS symptoms have usually been.

74. During the session, my neck, throat, right shoulder and head felt full of wool and as though I could not move or swallow, though I actually could—and did! At another time, my hands felt too heavy to move. I feel as though I could go for a good sleep now.

75. I felt tingling where the healer was touching. When lying down, I usually hear my heart beat quite loudly but this was much reduced during the session.

76. I felt warmth in the area that had been painful when the healer's hands were on that area. Just perfect.

77. It feels like a weight has gone. Excellent! I feel more alive.

78. I had a vision of purple clouds against a black background. The black background changed to purple with little bits of black that drifted away. The headache that I came with has disappeared.

79. I felt tingling in my arms. My left eye could see only purple light. At the same time, my right eye was seeing only the healer in white light. My eyes were shut throughout.

Effects on Hospital Patients

80. I felt as though I had lit up to begin with and felt a little afraid but this passed about halfway through. Then I saw golden light with purple appearing in the middle. The turmoil within me, that I had arrived with, has now changed to a calmer feeling.

81. At the beginning, I saw lights with red and green continually flashing out from my body. It seemed as though the healer was a golden blob. Another golden blob appeared then quite a few more appeared. I saw golden hands with extended long fingers of gold.

82. The healing session was absolutely relaxing—like I would feel when I am on holiday. There was tingling in the end of my fingers that spread throughout the whole of my body.

83. During the first half of the session, I felt waves of energy going from head to foot. Then, during the second half, the waves were going up my body.

84. I am feeling more positive now and there is tingling in my arms, shoulders and legs. I am quite surprised at my peace of mind throughout the session.

85. I have never experienced something like this before. I enjoyed the one-to-one experience. Everything is tingling now.

86. This was a magical experience and helped a great deal because the pain has literally gone.

87. It took a while for me to switch off, but then I was able to relax fully for deeper and longer than I can remember. I feel more positive now. I felt warmth in my legs during the session.

88. Half way through the session, I felt heat and comfort in the pelvic cradle that became more intense. I became the most relaxed that I have ever been in my life.

89. I felt warmth throughout, except for my feet. I was aware of the colour lilac throughout. When the healer worked on my feet, I

was aware of lilac and green. When the healer worked on the hip to knee area, I felt blood flow through, which made my knee ache. My right eye has been a problem for two years. When the healer was working in that area, it was as though a sharp needle (that did not hurt) had pricked the right eye and it feels better now, as though it has cleared.

90. My head feels clearer now. I felt warmth when the healer's hands were on my stomach and also on the back of my neck. I felt light-headed and woozy when I got off the couch but that cleared within a few minutes.

91. As an ex-nurse, I was paying attention to what was happening with my logical mind but I soon went with the relaxation. It felt as though my hands had raised by an inch and as though the healer had put my hands back down—but she had not done so. (Note: A medical student from the University of Birmingham was present and witnessed that the hands had not raised or been put back down.)

92. It felt as though certain areas in my body were being gently wrung. The healer's hands felt warm on the joints.

93. I soon relaxed and did not worry about a thing. I felt warmth in the belly and very chilled out.

94. I arrived with extreme pain in my left leg and hip but this disappeared at the beginning of the session. I had the sensation of my leg and hip being in lapping water. Extraordinary!

95. Excellent! I had arrived with a painful trapped nerve in my neck and right arm but this disappeared. I also had a distended stomach, which has noticeably reduced. Wow! I can't believe that my arm is normal again. It felt as though I dropped off to sleep a few times. When the healer was around my head area, I felt pressure, although the healer was not touching me, which I thought would develop into a headache but it simply disappeared instead.

96. I felt heat in the part where the pain was, and that pain is barely there now. When the healer touched my shoulders at the beginning, I felt tingles in my hands. Later, the healer touched my feet and I felt tingling in the base of my head.

97. Everything seems much better wherever the healer's hands had been. Her hands left a warmth behind, as though her hands were still there.

98. All of the aches in every joint disappeared except for in my right ankle and the bottom of my foot. I felt happiness during the session.

99. My shoulders feel freer and lighter. I feel really relaxed and a lot better. I am very pleasantly surprised and really chuffed. I can't believe how much better I feel now.

100. Tingling started in my head and spread all over my body. (Note: This patient also made the following comment about a previous session: I have not had abdominal pains since having the healing session that I had at the hospital nine months ago and also by following Dr Singh's advice of how to deal with worrying situations.)

101. I had felt concerned about my consultation with the doctor, but I feel better about it now. Bizarre! I didn't expect healing to work as well as it did. I felt tingling in my hands mostly and both arms. I loved it!

Regarding the first audit, only half of the people had sent in their 'one week later' forms, and I hoped to improve that rate of return. Instead of handing them the form as they left, I arranged for it to be mailed a few days later along with a stamped, addressed envelope. I hoped that this would serve as a timely reminder to fill it in and drop it in the post. Disappointingly, the return rate was lower than before, but on closer examination it was clear that the non-returned forms were in weekly batches. For those weeks, the forms had clearly not reached the postal service. Nevertheless, enough forms came back to confirm that people were continuing to benefit from the previous week's healing session.

Out of the 192 patients in this second audit, 67 sent their feedback one week later. This was a high proportion, considering how many forms did not reach the patients. The following comments are the ones that add some interesting insights:

1. I have felt a lot calmer and more peaceful since the healing session. I am not rushing around so much.

2. I have benefited from the session for four weeks now. I am much less anxious.

3. Before the healing session I felt terrible, but I was a different person afterwards. It was an amazing session.

4. I am amazed that I still have no pain!

5. I have lost weight since the healing session but I am still smoking.

6. I have not felt like myself in some situations, but every day my anxiety has been better. I have felt calmer and I am willing to try anything that will help.

7. This treatment helped a lot with stress and sleeping.

8. I have been more peaceful at home.

9. I have been sleeping well for the past three weeks and have been feeling well in myself. Since the session, and having had one counselling session elsewhere, I have come on in leaps and bounds.

10. There has been a positive effect since the healing session and, hopefully, this will get better. I do find healing very beneficial and would like regular sessions.

Effects on Hospital Patients

11. I have felt more able to relax and more able to get problems into perspective. I would definitely like to have more sessions as I am sure that it can only bring more improvement.

12. I feel that I can cope with situations a bit better now.

13. This has been a journey of discovery for me and has made me more aware of other aspects of events and situations.

14. Since the healing session, I have felt a lot more relaxed and have been able to sleep well most nights. However, I am still tired all the time and so I find it hard to concentrate well, although this has improved a lot.

15. I have noticed a vast improvement since the healing session.

16. After the session, the symptoms were less troublesome for a total of six days.

17. After the first healing session, I felt good for a few days, but then the IBS started again.

18. The one session I had was very uplifting and I feel that there has been some improvement.

19. Since having this session, I have been constantly eating fruit. From having just one piece of fruit every two weeks, I am now having more than five per day. I felt very sick half an hour after the session, but since then I have had a constant craving for fruit every day. Monday this week, I just ate fruit all day. Before, I struggled to eat an apple once every two weeks. I would usually eat chocolate every day and, for a week after the session, I had not touched a piece. Usually, I would eat lots of chocolate every day, even when feeling unwell. I really think that the healing session has made this happen.

20. Since the healing session, I have not been responding in my customary knee-jerk way to pressures placed upon me. I have actively sought measures to reduce stress and I feel better for it.

Healing in a Hospital

Initially, I was sceptical but the session proved wholly worthwhile and points out things that a person does not always see.

Healers all around the world probably witness similar responses to those that fill my two audits. The difference is that many of the improvements described here have been witnessed by a senior consultant physician.

Another unusual aspect is that it is highly unlikely that any other healer has had the opportunity to give healing to people who had no prior intention of having any.

Added to this, few healers would be prepared to devise and complete the paperwork necessary to produce an audit. It took two and a half years to conduct the healing sessions involved in these two audits, and this part of the venture was a real pleasure. The administrative elements took many laborious hours, but it simply had to be done.

The results of the second audit provide almost identical results to the first. This correlation between the two further underpins the reliability of their respective findings. In research terms, 'reliability' means that if the same exercise were to be repeated, we could expect similar results.

Anyone is welcome to use the primary data of these two audits for their own research purposes. I would simply ask that I be provided with any results as it would be useful to link the studies together. Requests can be sent to me via my website.

After completing both of these audits, I continued to see patients as usual but I no longer documented their responses. Conducting an audit is a time-consuming business, and I felt that the results of 267 patients must surely be enough to pique the interest of medics, researchers and patients who are willing to enquire.

With the results of the audits being so impressive, I wanted to be able to give talks about these exciting findings. I discovered a two-day residential course where I could learn how to produce slides and a script for a PowerPoint presentation. Designed for people who had no prior knowledge or experience, it suited me perfectly. The main building of Fircroft College was a former home of George Cadbury, which was a delight to experience. Sumptuous and spacious, set in acres of beautiful greenery, it was conveniently

Effects on Hospital Patients

located near to Birmingham city centre. George Cadbury had initially founded the college to help educate workers at his family's famous chocolate factories, and its philanthropic ethos continues. Courses are geared for those who have not attended further education, and also for charities and volunteer workers. Accordingly, the fees are unbelievably affordable, even though the courses are residential and fully catered.

A few days later, armed with my PowerPoint presentation and new skills, I was ready to put my graphs to good use, as you will read later.

Key Points

1. A senior consultant physician witnessed his patients benefit from one 20-minute healing session, some to a remarkable degree.

2. Few of these patients had accessed complementary therapies before, and almost all were highly sceptical that healing could help.

3. These patients' symptoms were resistant to standard and specialist treatment, but they were helped in various ways by one session of spiritual healing.

4. Figures 3, 4 and 5 reveal

    a. the placebo effect associated with compassionate care from a doctor (the grey columns), and

    b. the additional gains resulting from a healing session (the white columns).

5. Patients with longstanding addictions were helped by one healing session.

6. One 20-minute healing session resulted in substantial improvements regarding pain relief, wellbeing, relaxation, relationships, energy levels and sleep quality.

7. Improvements were retained for at least one week by almost all the patients who returned their 'one week later' form.

8. Patients who received healing were keen to have more.

9. Patients who attended follow-up appointments months later confirmed that they had continued to benefit.

10. Improvements may have been permanent for some.

Effects on Hospital Patients

11. The two hospital audits—of 75 and 192 patients respectively—resulted in similar findings to each other, thereby confirming the reliability of both.

12. Hardly any of these patients had received healing before and did not know what to expect, yet their comments reveal similar themes.

13. Of those who witnessed colours, most mentioned seeing purple. It was suggested to all patients that they imagine golden-white light, simply as a means of focusing their mind on something positive. Interestingly, most saw purple instead, and this is the main colour associated with healing.

An Instant Recovery

Dr Singh does not normally treat children, but a paediatrician who knew of his reputation asked if he would see a young teenager. The boy's symptoms continued to rage, despite all appropriate treatments with medication.

At his consultation with Dr Singh, the youth was in a great deal of pain, and there seemed no drug or treatment to alleviate his suffering. Dr Singh suggested that he have a healing session with me, and the boy—whom I shall call Joe—agreed. Joe left the healing session half an hour later, completely free of pain and feeling elated. When he returned to his waiting mother he walked with a confident stride and a beaming smile. I saw the colour drain from her face when she saw him, and her jaw literally dropped. She was speechless. But, within a moment, she regained her wits and whisked him straight off for a blood test.

When I returned home in the evening, the telephone was ringing. It was Joe. He told me that he had already tried calling me 15 times because he was so excited about the outcome of the healing session.

He admitted that, in the few strides from Dr Singh's room to mine, he suddenly felt fear rising up within him. He realised that it was fear of the unknown, and he was gripped with worry about what might happen to him. However, I seem to have a knack for putting people at ease, and he told me that he soon relaxed, once he was on the couch.

Dr Singh was keen to learn more about Joe's astounding recovery so he arranged to visit him at home a few weeks later. Joe and his mother agreed that their interview could be recorded. They gave permission for it to be shared with medical professionals and to be used in any other way that could help others.

A Grand Round is where doctors, surgeons and medical students gather in a lecture theatre on the hospital campus, and one of their number shares their new knowledge with the rest. When Dr Singh first presented this recording at a Grand Round, he invited me along. It must have been a surprise for the medics to hear a discourse that involved spiritual healing. I had not heard the tape before and it was clear to any listener that Joe was intelligent and, despite his young age, highly articulate. Hearing him speak directly to us in the audience had great impact.

To avoid repetition, the following transcript is an amalgamation of the tape recording and the written account that Joe provided later.

'Chest pain had been a problem for years but for about ten days prior to the hospital appointment, it had been a terrible burning sensation, going up and down all the time and made worse by eating. I had vomited several times, which badly hurt my throat, making it feel as though it was on fire. Several previous bouts had each lasted for two or three weeks but settled down with medication. Each bout seemed worse than the last one and really, really hurt.

'I love school and sports but was unable to attend either. I had no energy to get up in the morning; I felt down and was unable to face the day. Eating only plain, bland food stopped the vomiting but that did not help the symptoms.

'When I saw the consultant (Dr Singh), I believed that only tablets and more medicine could help so when he suggested that I have a healing session, I thought the idea was rubbish and plain silly. I was in such a fragile state, though, that I was willing to do anything and thought 'Well, it can't make me any worse', so I gave it a shot. In the few steps from the consultant's room to the healer's, I suddenly worried about what she was going to do to me, but I decided to try it anyway.

'Sandy, the healer, made sure that I was comfortable on the couch and told me to close my eyes. When she asked me to imagine certain pictures in my mind, I wanted to laugh but stopped myself from taking the mick and decided to take it really seriously. I did exactly what she said. Throughout the session I felt relaxed and, towards the end, she guided my thoughts to imagining a happy future and feeling good about myself.

'The burning in my chest was slightly better by the end, but it was still there. When Sandy said to open my eyes it felt as though I had been asleep, yet I knew for sure that I had been completely awake throughout. She asked if there was any pain still so I told her of the pain in my chest. She told me to close my eyes and imagine light shining into my chest and in 30 seconds or so it disappeared. I thought, 'Is this a dream?' because the pain in my chest had really gone. Then I had a cramp in my right shoulder so I told Sandy, and we used the same technique on my arm and that pain went.

'I have never liked having blood taken. I had to go for a blood test straight after the healing session and, as always, asked for the area to be numbed. But it was going to take 45 minutes and there wasn't time so, for the first time ever, I had to have blood taken without being numbed. I felt a sharp shooting pain so I closed my eyes and repeated the white light technique. The pain went in five seconds! I opened my eyes to see if the needle had been taken out but it was still in there. I thought, 'This is wicked!' The nurse did not manage to get any blood from that vein so she had to do it again with a smaller needle. But I was not scared this time because I knew I could make the pain go away. It felt really cool to be able to do that.

'That evening, I felt amazing—on top of the world. I wasn't stressing about anything; I felt happy and calm. We went out for a McDonald's to celebrate. On the way there, I had a headache so I asked mom to turn the radio off and closed my eyes to imagine white light shining on my head. The headache went! Strange isn't the word! It felt wicked. When I think about it, it makes me feel happy in myself.

Healing in a Hospital

'For the rest of the day after the healing session, I kept thinking 'Did that really happen?' When I got home, I felt pleasantly tired and just wanted to relax.

'Previously, I would be constantly worried that the pain would come back. In addition to that, I had always worried about stupid things, just like my mom does. When in school, I would think about the next lesson and check that I had done the homework, even though I knew that I had already done it. I always felt scared about homework. School projects would worry me loads. I would go around all my mates to see how many pages they had done to make sure I had done enough. But now, I know in myself that I've done what I should and I know that it's good work. I'm not worried about it any more.

'Sandy gave me her Sleep Easy & Be Well CD and I listened to it every night for a week. Ever since then, though, I have been relaxed enough to fall asleep naturally.

'Things that Sandy said have stuck in my mind and help me in day-to-day life. For instance, to relax any muscles whenever they might get tense; to imagine white light filling all the cells of my body; to understand that the past is gone and that the future will never come; that what will come, will come anyway so there's no need to worry about it

'I don't know what happened in the healing session and nor do I care! I am just amazed that I have no pain. It's just brilliant. I think my illness was caused by stressing about random stuff and it just built up and up.

'Before the session, I didn't have much of a faith but, ever since, I've been asking my mum if we can go to church on a Sunday. We haven't got around to it yet but I've been meaning to go every single Sunday. I don't know why but it's as though I feel a bit closer to God. That might sound weird to other people, but you have to experience it for yourself to know what I mean.

An Instant Recovery

'Ever since that healing session, I have never felt better; I never stress any more and I always feel calm, relaxed and very happy.

'I would recommend healing to anyone because it's so amazing.'

Joe's mother also kindly took the time to write to Dr Singh about her observations and gave permission for me to reproduce her letter. This is what she had to say:

'I didn't expect my son to benefit from the healing session except for perhaps some relaxation. Nothing prepared me for beaming smiles and colour in his cheeks! I was floored! I could not have believed it.

'That first night I looked in on him, as I always do, and I had never seen him looking so rested, so asleep and so peaceful.

'It's not just an improvement in his health; it's his whole character. He is so much more relaxed. I am still astonished at the phenomenal success of that healing session. My son experienced total and immediate relief from pain.'

When Joe later came for a follow-up appointment with Dr Singh, I did not recognise him at all. Young teens change so quickly, and he was now tall, strong and confident. He snapped up the opportunity to have a healing session with me, but not because he was sick. He knew from experience that healing sessions are enjoyable, energising and empowering.

Much later on, he attended a further and final appointment. Again, I did not recognise him. Eight years later (2016), I understand that Joe continues to be free of symptoms, and Dr Singh still plays his recording at Grand Rounds and to cohorts of medical students.

Incidentally, noticing Joe's reference to his mother's constant habit of worrying, I offered her healing but she declined each time. As she had witnessed the difference in her son, I thought she would be keen. Although I am eager to give healing to anyone who is suffering, I must respect their decision if it is not their wish.

Healing in a Hospital

Just one healing session changed Joe's life. However, most people need a series of weekly sessions before they notice substantial improvements. Other healers must experience similar variations with their own patients. Why the difference? If the healer is the same person, the healing energy could be expected to be reasonably constant, and therefore the only major variable must be the patient. There may be a difference within the patient that affects the level of healing that can be achieved. Joe, for example, was at the end of his tether. He had no other options left and he admits in his testimony that he surrendered himself to the process. My view is that this level of submission is key to achieving the greatest and swiftest healing results. If one person can reach that point, so can anyone else.

Key Points

1. A complete and permanent recovery occurred within half an hour, despite the patient's extreme scepticism.

2. Fear had been an underlying issue, causing persistent stress and worry.

3. The symptoms disappeared along with underlying concerns.

4. The patient had not realised how stressed he had previously been until after the healing session.

5. A senior consultant physician and a paediatrician were witness to the recovery.

6. Individual cases like this will not convince the scientific and medical community that healing is beneficial, no matter how many there are.

Chasing the Research Grant

Two months after starting work at the hospital, I received an email from a fellow Healing Trust member that ignited a frisson of excitement within me. That morning, the National Lottery had announced that it was offering a total of £25,000,000 to charities and to the voluntary sector to conduct research programmes. The grants were specifically for health and social wellbeing projects that would normally be too difficult to find funding for. This certainly applied to healing.

Incidentally, this particular fund is called the BIG Lottery but, for ease of reading, I am referring to it simply as the Lottery.

The scientific and medical communities often point to the lack of evidence in favour of complementary therapies, and contend that trials are often of poor quality. Nevertheless, the use of complementary therapies remains widespread, with estimates of up to one in four people using them (41), though this figure varies depending on how it is measured. Approximately £1.6 billion a year is spent on complementary treatments, and an NHS survey showed that as many as five million patients consulted a CAM practitioner during 1999.

Among patients with gastrointestinal complaints, other surveys have estimated that as many as 50% commonly use complementary therapies (42) (43). This high level of usage was in no way reflected by the hundreds of patients I saw at the hospital. All but a few told me that they had not tried a complementary therapy of any description.

Medical research councils, medical charities and drug companies are the main funders of medical research, but these organisations provide little support for the type of research we had in mind. Taken together, it has been estimated that they spend less than 0.01% of their total budget on investigating complementary therapies (44).

High quality research is extremely expensive to conduct but, if research were to show that healing is beneficial to patients, a number of groups could gain from its use:

1. Cost savings could be made by the NHS—and therefore taxpayers—if medication and surgery bills were found to be reduced.

2. Businesses could gain financially by reduced sick leave payments. Furthermore, staff attending work regularly are likely to be more productive, and especially so if they feel well.

3. With fewer people off work with long-term sickness, the Government—and therefore taxpayers—could gain financially by reduced welfare payments.

4. Individual members of the public may benefit—and therefore their families—in the many ways illustrated by the 267 patients included in my two audits and by the 200 patients involved in our trial.

However, not one of the above groups is likely to offer research funding for healing.

I took the news of the Lottery's announcement along with me to Dr Singh's clinic. It was clear that this was a 'one time only' opportunity, because Lottery money had never before been made available for research, and they stated that it would not happen again. What were the chances of this occurring within the first weeks of my working with someone influential enough to do something about it?

Dr Singh agreed that this was a special opportunity that should not be allowed to pass by without a serious attempt to apply. Intrigued that healing seemed to be making a positive difference to his patients, he felt motivated to bring together the necessary parties to make an application.

The Lottery was aiming to fund:

'...organisations that would produce and disseminate robust, research-based knowledge that will influence local and national policy and practice, to develop better services and interventions for people'.

So far, so good—healing would meet the basic criterion of providing an intervention that could help people.

The first condition of the grant was that a charity or voluntary organisation must make the application and administer the programme. Dr Singh was a Trustee of a Birmingham medical charity called Freshwinds that provides integrated care and support to those with life-threatening and life-limiting illnesses. The term 'integrated care' means providing and coordinating the range of services a patient may need, as well as their medical care. At Freshwinds, this includes the provision of complementary therapies, which are delivered by a bank of volunteer practitioners. Spiritual healing had been a part of their usual portfolio for many years, so Freshwinds was well acquainted with the benefits. They were happy to take up Dr Singh's suggestion that they apply for the grant.

In fact, it had been at Freshwinds that Dr Singh had first picked up the leaflets about our healing group, some years before. When I had initially asked Freshwinds if our leaflets could be displayed there, they were happy to oblige but they felt that our venue was too distant for their patients to be able to reach us. They were right about that, but when Dr Singh noticed our leaflets in their reception area, the eventual outcome was far greater.

Although the applying charity could conduct the research itself, it was strongly recommended that research professionals at a university or research facility should undertake this complex task. The Lottery was looking for research that could stand up to peer review and be accepted for publication in scientific or medical journals.

With his connections at the University of Birmingham, Dr Singh knew that Lesley Roberts PhD had considerable research expertise that would be invaluable for our project. He was delighted when she agreed to join the Steering Group. Another researcher from the University also joined, primarily to focus on a secondary element of the research, explained later. After the study had been completed, a statistician from the University would analyse the data. It was all coming together.

As a research-intensive institution, the University of Birmingham's website states that it is committed to research that is world-leading in terms of its originality and distinctiveness, significance and rigour. To my knowledge, no other Russell Group (UK) or Ivy League (USA) university—each known for first-rate research—had ever conducted a trial on spiritual healing. Having the University of Birmingham on board was a major achievement and very exciting.

To be able to conduct a clinical trial, a Primary Care Trust (PCT) needs to be involved. The PCT that governs Good Hope Hospital was the obvious contender as the healing work was anticipated to be at Dr Singh's clinic.

Evidence also had to be provided that the project was beneficial to members of the public, and my hospital audits confirmed this. In addition, proof was needed that people wanted the project to take place. As luck would have it, the final question on my 'one week later' form asked if the patient would be interested in a series of six healing sessions, if offered. The patients in the first audit were overwhelmingly in favour (Figure 12), as were the patients in the second. In any case, the positive comments littering both audits made it abundantly clear that this would be the case.

Responses of hospital audit patients when asked if they
were interested in receiving a series of 6 weekly sessions

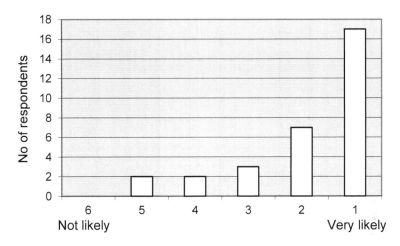

Figure 12: Audit Patients wanting more healing sessions

Any research programme needs to minimise anomalies so that reliable comparisons can be made. Consequently, I felt that it was essential that all of the healers involved must deliver healing using the same technique. For uniformity of the healing method and to ensure professional standards, I proposed that all of the healers involved must have been trained by The Healing Trust. In addition, I recommended that they be current members of The Healing Trust to guarantee that the healers would be subject to a strict code of conduct and disciplinary procedures.

Although trained to deliver healing in the same way as each other, there might be subtle differences between how experienced healers work. This is bound to be the case for any clinical trials that involve more than one practitioner, whether it be a medical procedure or a therapy, so this detail was of no particular concern to the researchers.

In my view, another benefit of using Healing Trust members was that, if the success of the project encouraged NHS outlets to incorporate healing into their provision of care, they would know of at least one appropriate organisation from which to recruit. They might also be willing to signpost patients to The Healing Trust's national network of voluntary healing centres that are spread across the UK. Other healing organisations with similarly high standards are listed on page 296.

When I first designed our voluntary group's promotional leaflet, I incorporated a sentence that encouraged people to try a series of five or six weekly sessions before deciding whether or not healing was helping them. This was based on my own initial experience of having healing, when I was so slow to notice the difference within me. Later on, I introduced the same guidance to The Healing Trust's national documentation and website. The Steering Group went along with the idea and each patient was to receive five weekly sessions. Six would have been better but more costly, and it was felt that a grant application asking for less money would stand a better chance of success.

Freshwinds had previously told me that each patient needed to have an hour of care and attention to gain maximum benefit from healing but I disagreed. My hospital audits confirmed that 20 minutes is sufficient, and the trial was therefore designed around using half-hourly appointments.

As the Lottery was not going to make research money available again, it was vital that we submit as strong an application as possible. The first Steering Group meeting between Freshwinds, the University researchers, Dr Singh and me was in January 2008. By now, 15 months had gone by since I had first mentioned the Lottery grant to Dr Singh. The delay was because Freshwinds, upon hearing of the grant opportunity from Dr Singh, had chosen to make an application of their own instead. Their design involved a range of complementary therapies and different types of healing. But their submission had been rejected, so my original suggestion of trialling only spiritual healing was now back on the table. Although we had missed the first deadline, there was a second opportunity on the horizon and there was just enough time to make a fresh start. It was at this juncture that Dr Singh enlisted the research expertise of Lesley Roberts PhD at the University of Birmingham.

The Steering Group comprised a senior consultant physician (Dr Singh), four 'doctors' and me. It took me a while to realise that only one of the four was a medical doctor. I naturally assumed that anyone in a medical establishment with the title 'Dr' must be a medic, but the other three were actually academics with PhD research doctorates.

At that first meeting, everyone realised it would be a mammoth amount of work to put a strong application together—and it could all come to naught. Competition was bound to be immense, and the requirements were exacting. Despite these concerns, coupled with the weight of their existing workloads, each individual was nevertheless willing to commit themselves.

Completing the paperwork was such a demanding exercise that the Lottery provided workshops to assist the organisations wishing to apply. By the time I discovered that these were on offer, the Birmingham one had passed. Instead, I travelled to Warrington in June 2008, where I joined the representatives of 90 other hopeful organisations. Bearing in mind that this workshop was being repeated in various cities around the UK, it was easy to speculate that there must be many hundreds of applicants. Early on, Dr Singh had suggested that I email him with any queries or information relating to the project, and he would relay it to the appropriate individuals within the Steering Group. I therefore sent him everything gleaned from the workshop, eager that we take every possible step to put a qualifying and competitive application together.

Five months later, I attended a second, more detailed workshop on my doorstep in Birmingham. After Warrington, I expected the place to be packed, so I was surprised to find that there were fewer than 30 organisations at this event. It was another fascinating day where I gathered more guidance and understanding. Again, I relayed this to Dr Singh for him to pass on to appropriate others.

At this second workshop, I was surprised to learn that it is not acceptable to know that something works and then conduct a research trial to prove it. I had thought that this was exactly what research is for. Instead, a research question needs to be devised that is focused enough for the trial to produce an answer. For instance, our question was: 'Is healing therapy beneficial as an adjunct to conventional management in patients with irritable bowel syndrome (IBS) and inflammatory bowel disease (IBD)?' The trial would then be designed to answer this question.

Healing in a Hospital

Incidentally, since the letters IBS and IBD are almost the same despite meaning quite different conditions, I shall write them out in full now and again for clarity. The physical difference between these two medical conditions will be outlined shortly.

Unusually for a research grant, the Lottery stated that 'users' needed to be involved from the very beginning of the design process. 'Users' are the people whom the trial is intended to ultimately benefit, which, in our case, were people with IBS or IBD. The Lottery wanted to ensure that programmes focused on outcomes that would address the needs of people who were suffering, not simply satisfy academic enquiry. My hospital audits were more than sufficient to satisfy this stipulation up to the application stage, but if our bid were successful we would need to invite someone with IBS or IBD to join the Steering Group for the duration of the project.

Another unusual requirement for a grant application was that the Lottery needed to see that the applicant (Freshwinds) had a formal agreement with its chosen research establishment, in our case the University of Birmingham. This was to make it clear before the outset who was doing what and how much it would cost. It was also recommended that the partners be local to each other to make regular meetings feasible.

For clinical trials such as ours, the scientists conducting the Lottery grant workshops emphasised that they would be looking for randomised controlled trials (RCTs), the gold-standard for research. RCTs were originally developed for the pharmaceutical industry to test the specific effects of drugs (45). As we shall see later, they have their limitations when applied to other fields, including that of healing.

In an RCT, patients are randomly assigned to one of three groups. The first group receives the bona fide treatment, such as a real drug that is being tested. The second group receives a placebo, a fake version of the treatment, which might be a sugar pill. The word 'placebo' is Latin for 'I shall please' and conveys that the pill or treatment will do nothing more than please the patient. The third group receives no treatment at all, real or fake, and is called the 'control' group. Scientists then endeavour to compare the results of the three different groups to establish whether the drug or treatment being trialled is effective.

Chasing the Research Grant

If a pill is being trialled, the people taking them must not know whether they are taking real or fake ones. Neither must the healthcare professionals administering the medication, or the researchers who are analysing the data.

In the case of drugs, it is vital that the investigators establish that the group taking the real drugs have gained substantially more improvements than the group taking sugar pills. Without a convincing difference between these two groups, drugs could be prescribed that are little or no more efficacious than sugar. Strangely, people often improve even if they are told categorically that the pills are made of sugar and cannot possibly help them. This is a striking example of the placebo effect in action.

For our trial, we needed a method of demonstrating that the positive effects were due to more than the placebo effect. Ideally, there would need to be trained healers giving treatment, and sham healers providing the placebo by mimicking a healer's actions. However, the practitioners and the actors would obviously know which people were being treated by trained healers, and which ones were not. This immediately contravenes the conditions of an RCT, because nobody involved is to know who is having the real treatment and who is having the sham. In addition, this method cannot be relied upon because every person has the natural potential to be a healer, trained or not. Accordingly, studies using sham healers to provide the placebo have shown no difference between the so-called fakes and the trained healers (46). In these trials the 'bogus' and the 'real' healing were equally beneficial in comparison to the control groups who had neither.

Physiotherapy is another treatment for which it is impossible to provide a placebo. When physiotherapy was being trialled, the patients must have received either the real treatment or no treatment at all. As a result, its effects are often claimed to be due to nothing more than placebo (47). Counselling, too, is impossible to fake and, again, its benefits are thought by many to be attributable to placebo (48). Nevertheless, both physiotherapy and counselling have been accepted into mainstream healthcare and are prolifically available. It must therefore be equally possible to test healing by a method that satisfies the scientific and medical community sufficiently enough for it to be provided by the NHS.

Healing in a Hospital

Designing a placebo is also difficult in respect of many surgical operations, and some aspects of surgery present special difficulties for randomised trials (49). Research shows that operations are half as likely to have been based on RCT evidence than medical therapies (50). A medical therapy is any treatment that affects physical or biological processes of the body, such as medication.

Remarkably, there are surgical operations that have been shown to be ineffective as a result of RCTs, yet they continue to be widely used. In the following example, a placebo—a fake operation—was possible because the medical condition was not life-threatening.

Medical staff simulated knee operations, cutting and sewing up the skin to give a convincing scar, and following up with the usual aftercare. Thus, an RCT in 2002 of 165 patients established that patients gained the same level of relief from symptoms whether they received a real operation or a fake one for osteoarthritis of the knee (51). Assessments over a two-year period showed that there was no difference between the groups at any point. Pain relief and their ability to walk and climb stairs had improved whether they had received the real operation or the fake one.

The type of operation involved is called an arthroscopy, where keyhole surgery gives access to the joint with minimum damage to the skin and muscle. This same method was used in a subsequent Finnish study in 2013, involving 145 patients. The participants had each been diagnosed with a common knee problem (degenerative medial meniscus tear) and were randomised to have either a real operation or a fake one. Again, both groups benefited and there was no difference in outcome between them (52).

Yet arthroscopic surgery continues to be routinely provided for these two conditions.

If a fake operation gives as good results as a genuine arthroscopy, then healing might as well be administered instead of surgery. The cost of just one of these operations—even a fake one—could pay for a number of patients to have a series of healing sessions. Receiving healing sessions would be far more pleasurable for the patients than an operation, and has the added potential of bringing about the range of benefits reported by my audit patients and by the people involved in our research trial. If they continued to be in pain after completing the healing sessions, these patients would still have the option of undergoing an operation—real or fake.

An article in the British Medical Journal (1991) quotes David Eddy, Professor of Health Policy and Management at Duke University, North Carolina, speaking at a UK conference. Professor Eddy stated that only about 15% of medical interventions are supported by solid scientific evidence, partly because only 1% of the articles in medical journals are scientifically sound, and partly because many treatments have never been assessed at all (53).

Professor Eddy had begun his career as a cardiothoracic surgeon but became concerned about the evidence to support what he and other doctors were doing. He decided to select a common problem for which there was a standard treatment, and then search published medical reports for the evidence to support that treatment. He found that there were no RCTs to support several common treatments routinely given, including radical surgery. This discovery changed his life. Eddy coined the term 'evidence-based' and began a crusade to bring logic and rationality to the medical system. By 2006, the proportion of medicine proven to be effective was thought to be 20-25% (54). This percentage is likely to have improved in the interim, but there is probably still some way to go.

Obviously, the medical profession would not continue using a particular procedure if patients did not improve sufficiently as a result of it. The point is that the improvement seen may not be due to the actual medical procedure.

Returning to our Steering Group meeting and the discussion about whether it was possible to utilise a placebo for our trial, it was decided that our researchers would devise a protocol that did not employ sham healers.

A 'research protocol' is the detailed description of how a programme will be conducted. It has to be precise in every detail so that other scientists can review the procedures and offer criticism if necessary. The aim is to develop a protocol that will produce results that can be relied upon. Also, if a future team of researchers wishes to conduct a similar trial, they can amend the same protocol to their needs. If their results are in keeping with the first trial, it helps to confirm the findings of both.

Healing in a Hospital

Every possible expense of the project had to be thought of to include in the grant application. The cost of employing a research assistant, and the expense of sick leave and maternity leave were permissible and recommended. The Lottery wanted to be certain that sufficient funds were granted so that projects would not run out of money before completion. Apparently, this is a common problem. At the workshops, we were told that the Lottery is more generous than most regarding the type of costs that it will cover, but that requests for additional funds later on would not be entertained.

It seemed that every aspect that had ever caused past research to fail or to be ineffective had been addressed by the conditions set out. It was impressive that their standards were so comprehensive and it was heartening to know that Lottery funds were being administered shrewdly.

Although the work involved in applying seemed highly complex, the scientists running the Lottery workshops advised that the chance of success for applicants who ticked all the boxes was much better than when applying to most other grant providers.

The subject of our research proposal was whether healing therapy, as an adjunct to conventional medicine, was beneficial for patients with IBS and IBD. These are both gastrointestinal disorders that have no known causes for them to develop. The unpredictability of embarrassing and painful symptoms significantly affects almost every aspect of a sufferer's personal life. Their physical health, psychological state, mobility, social life, sex life, work life and employment status are all adversely affected (55) (56) (57) (58) (59) (60) (61).

Irritable bowel syndrome (IBS) affects about 10% of the population although there could be many more because not everyone seeks medical attention (59) (55). Common symptoms include abdominal pain, diarrhoea, constipation, bloating and erratic bowels. There are no physical signs within the body to explain why someone should be suffering from these distressing symptoms. Blood tests, endoscopic investigation of the intestines and scans all give normal results. The cause of IBS is therefore a mystery and thought to be affected by psychological factors.

Inflammatory bowel disease (IBD) affects around one person in 1,000 or a total of around 50,000 individuals in the UK (62). IBD includes two conditions—ulcerative colitis and Crohn's disease. Unlike IBS, these are diseases, and there are physical reasons that cause suffering. Blood tests and endoscopic investigations disclose evidence of inflammation, and scans reveal abnormalities. It is not known why IBD develops in the first place. Both ulcerative colitis and Crohn's disease are intermittent, where there can be weeks or even months of mild or no problems, followed by periods of flare-ups. Outbreaks cause symptoms that can be excruciatingly painful and embarrassing. People with IBD are usually ill and miserable for a very long time.

Ulcerative colitis is a disease of the colon (the large intestine) that includes characteristic ulcers or open sores. The main symptom is usually constant diarrhoea mixed with blood, and abdominal pain.

Crohn's disease is an inflammatory disorder in which the body's immune system attacks the gastrointestinal tract. Common symptoms include recurring diarrhoea mixed with blood and mucous, abdominal pain, cramps, extreme tiredness and unintended weight loss. Despite a number of medical and surgical treatment options, symptoms continue to persist for many patients, and they generally experience a poor quality of life (62) (60). Around 50% of Crohn's disease sufferers receive surgical treatment, but it is not always effective.

The persistent and fluctuating nature of both IBS and IBD means that patients need regular check-ups over a long period of time, thereby presenting high demands on healthcare resources (63) (64).

Any chronic condition brings with it the risk of depression. Although 'chronic' refers to illness lasting for three months or more, people with IBS or IBD usually suffer for many years. The bleak outlook of knowing that a distressing illness will last for a long time and cannot be cured must be devastating.

According to the National Institute for Health and Clinical Excellence (NICE), depression is two to three times more common in people with a chronic physical health problem (65). The symptoms of depression may range from lasting feelings of sadness and hopelessness to losing interest in the things that used to be enjoyable, and feeling tearful or anxious (66). Research indicates that the physical features of depression, such as poor appetite, weight loss, sleep disturbance and fatigue may be misinterpreted as signs of a physical illness (67). Some of these symptoms are typical of IBS and IBD, and they can also be side effects of the medication involved, thereby making it even more difficult to identify depression.

Patients do not always ask for help with depression, sometimes because of their fear of being stigmatised for having a mental problem, but others do not realise that they are depressed. Around 30–50% of depressed people are not recognised as such in consultations (68), and this is even worse among people who have a long-term condition (69). Healthcare professionals are not necessarily trained to check that a patient is suffering from depression because the health service separates mental health and physical healthcare (70). In addition, some health workers naturally believe that feeling dejected is a normal response to the physical illness. It is known that all illnesses have a psychological effect and that the level of impact depends on the individual's perception of the illness and its severity (71).

No universally effective treatment exists for IBS or IBD, and options are limited. With so few conventional methods to help them, these patients surely ought to be interested in any therapy that could help bring them some relief. It would be fascinating and constructive to see whether healing could be of benefit to either or both of these two very distinct and distressing conditions.

An electronic search of existing medical literature revealed no other clinical trials of healing for IBS or IBD. It also seemed likely that, with 200 patients each receiving five sessions, ours must be one of the largest healing trials in the world.

Discussions about how patient improvements could reliably be measured resulted in the decision to use a variety of questionnaires. These would gather the maximum amount of data across all aspects of the particular ailments, as well as how the programme had affected their lives. Interviews with selected participants would add a further dimension. It would be impracticable and too complex to ascertain whether there had been an accompanying reduction in medication for these patients.

Time was ticking by towards the Lottery's final deadline for submissions. We had already missed the cut-off date for Round 1 in

Chasing the Research Grant

2008, as explained earlier. Although there were originally going to be three rounds, so many excellent applications were submitted in Round 1 that the third one was withdrawn. Round 2 was our last chance, and the closing date (May 2009) was beginning to loom.

By this time, I was well into my second audit of hospital patients and had seen an additional 100 patients. The responses of these patients mirrored those of the first audit, so our application was able to state with confidence that the vast majority of 180 hospital patients had reported benefiting from a single 20-minute healing session and were keen to have more.

It was a great relief to hear that our application had been despatched in time for the deadline. It would be thrilling if our bid were successful, but now we could do nothing but wait.

Over 450 applications had been submitted, but only between 35 and 50 grants would be awarded. An announcement was soon made by the Lottery that a number of applications had not met the basic criteria and had been disqualified. Those organisations would receive notification shortly. We had no idea how many hopeful organisations were affected, but we heard nothing ourselves and no news was good news. A few months later, another tranche was rejected on more detailed grounds. Again, we heard nothing so we were still in the running. Then more news that another batch was being cast off. We held our breath but heard nothing.

At last, in November 2009, we received the tremendous news that £205,000 had been granted for our project. Our proposal had successfully met all the stipulations demanded by the panel of scientists appointed to the task by the Lottery.

Dr Singh and I heard the news just before the Wednesday morning clinic, and we were like Cheshire cats. Once our jubilation had subsided a little, Dr Singh reflected upon the sobering amount of work that lay ahead, but nothing could contain our triumphant mood. Congratulatory emails flew between the members of the Steering Group, and a press release was despatched.

I immediately spread the news of our success to a myriad of groups and individuals connected to healing, many of whom forwarded it to their contacts. National healing organisations large enough to have a members' magazine printed an article, and the story also featured in the Journal of Holistic Healthcare (72).

Healing in a Hospital

I was invited to give talks at several events where I delivered my newly produced PowerPoint presentation of the hospital audit graphs, culminating with information about the Lottery funding and the research programme. Broadcasting our success helped meet a condition laid down by the Lottery that we must publicise our award along with details of the project.

The Society for Psychical Research invited me to speak at one of their study days in London. During the lunch break, I chatted with a surgeon who recounted a story about his medical training. He had been in awe of two of his tutors, who were both highly regarded surgeons. The first had a clinical, brusque manner with his patients whereas the second had warmth and empathy. Technically, they were as excellent as each other, but everyone knew that the patients of the second surgeon had a better recovery rate. Before his career had even begun, the surgeon telling me the story had already learned the importance of a patient's feelings in relation to their physical recuperation. He was curious about healing and commended my presentation.

I gave the same talk to other national organisations—the Doctor Healer Network (London), the Confederation of Healing Organisations (London) and the College of Healing (Malvern), as well as to various self-help groups local to home.

When I was invited to speak at the Royal Geographical Society's annual conference at the University of Edinburgh, not only was there was no offer of expenses, but speakers had to pay for the privilege. The cost of travel and attendance was out of the question but I did not want to let the opportunity pass without an attempt. I looked for sponsors and, thanks to the generosity of the Doctor Healer Network, Dr Singh and Dr Jean Galbraith, I was able to attend. Dr Galbraith was a retired GP who had employed healers in her surgery for many years and was a practising healer herself. The audience at the Royal Geographical event was smaller than I had envisioned, but my presentation was received with keen interest and generated animated discussion afterwards.

Until a handful of years before these talks, public speaking in any capacity had always been tortuous for me. Although confident in social situations, I could not read out loud the simplest words from a sheet of paper to an audience. No matter how small the group, or how well I knew the people, the page would be trembling in my hands and the words jumbling up in front of my eyes. Without a script was even worse. My brain would empty itself of every relevant thought. No amount of practice made a difference, even if I was fully conversant with the topic. Yet it was vitally important that I be able to speak coherently and eloquently in front of an audience to spread the word about healing. I wanted to be able to speak with the same ease and confidence at public events and interviews as I would with friends. So I determined to overcome the problem once and for all. I healed myself out of this ridiculous state of mind, almost overnight and nearly completely.

To advertise the news of our grant, I had contacted the media. Some local papers and radio stations covered the story, but the best coverage came the following year.

Thanks to a grateful patient, I had been nominated for the Primary Care Trust's 'Volunteer of the Year Award' and I attended the presentation event. After the proceedings, everyone retired to the bar area to relax and mingle, including the BBC newscaster who had presented the prizes. Although there were healthcare executives milling about, the newscaster headed straight for the small knot of people I was with. While chatting, it suddenly popped into my head to suggest to him that our Lottery-funded healing research could make a news item with a difference. He offered to put me in touch with one of his colleagues and, in due course, a BBC reporter and a cameraman came to the hospital to interview Dr Singh, one of his patients and me.

The patient who agreed to be filmed had suffered for a long time with Crohns' disease. When asked by the reporter what she had to say about healing, she replied:

> 'Fantastic! I've had constant pain for nine years, literally crippled and brought to my knees. For four days after seeing Sandy, I didn't have a pain in my body at all. I thought I had died and gone to heaven!'

When Dr Singh was filmed, he stated the following:

> 'We have seen benefits, sometimes unexplained and amazing benefits to some patients. [Yet] conventional scientific wisdom is that if you can't explain something then it can't be true.'

143

Healing in a Hospital

The programme was broadcast that evening during prime time viewing, immediately after the 6 o'clock national news on Midlands Today. Afterwards, I was invited me to contact them again when the research had been concluded.

As well as helping to satisfy the Lottery's requirement to publicise the news of our grant, the programme brought awareness of healing to a terrific number of people. Some viewers found their way to our voluntary healing centre while others asked their doctors to refer them for healing. Members of staff at the hospital also saw the programme and asked if I could arrange healers for their department but, alas, I could not find additional volunteers.

Key Points

1. Applications for a Research Grant from the BIG Lottery had to be beneficial to the public.

2. Successful applicants had to produce robust research that would be published in a scientific or medical journal and capable of influencing local and national policy and practice.

3. Irritable bowel syndrome (IBS) accounts for at least 10% of the population, and there is no medical cure.

4. Inflammatory bowel disease (IBD) affects 0.1% of the population, and there is no medical cure.

5. Symptoms of IBS and IBD cause significant difficulties in all aspects of a sufferer's life.

6. IBS and IBD patients usually suffer for many years.

7. Depression often accompanies chronic medical conditions, including IBS and IBD.

8. No universally effective treatment exists for either condition, and options are limited.

9. It would be highly beneficial for patients if a treatment could be found that alleviates symptoms.

10. NHS resources would be relieved if an effective and affordable treatment could be found.

Existing Healing Research

To enable our grant application to be considered, a search of all related research first had to be made, to ensure that we were not repeating work that had already been completed or was in progress. Research has to extend the boundaries of what is already known.

Although the worldwide search of medical literature revealed no clinical trials of healing in IBS or IBD, it did find trials where healing had been found beneficial for other conditions.

Trials evaluating the effect of Therapeutic Touch—an American version of healing—in chronic pain sufferers found significant benefits in reducing pain and reducing the use of pain killers (73). In other trials, healing had been found beneficial for osteoarthritis of the knee, burns patients and fibromyalgia (74) (75) (38). Additional studies were found involving cancer, chronic pain, anxiety, wound healing and HIV. Each study concluded that healing had helped to reduce pain and anxiety, and had improved the patients' quality of life (73) (76).

Quality of life can be seriously impaired by medical treatments, and various studies have found that healing helps alleviate debilitating side effects. This is particularly the case for cancer treatments.

The majority of women who have had breast cancer are given hormonal treatment for five years. Side effects include hot flushes, aching joints, stress, anxiety, depression and lack of motivation. Understandably, a substantial number of patients seek respite by not taking the medication but this can diminish the long-term treatment benefits.

Healing in a Hospital

The University of Southampton conducted a trial using 12 women who were struggling with these side effects (77). They were each given ten healing sessions by Healing Trust practitioners or equivalent. Not only were their symptoms alleviated, but they also spoke of feeling empowered and of experiencing a new serenity. Furthermore, they reported increased energy levels, enhanced wellbeing, emotional relaxation and re-engagement with pre-cancer activities. These positive effects lasted between sessions and continued for varying lengths of time after completion of the course. One of the ladies admitted that she had previously been so badly affected by side effects that she had considered stopping her medication. Once she began having healing sessions, the symptoms were alleviated to such a degree that her intention to have a drugs holiday evaporated. In fact, while these women were receiving spiritual healing sessions, not one of them felt tempted to give up their hormonal treatment. This illustrates a valuable way in which healing can support conventional treatment.

There was no control group in the above study, but the positive outcomes demonstrated the safety and effectiveness of healing, and the results were significant enough to warrant controlled trials being conducted. With only 12 participants, the trial was too tiny a sample size, in research terms, to achieve statistical confidence in its findings. However, it adds to the existing body of evidence, and scientists can group together any number of these small trials to look for patterns and trends on a grander scale. This method of research is called a review.

A review of healing trials that did include a control group—called a controlled trial—has been produced by David Hodges PhD at the University of London (78). To give meaning to the probability figures quoted in his research examples, Hodges first explains that probability figures (p) are more impressive the smaller they are. For example:

p=0.05 means odds of one in 20 (statistically significant)

p=0.001 means odds of one in 1,000 (highly significant)

p=0.0001 odds of one in 10,000 (very highly significant)

Existing Healing Research

The phrase 'p<0.05' means that the probability that the difference between the treatment group and the control group is due to chance is less than one in 20. (To arrive at this figure, divide one by 0.05.) Thus, the smaller the probability numbers in the following research trials, the less likely that the change was due to chance. The studies that Hodges cites include the following:

1. Healing on enzymes gave a significance of $p<0.001$, which means a probability of less than one in 1,000 that the changes in enzyme activity were due to chance (79).

2. Healing on stressed human blood gave a significance of $p<0.00096$, meaning a probability of less than one in 1,000 that the changes seen in the blood were due to chance (80).

3. Healing on fungi and yeasts gave a significance of $p=0.00014$, a probability of 1.4 in 10,000 that the changes were due to chance (81).

4. Distant healing on fungal cultures gave a significance of $p<0.00003$. Healers worked 15 miles away from the laboratory and sent distant healing. The probability that the healing effect was due to chance was less than one in 30,000 (82).

5. A range of different trials on plants each gave a significance of around $p<0.001$, giving a probability of less than one in 1,000 that the changes seen were due to chance (83).

6. A range of different trials on animals each gave a significance of around $p<0.001$, again meaning a probability of less than one in 1,000 that the changes seen were due to chance (84).

All experiments on cells, plants and animals prove to demonstrate that the placebo effect has had nothing to do with the positive effects achieved. Giving healing to cells in Petri dishes must have been a strange experience for the practitioners involved, yet the results show that they overcame the challenge.

Medical research on animals is popular because it is cheaper and easier than using people. If a drug for a particular problem is being trialled, the researchers have to find patients who already have that particular illness. Animals, on the other hand, can be inflicted with it in preparation for the trial. In addition, they will definitely be in their cages for the next step of the procedure whereas people have to be relied on to attend at the allotted time. Animals have no choice but to continue with the programme until its conclusion, whereas people can choose to drop out of a trial at any time. Some people have genuine reasons for not being able to continue with a programme, but they are equally within their rights to simply change their mind. A number of animals can be accommodated in a single room where the scientist can move swiftly from one beast to another. In contrast, human research subjects need to be welcomed and put at their ease; they need to have the procedures explained to them and their permission gained. Then they might need a private room to receive the treatment and, at the very least, their travel expenses reimbursed. It is easy to understand why research on animals is so much cheaper and easier, and therefore prevalent.

Many people naturally recoil at the thought of animals being harmed, and more so if they are wounded on purpose. To molest animals so that the effect of healing can be measured seems paradoxical and must have been an issue for the healers involved. It makes grim reading, but this section has to be included to convey the extremely positive contribution that these animals have made in showing that the placebo effect cannot have been a factor in these instances. The following examples are also taken from Hodges' report:

1. Identical wounds were caused on the backs of 96 anaesthetised mice, and the rate of wound healing was measured on a daily basis. Healing was given for 15 minutes per day. By day 14, the wounds of the treated group had healed significantly more rapidly than those of the control group ($p<0.001$) (84).

2. Newts naturally regenerate severed limbs, and a complex set of experiments sought to discover whether healing would make a difference to their regrowth. All of the newts had part of one forelimb amputated, and four different healers gave treatments to their allocated newts. The results were compared with those of a control group whose limb regeneration was left to nature. Measurements were taken at two different stages. Healer 1

showed no significance at either stage, but the other three healers showed significance at both stages, ranging from $p < 0.05$ (significant) to $p < 0.01$ (highly significant). Some of Healer 2's work achieved $p < 0.002$ (very highly significant) (85). These results show that healing is effective, but results can vary when using different healers.

3. Goitres were created in mice, either nutritionally or chemically, and the rate of goitre development was measured over a period of 40 days. The development of goitres in the group receiving daily healing was significantly slower than in the two control groups ($p < 0.001$). A second experiment using similarly afflicted mice involved indirect healing. The healer held wool or cotton in his hands, after which portions of the treated material were placed in the mouse cages. Interestingly, the goitres developed just as slowly in the group of mice that had this treated material in their cages as those in the first experiment where direct healing was used ($p < 0.001$) (84).

4. Tumours were developed in mice by injecting them with tumour cells, and then daily healing was given to see if this influenced the growth of the tumours. The results showed that the average tumour area was significantly smaller in the treated group than in the controls after 16 and 22 days ($p < 0.001$) (86).

5. Ether-anaesthetised mice were given healing to see if recovery time was improved by healing. In a large number of these experiments, each of which comprised many trials, the majority of the results showed a significant effect. Across the trials, the probability levels varied from $p < 0.05$ to $p < 0.001$ (87) (88) (89) (90) (91).

It is with a sigh of relief that we now turn our attention to healing trials on humans who, of course, were not harmed in any way. Again, these are taken from Hodges' report:

1. Experiments were conducted to see if healing could raise blood haemoglobin levels in patients. Over 250 patients were involved in the trial, along with four trained healers. Results ranged between $p < 0.01$ and $p < 0.001$ (92).

2. Another experiment sought to discover whether training to be a healer made a difference to the trainees' blood haemoglobin levels. A group of 48 trainees were blood sampled before and after their first degree reiki training. Measurements of haemoglobin and haematocrit showed significant changes in the test group, compared with the controls ($p<0.01$) (93).

3. A well-organised, double-blind study on wound healing, using non-contact healing, measured wound size on days 8 and 16. There were significant differences between experimental and control groups on both days ($p<0.001$) (94).

4. A double-blind study was conducted on 96 hypertension patients, who were divided equally into two groups. The one group received distant healing and the other did not. Both groups continued with their usual medical treatment. The results showed a significant improvement ($p<0.014$) in the systolic blood pressure (when the heart contracts) of the group receiving healing, compared with the controls, but no significant changes in the diastolic blood pressure (when the heart is at rest and refilling with blood) (95).

The beneficial effect of healing on pain, anxiety and quality of life issues is complex and therefore difficult to measure. Studying these issues usually involves more variables and a greater possibility of patients misunderstanding the questions. However, specialised questionnaires designed for the particular illness concerned have proved to be the most effective and reliable tool, and were utilised in the following experiments:

1. A total of 60 volunteers suffering from tension headaches were split into three groups. The first group received a healing session, the second group received a sham healing session and the third received nothing. Pain relief was measured immediately after treatment and again four hours later using a specialised questionnaire. Results revealed significant differences between the groups ($p<0.005$ to 0.01 depending on the questionnaire used) (96).

152

Existing Healing Research

2. A total of 90 patients in a hospital cardiovascular unit suffering from anxiety were split into three matched groups. One received five minutes of healing, the second received five minutes of touch without healing, and the third received no touch or healing. The people receiving healing showed a highly significant reduction in anxiety following the treatment ($p<0.001$). They also showed significant anxiety reductions, compared with both the 'touch without healing' and 'no touch' groups ($p<0.01$ in both cases) (97).

3. A total of 60 hospitalised cardiac patients suffering from anxiety were randomly assigned to one of two groups. The first received five-minute treatments of non-contact healing given by an experienced practitioner. The patients in the other group were given inexperienced practitioners who went through similar procedures but while doing mental arithmetic. Results showed that the group receiving healing experienced a very significant reduction in anxiety ($p<0.0005$) (98).

4. A double-blind, crossover study was conducted on the effect of distant healing on post-operative pain. Of people needing surgical removal of both impacted lower molar teeth, 21 were randomly assigned to control or treatment groups. The healers were located several miles away and concentrated on photographs of the patients. The resultant data showed a highly significant improvement in reduced pain levels as a result of the distant healing ($p<0.0001$) (99).

All of the above experiments appear in greater detail in Hodges' review, along with many others.

David Hodges and his colleague Tony Scofield PhD conducted experiments of their own at the University of London. They soaked cress seeds in salt water to make it difficult for them to germinate and grow properly. Then, in nine different experiments, the gifted healer Geoff Boltwood held his hand over the treatment group seeds for just two minutes each. Over the next several days, the scientists photographed the treated and untreated seeds, and the pictures offer visible evidence that the seeds given healing germinated sooner and

153

grew substantially in comparison to the untreated seeds (100). The researchers stated that:

'The results obtained do support the contention that a healing ability exists.'

They also affirmed a prejudice often encountered by healers:

'It is unlikely that any laboratory model is ever likely to satisfy those who do not wish to know.'

The BBC visited their laboratory and filmed seeds that were visibly germinating in Geoff's hands. This dramatic visual demonstration of healing energy in action could have been broadcast to the public, but the programme was never aired.

Another experiment on plants was conducted in a commercial setting where a healer was asked to treat lettuce seeds before they were planted at an organic farm (101). By the time the plants were ready to go to market, the lettuces that had received healing energy had yielded 10% more crop than the others and had less slug and fungal damage. The researchers reached the obvious conclusion that there could be a commercial use for healing.

After having conducted research into various complementary therapies, Hodges and Scofield concluded that:

'If most complementary therapists were to recognise that they primarily harnessed healing energy and that the techniques...they used were largely part of the ritual for achieving this, then complementary medicine would be in a much stronger position to defend itself from criticisms by conventionally trained scientists (102).'

They also jointly produced a scientific paper (103) that was published by The Royal Society of Medicine. Its conclusion states:

'Healing is...largely viewed with scepticism by medical science, in spite of evidence that points strongly towards the need for an objective investigation and assessment of the phenomenon.

'If integrated into medical practice, [healing] could be a major advance in healthcare and potentially a significant factor in controlling medical costs.

Existing Healing Research

'The mechanisms underlying healing appear to be radically different from those underpinning modern medicine.'

Experiments at the University of Connecticut further support these statements. A series of laboratory trials were conducted on human bone and tendon cells in Petri dishes (104) (105) (106) (107). Professor Gloria Gronowicz, who led the studies, has spent much of her career studying the biology of bone cells. A colleague had asked her to collaborate on an experiment looking into the power of healing. Although sceptical, she was intrigued. As a full professor with tenure and respect, Gronowicz had the stature to conduct research that scientific colleagues might well criticise. She admits that it would have been impossible to consider the proposal had she been at the beginning of her career (108).

In one of the trials, cells were divided into three groups. One received genuine healing by trained practitioners while a second group was given sham healing by medical students. The students were instructed to simply hold their hands a few inches over the Petri dish. The third group was completely ignored. The healing and sham treatments were given twice a week for ten minutes each. The scientists who later examined the cells did not know which group each dish had been in.

To Gronowicz's surprise, the healthy cells treated by trained healers grew faster and stronger than those in the other two groups. Some had grown at double the rate of the untreated cells. In addition to increased cell division, the bone cells had also absorbed more calcium, the essential mineral for growing strong bones.

Gronowicz investigated the healing effect on bone cancer cells and found that they had not been stimulated in the same way. This is an extremely positive result because cancer occurs when cells multiply out of control, and a treatment that stimulated the growth of cancerous cells would be detrimental. In addition, these cancer cells decreased differentiation and decreased mineralization, both of which are highly beneficial for a patient.

After four treatments in two weeks, healthy cells had become stronger and cancerous cells weaker. Compared with controls, the probability figures for this happening ranged between $p = 0.03$ (statistically significant) and $p = 0.0007$ (very statistically significant), depending on which element was measured. The conclusion of a 2010 paper authored by Professor Gronowicz (109) states:

> 'Our experiments are the first to demonstrate that Therapeutic Touch treatment of human bone cancer cell lines caused a significant decrease in matrix synthesis and mineralisation, and differential effects on cell growth. These findings suggest that experienced energy medicine practitioners are able to affect cells in culture, that the practice of energy medicine may be beneficial to patients and that this technique...has scientific validity and should be studied in more depth.'

Earlier laboratory experiments on human cells employed Matthew Manning, a well-known healer. In his book *The Healing Journey*, he describes giving healing to blood that had been mixed with saline solution. Normally, saline kills blood cells within five minutes. The cells given healing lived for 20 minutes—four times longer than the controls.

In other experiments, Matthew gave healing to cancer cells placed in liquid protein feed. Under these conditions, the death rate of cancer cells is usually 1,000 per ml of liquid. In 27 trials out of 30, the death rate of the cancer cells given healing increased by between 200% and 1,200%.

One of the scientists involved, William Braud PhD, described the results of Matthews's healing as 'impressive'. These and many other experiments are presented in Braud's book *Distant Mental Influence: Its Contributions to Science, Healing and Human Interactions*.

As with Gronowicz's experiments, it was shown that healing improves healthy cells, yet simultaneously depletes cancerous cells.

The National Health Service (UK) funded research at the University of Aberdeen to ascertain the effectiveness of spiritual healing in restricted neck movement (110). A total of 68 patients received three healing sessions each, over a three-week period. Not only was neck movement in each direction significantly improved in comparison to the control group ($p<0.001$), but the severity of pain was also reduced ($p=0.03$). In addition, the treatment group significantly improved their scores for physical function, energy and vitality in comparison to the group that had not received healing.

Existing Healing Research

Research aims to stretch the boundaries of knowledge and understanding, sometimes using different methods or by applying the same methods in a different context. Besides running a clinical trial, another means of conducting research is to undertake a 'systematic review'. This is where a research question is posed and then a review of all the research evidence relevant to that question is used to arrive at a conclusion. It is a method of combining all the available evidence and is regularly employed in healthcare. The Cochrane Collaboration, for instance, is a group of over 31,000 healthcare specialists in more than 120 countries who volunteer to routinely organise medical research information in this way. As a result, more informed choices can be made regarding the provision of care.

Another option is a 'meta-analysis' where the statistics from different studies are contrasted and combined in the hope of identifying patterns or other interesting relationships. It is a mathematical technique that combines the results of individual studies to arrive at one overall measure of the effect of a treatment. Again, this method is often used to assess the clinical effectiveness of healthcare interventions.

Dr Daniel J Benor, an American medical doctor, has amassed a wealth of clinical trials, systematic reviews and meta-analyses regarding healing (111). Of the extensive alphabetical list available on his website, the following selection is taken only from within the letters A to C, otherwise it would be too lengthy. For ease of reading I have slightly reworded some of the text.

1. A systematic review focused on the efficacy of distant healing and involved a total of 2,774 patients (112). A total of 23 randomised studies were reviewed—five with prayer healing, 11 with non-contact healing and seven miscellaneous distant healing approaches. A positive effect was found in 57% of these. Overall, for the 16 trials with double blinds, the average was $p<0.001$. The authors concluded that 'the evidence thus far warrants further study', which, in research terminology, means that the evidence has merit. One of its authors was Professor Edzard Ernst, the first Professor of Complementary Therapies in the UK.

2. A meta-analysis was conducted regarding the effect of healing on electrodermal activity (EDA) (113). This is a measure of electrical conductance of the skin, which varies depending on the amount of sweat-induced moisture present. When a threatening situation occurs, the 'fight or flight' response is activated, which creates the tension needed to deal with the situation. One of the effects is instant sweat production, and this means that EDA reflects a person's state of anxiety. By attaching a meter to the patient's skin, it was found that healers could selectively lower and raise a patient's EDA. In a series of studies there were 323 sessions with four experimenters, 62 influencers and 271 subjects. Of the 15 studies, six (40%) produced significant results. Of the 323 sessions, 57% were successful (p=0.000023).

3. A meta-analysis was conducted in 2000 regarding the effects of Therapeutic Touch on patients with anxiety (114). A total of nine randomised studies were reviewed that met the criteria specified by the researchers. They concluded that Therapeutic Touch significantly reduced transient anxiety.

4. Using imaging technology, a study in 2005 demonstrated that sending thoughts at a distance correlates with the activation of certain brain functions in the recipients (115). The recipient was placed in an MRI scanner and isolated from all forms of sensory contact from the healer. The healer then sent distant healing at random two-minute intervals that were unknown to the recipient. Significant differences between experimental (send) and control (no send) procedures were found (p=0.000127). The researchers concluded that a healer can make an intentional connection with a person who has been isolated from the healer in every way, as this can be correlated to changes in brain function of the target individual.

5. A randomised control trial of healing was conducted that involved approximately 400 patients undergoing coronary artery bypass surgery at an American hospital (116). There were three groups—one received healing, another received a visit, and the

third was a control group that received neither. It was found that participants who received healing had a shorter hospital stay.

6. Double-blind preliminary studies were conducted to see if hands-on healing affected enzyme activity (117). Pepsin is an enzyme in the stomach that breaks down proteins and is therefore vital for digestion. A pepsin solution was added to egg albumen in test tubes, and measurements were made to track the level of protein breakdown. Prior to mixing, one test tube of enzyme was exposed to a healer's hands, a second to a non-healer's hands, and the third remained untreated. In all three trials the 'healed' enzyme was found to have a significantly higher level of activity than the untreated control. These results suggest that healing aids digestion. [Incidentally, this last point should be of particular interest to Dr Singh's patients and could be relevant to our trial results.]

7. A study was conducted in order to determine whether healing could exert a beneficial effect on peak expiratory flow rates (PEFR) in asthmatics (118). A total of 22 asthmatics each received healing for a ten-minute period. Their PEFR was found to improve significantly (p=0.009), and 18 of these subjects showed greater improvement a week later (p=0.003).

8. The following study involved only one patient, but the results surprised the researchers and medics (119). The patient's blood flow was blocked by clots, causing paralysis in the mid-chest level and below. The maximum improvement thought possible was to the level of three vertebrae lower in the chest. Treatment consisted of a 15-minute telephone call each day, followed by a distant energy healing session. Every three to four weeks there would be a three-day break. Recovery after five months reached the lower back. MRI and neurological examination confirmed that the subject had functionality almost to the base of the spine (L5/S1) and was continuing to improve.

9. A series of experiments was performed utilising okra and zucchini seeds germinated in acoustically shielded, thermally insulated, dark, humid growth chambers (120). Healing energy

was administered for 15–20 minutes every 12 hours with the intention that the treated seeds would germinate faster than the untreated seeds. The objective marker was the number of seeds that sprouted out of groups of 25 seeds, counted every 12 hours over three days. Temperature and relative humidity were monitored every 15 minutes inside the seed germination containers. Healing energy had a significant effect compared with an untreated control ($p<0.0006$) and over time ($p<0.0001$).

As well as providing an extensive list of published healing research on his website, Dr Benor has also written a number of books on the subject. In his book—*Spiritual Healing: Scientific Validation of a Healing Revolution*—he collates and ranks a range of fully referenced studies. Of 191 controlled research programmes, 124 (65%) demonstrated a statistically significant effect and, of 50 high standard studies, 38 (76%) were statistically significant. A meta-analysis of 100 distant healing studies found 23 high standard studies, of which 13 (57%) demonstrated significantly positive effects.

A number of other medical doctors have written books that promote the use of healing alongside conventional treatment. Among them are Dr Deepak Chopra, Dr Andrew Weil and Dr Bernie Siegel, who have each produced inspirational bestsellers that are littered with references to research trials from around the world.

Maxwell Cade was the first to work towards developing scientific equipment that could visually display brainwave changes during a healing session. Cade was a highly qualified British scientist who worked in radiation physics for the Government and for industry. In 1976, he and Geoff Blundell developed a Mind Mirror (121). This was an electroencephalograph (EEG) that demonstrated the connection between healer and patient. Its screen revealed that, when giving healing, the healer's brainwaves quickly changed to low frequency alpha waves. Alpha waves are linked with passive, meditative mental activity, the state associated with biological self-repair or 'homeostasis', mentioned earlier. Within moments of the healer beginning to work, the Mind Mirror showed that the patient's brainwaves entrained to the same alpha wave pattern as the healer's. This phenomenon was demonstrated at the

Existing Healing Research

Wrekin Trust 1978 Conference, held at Loughborough University, with an audience of 400 doctors, psychologists, scientists, healers and other professionals watching on closed circuit television.

Further tests by Cade involved placing the patient in a separate room from the healer so that no communication between them was possible, and nor could they see each other. An EEG was attached to each participant, and the patient had no idea when the healing would begin. Nevertheless, the EEG revealed the same entrainment within the patient, moments after the healer had begun to work. Cade's passion and enthusiasm was the driving force behind this investigative work, and his sudden death in 1984 tragically marked the end of further research.

A more recent study in America confirmed that a person's positive healing thoughts have a noticeable impact on someone else's mind and body (122). Dean Radin PhD at the Institute of Noetic Sciences in California wanted to see if the partners of cancer patients could help their spouse by sending healing energy to them. The healthy partner attended a training course for three months in preparation for the trial. They were then directed to send healing at random periods chosen by a computer. The receiving partner relaxed in a distant, shielded room for 30 minutes, not knowing which periods of time during this half hour that healing would be sent. The double-blind study ascertained that, overall, the skin conductance of the receivers increased during the periods that healing was sent ($p=0.00009$). Increased skin conductance means that more sweat is on the skin, the production of which is stimulated by the sympathetic nervous system. Changes in a person's state of nervousness or calm can thus be measured and this is the principle upon which lie detectors work. Telling a lie causes stress, and stress stimulates sweat production. As well as physically measuring a change in the mind and body of recipients, these patients also described experiencing a warm feeling inside (123). This sensation mirrors the comments that patients often make about healing. However, the study was not designed to discover whether these responses actually promoted healing in any way.

Various trials confirm that directing healing to someone who is absent can have an effect on them. However, it is probably rare for a healer to receive convincing evidence themselves that their distant healing work has made a difference. If I feel doubtful that sending healing to someone could be beneficial to them, I bring to mind the work of people like Cade and Radin, and also the following particular cases.

A man had been recommended to me for healing, but a visit was out of the question because he lived hundreds of miles away. His wife telephoned and explained that her husband was constantly troubled, affecting their lives day and night. This had been the case for a long time and was getting worse. They were at their wits' end. Although I was keen to help quickly, I was unable to say which day or time I would have a chance to sit quietly and send healing. An opportunity soon came along and I planned to call later that day to let her know. Before I could do so, she called me to say that her husband's difficulties had suddenly evaporated. Discussing the details, we came to realise that he had resumed normality at the particular time that I had sent healing.

Another occasion was when flying home from a holiday. Substantial delays at our departure airport caused passengers to strike up conversation with each other while waiting to check in. An elderly lady travelling alone on our flight explained that she was a regular flyer but dreaded landing because of the terrible pain that would build up in her ears. She was fascinated to hear about healing, and I offered to send her absent healing as soon as our aeroplane began its descent. When I felt the loss of altitude begin, I went to the back of the cabin to let her know that I had not forgotten. Later, while I was waiting at the baggage carousel for our cases, she rushed up to me. She was incredulous that the landing had been pain free and enjoyable for her. In this particular case, she may have healed herself simply through the power of suggestion. Either way, healing occurred.

Probably the most dramatic example of absent healing in action is the story of Dr Hew Len (124). Over 30 years ago, he began work as a clinical psychologist at the Hawaii State Hospital. His clinic was a special ward specifically for mentally ill criminals who had committed extremely serious crimes. They were so dangerous that they were permanently shackled and never allowed outside. No day passed without an attack on a fellow inmate or on a member of staff. Up until the arrival of Hew Len, previous appointees to his post had

162

not stayed much longer than a month, and staff members were often off sick with stress. Instead of seeing any patients, he quietly viewed their files and photographs in his office and conducted an Hawaiian method of distant healing in his mind. As time went by, the patients began to improve. Medications were reduced, and some inmates were allowed outside, no longer shackled. Staff absence dwindled. In less than four years, all but a few of the prisoners had been released. The last few were sent elsewhere, and the secure unit was closed down.

Hew Len's example points to the value of sending healing to perpetrators of crime. It is natural for us to feel empathy for victims, but there may be fewer victims in the future if we also send healing to offenders. With the obvious advantage of not needing proximity to such people or their permission, the scope is limitless.

It may seem impossible that distant healing could be effective, but the work of Cade, and those who came after him, seems just as outlandish as what quantum physicists term 'entanglement'. This is something that happens to sub-atomic particles called quarks. If quarks with identical spin are paired and separated, changing the spin on one will instantaneously change the spin of its partner. It does not matter how many miles apart they are (125). The principle seems very similar to entrainment—explained earlier using the example of tuning forks—except that the mirroring behaviour of quarks can be across a vast distance. Since this is the case within the atoms that make up the cells of our physical bodies, then perhaps we are subject to the same effect in some subtle way.

The work of physicist Amit Goswami seems to demonstrate this. Goswami is the author of the highly successful textbook *Quantum Mechanics* that is used in universities throughout the world. In an experiment, he demonstrated entrainment between two people after they had meditated together. He placed them in two separate chambers that were electromagnetically impervious and where they could not see or hear each another. Then he repeatedly flashed a light near the one person's eye, causing the firing of a certain frequency in the brain. At the same moment, the other person's brain fired similarly, despite not being able to see the actual light.

Healing in a Hospital

If distance is no barrier to sub-atomic particles being affected by each other, then maybe the same applies to healing energy. Whatever the reality is, I focus on thinking that healing energy is working at this quantum level, whether the patient is with me or not. Even if my understanding or explanation of the physics involved is primitive, the concept allows me to think in a way that goes beyond the boundaries of Newtonian physics. Newtonian physics describes the physical world that we experience every day through our five senses. If the particles that create the foundation for this physical world behave differently, then there must be two types of physics occurring in the same space. Eminent physicists have made the following statements about the quantum world:

'Those who are not shocked when they first come across quantum theory cannot possibly have understood it.' Niels Bohr (126)

'I think I can safely say that nobody understands quantum mechanics.' Richard Feynman (127)

'In the world of the very small, where particle and wave aspects of reality are equally significant, things do not behave in any way that we can understand from our experience of the everyday world...there is no physical analogy we can make to understand what goes on inside atoms.' John Gribbin (128)

Judging from all of the above, it would seem that quantum physicists ought to have less difficulty accepting that beneficial healing energies exist than conventional scientists might. Throughout history, the scientific community has found it very difficult to accept a new paradigm that contradicts established knowledge.

A classic example was when Guglielmo Marconi proposed, in the early 1900s, that it should be possible to use short wavelength communications across enormous distances, allowing a greater volume of traffic at much higher speeds. His vision was derided by leading British and American scientists, including those involved in a Royal Commission that was advising the British Government. But the expertise of Marconi's technical team proved him right, and

164

their achievement laid the foundations for the modern communication systems that we now take for granted (129).

When a person is physically with me, I envision that beneficial electromagnetic forces are at work in the same fashion as a microcurrent electrical neuromuscular stimulator (MENS). A MENS machine sends weak electrical signals into the body that help alleviate pain and speeds the healing of wounds, tendons and ligaments (130). MENS machines are commonly used by athletes because it is a drug-free treatment that is non-invasive and highly effective. A study in 1969, for example, showed that skin ulcers achieved 200–350% faster healing rates than those of the control group, and they gained stronger scar tissue and antibacterial effects (131).

Whether a patient is with me or not, I also imagine the person being illuminated with brilliant light that is charging them with positive energy and elation. Bruce Lipton PhD was a cell biologist and professor at the National Institutes of Health, USA, and he maintains that positive emotion is a necessity for physical health. In his book *The Biology of Belief,* he writes about the chemical activity that is visible at cell level and how he discovered that too much negative emotion tips the health seesaw within the cell. He explains that health is, of course, supported by diet and exercise but is also affected by stress and optimism. The main thing that influences the cells of our body is our blood. If we see someone we dearly love, our perception causes a release into the blood of oxytocin, dopamine and hormones that encourage the growth and health of cells. But seeing something frightening releases stress hormones—cortisol, histamine, norepinephrine—which put the cells on alert and into a protection mode. Worry, stress and any other negative emotions have the same effect. If these emotions persist, Lipton contends that the imbalance can eventually develop into an illness or disorder. People usually comment on how uplifting healing feels, and Lipton's work indicates that this brighter state of mind causes a physical contribution towards the health of their cells.

Whatever my own thoughts as to how healing might work, nobody truly knows and can prove it, and probably every healer has a different opinion. The most detailed description of insights and perspectives has to be that of Barbara Brennan PhD, in her book

Healing in a Hospital

Hands of Light. Barbara was a NASA physicist who became a healer, and she now runs her own healer training organisation.

Academics who believe that healing should be further researched include Professor Peter Fenwick, a consultant neuro-psychiatrist at King's College London. He has studied the phenomenon of healing and says:

> 'There are four possibilities. Either we are dealing with fraud on a massive scale; or large numbers of able and gifted researchers are simply wrong; or hundreds of reports disproving healing have not been published. All these seem unlikely, so we're left with the possibility that the effect is real (123).'

Professor Harald Walach, a psychologist at the University of Northampton, is quoted as saying:

> 'We should take this phenomenon seriously even if we don't understand it. To ignore it would be unscientific. Our work shows that there is a significant effect, and despite it being the most widely practised alternative remedy, science has only recently begun to investigate whether spiritual healing actually works. Scientists and doctors simply assumed that it didn't (123).'

In answer to critics who say that much healing research is flawed and that any effects are due to the placebo effect, the Confederation of Healing Organisations (CHO) recently commissioned the University of Northampton to produce the largest ever meta-analysis of non-contact healing (132). It focused on two separate groups, the first being only plants, animals and cell cultures, so that the placebo effect could be discounted. The second group included only humans. The researchers excluded any studies that did not meet their standards, yet the results remained significant for both groups. Professor Paul Dieppe of the University of Exeter commented on the findings thus:

> 'This is a rigorous, high quality scientific report, and it clearly shows that healing intention can have beneficial effects on living systems, both human and non-human.'

Existing Healing Research

As a result of this study, the scientists found that it made little difference if they excluded all of the trials that fell below their standards of methodological excellence. This suggests that those trials that were below par did actually demonstrate that healing was effective; it was only because their methodology could be criticised that they were disqualified from the meta-analysis. To help future investigators to steer clear of such pitfalls, their work includes a section giving comprehensive guidance. However, for scientists to be able to investigate healing, they need financial backing, and they also need to know that they will not be ridiculed and ostracised by the scientific community.

Professor David Peters of the University of Westminster has this to say about the findings of existing research:

'Science now supports some of the key principles of traditional healing—that the body and mind are effectively inseparable; that the body-mind has untapped and in-built healing responses; that complex systems are self-sustaining because a flow of information organises them (133).'

At the time of the CHO's meta-analysis being published, our own research paper was on the verge of being sent to a medical journal. Academically, we hoped that we would be adding yet another piece of convincing evidence to the existing mass. In practical terms, I hoped that the positive results would persuade medics and patients alike that healing really does make a difference. Positive results might then take us a step closer towards my ultimate goal—having healing made available to the public via the NHS.

Key Points

Extensive research shows the following:

1. Healing is effective for people in respect of a wide range of issues, including physical, mental and emotional problems.

2. Healing is effective on animals and plants, and on human cells in Petri dishes.

3. Healing on human cells in Petri dishes strengthens healthy cells and, at the same time, depletes cancer cells.

4. The results of healing on animals, plants and cells in vitro demonstrate that the placebo effect cannot be a factor.

5. Distant healing is effective.

6. When distant healing is sent without the knowledge of the recipient and has been effective, the placebo effect cannot be a factor.

7. Healing has been found to support medical treatments by reducing side effects.

8. Healing has been found to support surgical procedures by alleviating distress beforehand and by speeding recovery afterwards.

The Research Programme

Soon after hearing the terrific news that we had been awarded a grant, our Steering Group met to begin getting the project underway. A plethora of technical and organisational aspects had to be addressed, but none of these responsibilities would be landing on my lap because I was the only volunteer on the Steering Group. Everyone else was employed by the respective organisations involved. My remit was to deal with anything relating to healing and to be an extra voice when opinions were needed.

The main priority for the researchers was to finalise the study protocol. Plenty of detail had been provided with the grant application, but they now had to design a carefully structured, written plan to ensure that the programme ran smoothly to a successful conclusion. It had to be robust enough to withstand peer review in order to validate the systems and procedures used. Questionnaires, an information booklet for participants, letters and forms all had to be devised and finalised. Only when all of this documentation was completed could ethics approval be applied for.

Whenever research involves interviewing people, giving them questionnaires, accessing their medical records or offering them a treatment, ethics approval is mandatory. This is to ensure that participants are treated with respect, are informed about the research, have given their consent and are not harmed in any way by the treatment. Every detail of the patients' involvement has to be outlined in advance and, if the Research Ethics Committee decides that an alteration is needed, the application has to be amended and resubmitted. Also, if the slightest change is required during the programme, official approval must be gained before taking any steps. Bearing in mind that an Ethics Committee might only meet once a month, it can sometimes take quite a time to get an application passed.

Another priority was setting up detailed, official partnership agreements between Freshwinds, the University of Birmingham and the Primary Care Trust. Each organisation needed to commit to devoting specific resources to the project, which included personnel, office space, treatment rooms and any other elements involved.

Also, a research assistant needed to be employed for the two years of the programme. It was considered ideal that he be based at the University campus, but the procedure for securing desk space there would take too long, so he was based at Freshwinds.

To satisfy the terms of the grant, we also needed to have a 'user' on the Steering Group. Mentioned before, this meant inviting someone who had IBS or IBD so that a user's perspective would be on hand throughout the programme. When the Steering Group was casting around for a candidate, I suggested one of my friends who suffered with IBS, and she was duly invited. In addition, nobody could be more aware than Dr Singh of the full range of issues that affect both IBS and IBD patients.

Healers had to be recruited, too. I was most surprised to learn that the healers would be paid for their work. Naïvely, I had anticipated that we would be seeing the patients in a voluntary capacity but, of course, it made sense that the employment of healers should be on a formal and professional basis. The healers had to be recruited in the usual, equal opportunities manner. A few of the healers at our voluntary group had shown interest in the project, and I gladly supported their applications. My own involvement thus far in the project was irrelevant to my employment prospects within it, and I interviewed along with the rest. The healers from our group were successful, including myself—although I must confess that I would have been most perturbed if I had been rejected!

Commercially, the payment per session was far too low to expect a healer to travel to the hospital in the event that there was only one patient to see. Added to this, the sum would be halved if that one patient did not show up, and no compensation for time or travel would be paid. To minimise losses for the healers, attempts were made to bunch appointments together, but this was not always possible. Thankfully, the healers employed on the programme were so keen to assist the project that this was more of an observation than a real complaint. The problem did not affect me at all because my own research patients were to have appointments on Wednesday mornings, when I would normally be at the clinic anyway.

The contract also required healers to attend health and safety training and additional meetings without payment or reimbursement of expenses. Again, the healers were prepared to overlook this in favour of supporting the project.

With the finalised protocol, ethics approval, partnership agreements and staff recruitments yet to be done, the Lottery nevertheless needed to be advised of our start date, otherwise we would lose the grant. It was decided to commit to 1 April 2010, which would give the Steering Group four months to put everything into place. As it happened, though, gaining ethics approval caused an unanticipated three-month delay, and our start date had to be adjusted accordingly. We therefore had until 5 July 2012, two full years, to complete the trial.

All research trials need to be registered centrally so that clinicians, researchers, patients and the public can find out about trials in progress as well as those that have been completed and published. This has a number of benefits, one being that it reduces the possibility of research being duplicated. Besides being a waste of money, duplication could cause patients to be subjected to treatments for which evidence is already available, or is in the pipeline. Our trial was registered with the International Standard Randomised Controlled Trial Number Register.

All the participants were to be recruited from Dr Singh's outpatients clinic. At their usual consultation with him, or with one of his colleagues, each suitable IBS and IBD patient was asked if they would like to be involved in the project. If they agreed, they immediately had an appointment with the research assistant, who attended the clinic every Wednesday so that he was readily available. Some had to be disqualified straight away. For instance, they could not take part if they were unable to fill in the questionnaires themselves. In line with clinical trial guidelines, pregnant women could not be included, or people who had recently been engaged in another clinical trial, even if it was totally unrelated. If patients had received healing within the previous six months, they had to wait until six months had elapsed before beginning the series of healing sessions on the trial. Eligible patients were given more detail about what was involved, and they were sent home with information to share with their families before making a decision.

A little while into the programme, it transpired that not enough patients were being enrolled from Dr Singh's usual outpatient appointments. Rather than fall short of the target figure of 200, invitations were posted to potentially eligible candidates who were on the hospital database.

Once their consent had been received, the patients were randomised between two groups, with equal numbers of IBS and IBD patients in each. The 'intervention group' patients would then embark upon a series of five weekly healing sessions, but the 'waiting list control group' would not receive treatment until 12 weeks later. That way, the results of the intervention group (those who received the treatment) could be compared at Week 6 and Week 12 with the waiting list group, before the latter began receiving healing sessions.

Research trials usually have a control group that does not receive the treatment at all during the programme. Our waiting list patients were the 'control' for 12 weeks but after this period they were given appointments for five healing sessions. The protocol was designed this way because all the patients who had agreed to be on the programme were willing to receive healing. The ones randomised to the control group would be bound to feel dismayed if they were denied the healing that was on offer. Equally, healers would be dissatisfied with the idea of withholding healing from someone who was willing to receive it.

The first questionnaires were to be completed at Week 0—before the healing sessions began—and then repeated at Week 6, Week 12 and Week 24. Given that the intervention group received healing and the other group did not, direct comparisons could be made between them until Week 12. After this, the waiting list group would begin to have healing sessions, so the intervention group's Week 24 would not have a control group to compare against.

The Research Programme

Instead, this data was to establish whether any benefits identified at the previous stages had been sustained.

Taken together, the battery of responses should answer the research question as to whether healing had made a positive difference to their lives.

Throughout the trial, both groups continued to receive their usual medication.

Out of every five patients who agreed to be on the trial, one did not turn up for the sessions. Such a level of drop-out is normal across research programmes. However, very few people left the programme after they received their first healing session. One person quit after their first session, saying that all of the symptoms had disappeared. Considering that this patient must have been suffering from the condition for quite some time, this was an excellent result. However, whatever the reason was for the recovery, this data could not be included in the study figures because the patient chose not to continue.

Naturally, some patients were unable to attend every consecutive week of their five sessions. If they missed a week, their fifth session would be tagged onto the end. In this instance, one would think that their Week 6 questionnaire should be shifted forward a week to ensure that they had received all five healing sessions before completing the form. However, in standard research terms, the shifted week would then be Week 7, and the comparisons would be skewed. Therefore, the Week 6 data includes those who had received fewer than five sessions at that point. The Week 12 figures would definitely be after all five healing sessions had taken place. However, if the patient benefited after their delayed fifth session but then slipped back by Week 12, the peak of their improvement would not be reflected in any figures.

One would think that it could be useful to compare the results of the patients on our trial with those who had refused to take part. There may be a difference between those who are willing to try a safe but strange approach and those who are not. However, this, too, is against standard research protocol. Only people who are prepared to be randomised can be included, which means that they must be prepared to have the treatment if they are chosen for that group. Therefore, people who are **only** prepared to be in the control group—the group that receives no treatment at all—cannot be accepted. This means, of course, that only people willing to have healing were included in the trial, thereby making the participants 'selective'. Ideally, research trials require 'non-selective' participants, picked totally at random so there is no bias. However, this is impossible for any trials involving human beings because people have to agree to take part.

All the patients were seen on a Wednesday, to save the research assistant from having to travel back and forth more than necessary. He arranged all of the appointments and anonymised the paperwork to ensure that patients were not identifiable on any document that left his desk. However, it would have been off-putting for patients if the healer addressed them by their reference number so, for the sake of decorum, we were given their names but under separate cover.

In the main, I had all the morning appointments while a second healer had the afternoon ones, and a third handled the evening shift. Two additional healers were on stand-by in case any of the three of us had to be absent. If a patient could make a morning one week and an afternoon the next, he or she would therefore see two different healers. Usually, though, patients stuck to a regular time of day to avoid getting confused with appointment times.

To gather information from the patients, each person completed three different questionnaires. Everyone on the programme completed a general questionnaire called MYMOP, described later, plus two others that were specifically intended for their particular condition. Thus, the IBS people completed a different set from those for the IBD patients, but both groups completed MYMOP. All of the questionnaires employed had previously been widely used in clinical research and were validated.

Validation means that these forms have been rigorously assessed to confirm their reliability, validity, reproducibility and responsiveness. Basically, this means that the questions are detailed and precise enough to avoid ambiguity and are able to register changes in a patient's condition. Thus, the data gained can be expected to provide meaningful and useful information. It was important to use questionnaires that had been thoroughly tested so that the results gained could be interpreted with confidence.

174

The Research Programme

Together, the various questionnaires used were designed to gather as much data as possible. They would establish whether healing benefited patients in measurable ways, and also how they felt within themselves throughout the course of the programme. In our study, a small number of patients were also invited to in-depth interviews to get a fuller picture of how the treatment had affected their lives.

Researchers talk of quantitative data and qualitative data. As the words suggest, one refers to quantities and the other to qualities. Quantities can be measured and weighed whereas qualities are sensed and perceived. Measured and weighed quantities can be thought of as solid, whereas perceived qualities can be thought of as soft. Quantitative data would therefore be the equivalent of the bare bones or skeleton, and qualitative data would be the flesh that brings those bones to life (134). With flesh, the bones have a purpose. Qualitative, 'flesh' data aims to discover the human elements that affect a person's life. With both types of data to work with, a clearer picture can be gained that brings real meaning to research results. In our study, the questionnaires would provide the quantitative data regarding quality of life and symptoms. The subsequent interviews with selected patients would add qualitative data, by discovering the personal perspectives of their experience.

All the participants completed a MYMOP questionnaire—Measure Yourself Medical Outcomes Profile (135). This was created by Dr Charlotte Paterson, a GP from Somerset who has made complementary therapies available to her patients for many years. She wanted to know, from her patients' point of view, whether their lives were improving as a result of the treatments received.

Published studies have shown that MYMOP is practical, reliable and sensitive to any changes in the patient's condition. These studies involved patients who had received treatment from both orthodox and complementary practitioners for a range of problems. MYMOP has been extensively used in clinical research and is a validated instrument, designed to gather highly individualised information that is particularly patient-centred.

The MYMOP questionnaire is brief, which increases its feasibility and acceptability, thereby leading to high response and completion rates. Its simple structure and straightforward scoring make it easy to chart the scores of individual patients over a period of time.

MYMOP aims to measure the outcomes that the patient considers to be the most important. The patient chooses one or two symptoms that are causing them the worst difficulty and for which they would like the most help. Then they choose an activity of daily living that they cannot do or cannot manage properly because of this symptom. These choices are written down in the patient's own words, thereby giving clarity about their situation. The patient then scores them for severity over the previous week. On each follow-up questionnaire, the wording of the chosen issues remains unchanged, and the patient scores them afresh. Although our trial was for IBS and IBD sufferers, their worst problems might have been caused by an entirely different issue.

All of these scores are added together to get a final figure and, in our study, the final figures for Week 0, Week 6, Week 12 and Week 24 would reveal a picture of the outcome. Week 0 questionnaires were completed before the first healing session, giving what is called the 'baseline', against which the subsequent figures would be compared.

As well as MYMOP, the IBS patients completed a widely used and validated questionnaire called IBS-QoL (Irritable Bowel Syndrome Quality of Life). This was developed by a team of researchers at the University of Washington in Seattle. Its questions cover eight specific areas of a person's life—feeling unwell or unhappy, daily life activities, body image, health, worry, food avoidance, social reaction, and sexual/relationship aspects. It also evaluates bowel issues and the body as a whole. The individual gives a score for each particular issue, ranging from scoring just one point for 'not at all' through to five points for 'extremely'. These scores are added together and then averaged for a total figure, higher scores indicating a better quality of life. The IBS-QoL was designed to be completed by the patient and takes about ten minutes.

In addition to the MYMOP and IBS-QoL questionnaires, the IBS patients also completed the Birmingham IBS questionnaire. This was developed at the University of Birmingham to ascertain the severity of IBS symptoms. Its questions ask how frequent and intense their physical problems had been over the previous four weeks.

All of the people with IBD completed a MYMOP and also an IBDQ (Inflammatory Bowel Disease Questionnaire). The IBDQ was developed at McMaster University, Ontario. The team of researchers initially interviewed patients with IBD and identified 150 problems experienced in four different domains—bowel symptoms, emotional health, body systems and social function. They also discovered that almost half of the patients under-reported the various difficulties and impairments experienced unless they were encouraged by a reminder list. Until this in-depth investigation, their doctors and spouses had not realised the full extent of their suffering. The IBDQ is a respected quality of life questionnaire used extensively in academic research and clinical trials.

The inflammatory bowel disease (IBD) patients were split between two groups—those suffering from ulcerative colitis (UC) in the one and those with Crohn's disease (CD) in the other.

The ulcerative colitis patients completed a Simple Clinical Colitis Activity Index (SCCAI) questionnaire. This was jointly authored by researchers at the Royal Free Hospital School of Medicine in London and the Queen Elizabeth Hospital in Birmingham, UK. Its questions focus on the main symptoms and is designed to help doctors evaluate the severity of colitis in an accurate and easy way. This allows doctors to prescribe appropriate medical treatment without the delay of lengthy investigations and also helps identify patients who need a detailed assessment. For the purpose of our study, this questionnaire would be useful to reveal any changes in the severity of symptoms during the programme.

The other IBD group—those with Crohn's disease—completed a modified version of the Harvey-Bradshaw Index questionnaire. This consists of just five questions relevant to Crohn's symptoms.

Every participant therefore completed three questionnaires at each of the four stages—Week 0, Week 6, Week 12 and Week 24. If none of the 200 participants quit the programme, there would be a total of 2,400 questionnaires to process and evaluate. Armed with this amount of data, our researchers and statisticians should have a wealth of information from which to produce meaningful results.

Healing in a Hospital

The healers were not involved with the questionnaires. Our only remit was to deliver healing sessions. Healers are often also trained in other helpful therapies but, obviously, we were only to give healing during these sessions, using the method taught by The Healing Trust. Many healers think that it helps the patient to talk about their worries and illnesses but I do not agree. I therefore do not ask patients to tell me about themselves or why they have come for healing. It is obvious that people in Dr Singh's clinic will have gastrointestinal disorders, but I do not invite disclosure or attempt to discuss any issues, medical or otherwise.

Although the healers employed on the research programme were all using the same method of healing, we were allowed to help the patients relax beforehand in our own individual way. Some healers simply instruct the patient to take a few deep breaths. I use this method if talking might disturb others, such as at our healing centre where a number of people could be receiving healing in the same room. If I am alone with the patient, as at the hospital, I use a short and simple visualisation that gives the patient a useful technique to take home with them. These few sentences may then help them at any other time that pain or anxiety occurs.

At last, our first participant on the programme arrived on a Wednesday morning in September 2010. Over the next 21 months, I had the pleasure of treating more than 70 of the research patients.

The healers had a form to complete for each appointment, to confirm that the patient had arrived and that they had suffered no adverse effects from the healing session. If the patient volunteered any feedback about the session that they had just received, or how they had been since the previous one, I would make a note on this form before passing it to the research assistant. These remarks were invariably positive and sometimes fascinating, but I was disappointed to learn, very much later, that only the research assistant had read them. I knew that this information could not contribute towards the main research results, but it seemed a shame that it would be unseen and lost forever. Any feedback about the sessions had to be provided direct to the researchers via the questionnaires that were completed by the participants at home. Only the MYMOP forms invited descriptive comments but those insights were not utilised for our trial.

178

The Research Programme

On two occasions during the course of the programme, small amendments to the protocol were needed. Official approval from the Lottery and from an Ethics Committee had to be gained before any changes could be made.

The first problem involved the recruitment of qualifying patients. Initially, this had gone well using Dr Singh's lists, but eventually it became clear that we could fall short of the target number if we did not expand the net. An additional hospital within the Primary Care Trust was therefore approached and a small number of patients were treated there by our back-up healers.

The second issue was finding enough people with ulcerative colitis to populate the IBD group. To overcome the shortfall, Crohn's disease was included, which is very similar.

These amendments took additional time and effort to gain the necessary approval. Time was of particular concern because one of the conditions of the Lottery funding was that the programme must be concluded within two years.

Both of the Lottery workshops that I attended, and also the grant documentation, emphasised the need to publicise that our research was in progress. We were to consult and inform policymakers such as politicians, medics and primary care trust chiefs throughout the course of the programme, and also the general public. But, other than the initial news that we had successfully gained the grant, there was nothing more that we could openly state about it until the full results had been officially published in a medical journal.

However, a patient who flatly refused to take part in the project had much to say about it and took her views to the newspapers. She was aghast that healing was taking place in an NHS hospital and horrified that Lottery money was being 'wasted' on researching it. A well-known online newspaper carried a provocative and sensationalised article about the study. Journalists were eager to find out more about the project, but they were fended off because information given part way through a programme can sometimes adversely affect the outcome. Holding to the marketing maxim that 'all publicity is good publicity', the newspaper at least advertised that the research programme was in progress. It thereby helped meet the Lottery's requirement that we raise public awareness about the project. It will be interesting to see if the same paper prints something more constructive after the results are published.

The above-mentioned patient refused to participate in the programme because she was convinced that healing must be a waste of time, and perhaps others declined for the same reason. But most of those who were asked did take up the offer. After suffering for months or years, it seems logical to try an additional and complementary option, especially if it cannot make the problem worse. The only cost to these patients was their time.

My final healing session on the programme, which was the last one of the entire project, was in June 2012. Once this patient's Week 24 questionnaire arrived, the researchers and statisticians would be able to conclude processing the mountain of data and reveal the outcomes.

Key Points

1. NHS patients were to be recruited who continued to have IBS/IBD symptoms despite treatment by their GP and specialist medical care.

2. Each of the 200 participants was to receive five weekly healing sessions via half-hourly appointments at the hospital.

3. The main questionnaire (MYMOP) would determine whether people's lives had improved, not whether issues relating to IBS or IBD had been alleviated.

4. The second type of questionnaire would determine whether people's lives had improved in respect of the specific difficulties caused by IBS or IBD symptoms.

5. The third type of questionnaire would determine whether the physical symptoms of IBS or IBD had been alleviated.

6. A small selection of patients would be interviewed to gain their personal perspectives.

7. Half of the patients were to be randomly allocated to the 'intervention' group, and begin their series of healing sessions almost immediately.

8. The other half were to be assigned to the 'waiting list control' group, and wait for three months before beginning healing sessions.

9. Comparisons were made between the two groups at Week 6 and Week 12 to see if the group that received healing gained more than the group that did not.

10. Comparisons were to be made between the two groups after the 'waiting list control' group had received healing to see if their results followed a similar pattern to that of the 'intervention' group.

11. The 'intervention' group's Week 24 figures would reveal whether benefits were retained in the longer term (19 weeks after their final session).

The Results

The unconventional subject matter of our study was likely to be a magnet for denigration, academic and otherwise. The Steering Group and the University's executive were bound to be alert to these risks, and will have aimed to minimise the possibility of criticism. Our researchers had their own professional reputations to protect as well as that of the University, which, as a member of the Russell Group, takes pride in being known for first-rate research.

Judging from the range of positive patient responses that we had personally witnessed when seeing our patients, the other two main healers and I felt optimistic that the research results should be impressive. However, a great deal can depend on how researchers manipulate and present data, and this can be affected by their beliefs and attitudes. If researchers are biased, either in favour or against the subject of a trial, then the presentation of the results can be slanted accordingly. But I had no doubt that the researchers on our Steering Group would present the results fairly.

Nevertheless, I suppressed any dreams of triumph. It seemed to me that the outcome of a research programme could be like a court case where, despite evidence pointing to a defendant's innocence, he is found guilty, or vice versa. Perhaps that is why a research programme is called a 'trial'.

Another similarity between a research project and a court case is that all of the information involved has to remain totally confidential until it has been officially revealed. In a legal case, the details are presented in a law court. In a research trial, it is officially published in a scientific or medical journal. If the evidence in a court case is leaked sub judice—that is, while the case is being considered and in advance of the sentence being passed—it can jeopardise the court's decision. Likewise, the findings of a research project should not be disclosed until the paper has been officially published. Prior disclosure could undermine confidence in the findings. Worse, if a research paper's robustness is disputed prior to its publication, an academic journal may not be prepared to print it at all.

At last, the meeting arrived where the research assistant was to present the findings. Until then, no hint had been given to the Steering Group of how the incoming data was panning out. Five years had gone by since I had first approached Dr Singh about applying for the grant; this would be the moment when we would know whether our efforts had been at all worthwhile.

Among all of the numbers and graphs being shown to us, it was clear to me that healing had indeed made a significant difference. Dr Singh and I were exultant. On reflection, it must have also been a relief for Dr Singh that the trial had been successful because his name was nailed to it. Also, if he were now to be quizzed about providing healing at his clinic, he could point to specific evidence justifying his decision.

During the presentation of the results, I wondered if I was misreading one of the graphs. It seemed to show that the control group had benefited slightly while they were waiting for their healing sessions to begin. I learned that this was true, and is a common feature of trials involving human beings. Even when people know that they are taking a sugar pill and are told categorically that it cannot do them any good, they often still improve. But in our study, the participants were not even getting a sugar pill. Their positive response may be due to the Hawthorne effect—described later—where patients improve when they feel that someone is taking an interest in their plight.

Although the control group in our trial improved by a small degree, the people who received healing sessions showed considerable improvements by comparison. Furthermore, the gains they reported followed a similar pattern to those in my audits.

Knowing that our study had been a success for healing was very exciting, but I was unable to share the cause of my elation with anyone outside of the Steering Group. Strict confidentiality was necessary until the research paper had been officially published.

The Results

It would be a very long while until publication because research papers typically take a significant amount of time and effort to write, agree and process. First of all, each of the co-authors has to contribute their part to it and then agree to the wording of the final draft. The paper is then sent for peer review, to academics within the originating university—in our case, the University of Birmingham—who were not involved in the trial. Any feedback is then considered and dealt with until a document agreeable to everyone is finalised. Our reviewers at the University of Birmingham were bound to have been advised by the Executive to take particular care on account of the adverse media attention that our trial had already attracted. It was likely to be under a spotlight when published.

Once a research paper has been finalised, a scientific journal can then be approached to publish it and, naturally, the most prestigious, appropriate journal is the first one to ask.

The receiving medical journal may not want to accept a paper on healing at all. The House of Lords Report, referred to earlier, provides the following evidence from the University of Exeter (41):

'[A] paper based on an orthodox medicine treatment [is] more likely to be accepted for publication by an orthodox medicine journal than [an] identical paper that provides the same results for a CAM treatment.'

Alternatively, the journal may have recently published an article about complementary therapies and does not wish to be overly associated with that field. Scientific journals have a reputation to protect, and endeavour to publish research that will add to their stature.

If rejected, another journal needs to be approached and so on until a suitable home has been found. The accepting journal then sends the research paper to its own choice of independent academics and, again, it is scrutinised for the legitimacy of its content and process. Any feedback is forwarded to the editor of the journal, who conveys it back to the authors. Even at this late stage, the paper could be ultimately rejected. But if the journal is satisfied, it is scheduled to fit into an upcoming volume and goes to print.

Healing in a Hospital

In our case, it seemed to take as much time to get the results published as it did to conduct the actual programme. From the day that we gained the grant through to the time that the research paper was eventually published, seven years went by. Throughout that time, I was naturally being asked for updates by healers, friends and healing organisations. Up until the last patient was seen, I had been able to respond to enquirers with something tangible and encouraging by giving details of the latest stage that we had reached. But after that last appointment I was unable to give any new information. As months and years slipped by, people could be forgiven for thinking that the project had failed or been abandoned.

Despite the information embargo, a small dissemination event was held at the hospital. The members of the Steering Group were present, and invitations were sent to the healers involved and to the participants. Only a handful of patients attended, probably due to the diabolical weather conditions that evening. Most members of the audience seemed to be volunteers from Freshwinds, some of whom were complementary therapists keen to know the results of the trial. No media could be invited because the research paper had yet to be officially published.

Two presentations were given at the dissemination event, one regarding the quantitative data and the other the qualitative data. Although the figures had successfully shown that healing had made a significant difference to our patients, these presentations seemed downbeat to me. I was relieved when Dr Singh and later confirmed my original understanding.

For the results of our trial to mean anything, the starting points first had to be established.

At the beginning of the programme, all of the participants completed Week 0 questionnaires to provide the 'baseline' information. Then the patient profiles were analysed to ensure that the people in the treatment groups were reasonably similar to their counterparts in the control groups. If there was a predominance of, say, drinkers and smokers in either group, future comparisons could be less meaningful. Our participants ranged between 33 and 62 years old and each person was taking between one and four medications to combat symptoms; 71% were female, 13% were

The Results

smokers, 59% were employed and 59% drank alcohol. On average, the participants had a marginally healthy body/mass index of 24.

The patients at Good Hope Hospital represent a broad spectrum of age, income and education, but not of ethnicity. Being located in a predominantly Caucasian area, only the tiniest proportion of the patients I saw—throughout my entire time at the hospital—were Asian or of African descent. Only one was of Southeast Asian heritage. Presumably, the participants of our trial followed similar lines. Curiously, there was a far greater proportion of non-Caucasians among the staff at Good Hope than among the patients, even though both groups must have been drawn from the same geographical district. Perhaps the disparity could be due to the spirituality of some cultures—discussed later—or to their use of ethnic remedies, such as Chinese herbal treatments and Ayurvedic medicine.

Overall, the patients had been diagnosed between eighteen months and ten years previously, though they will have suffered for longer than this. People with bowel problems can be reluctant to see their doctor, for fear of embarrassing investigations, and sometimes delay seeking medical help. Being outpatients at the hospital, every one of the people on our trial had already exhausted the standard treatments available from their GP. Once under the wing of a consultant, some people need a series of investigations for a proper diagnosis to be made. Consequently, many of these patients could have been suffering very much longer than one might suppose from the diagnosis figures.

Across both IBS and IBD, the baseline data at Week 0 revealed that it was the physical symptoms that caused patients the most concern. The main sources of distress were pain and problematic bowel activity. Unsurprisingly, these debilitating issues had a significant impact on all physical activity, including work life, social life and sex life. With all of these aspects affected, it is no wonder that some felt utterly miserable.

The 105 patients with IBS were split almost equally between the group to be treated and the control group. The 70 patients with ulcerative colitis were split similarly, and also the 24 patients with Crohn's.

In total, 241 patients expressed their willingness to taking part in the trial, which indicates the high level of interest that there must be among patients. For various reasons, 41 had to be excluded, leaving us with our target number of 200 participants.

Of the people who were allocated to the intervention group, 78% attended all five sessions and a further 12 people only missed one. The University researchers commented on how impressive these attendance figures were, compared with those of other trials. Our participants must therefore have had a positive attitude towards attending further sessions once they had experienced their first.

Completion of the questionnaires followed an encouraging pattern with 84% returning their Week 6 questionnaires, 79% completing Week 12, and 72% sending in their Week 24 form. Although these figures show that patients either dropped out along the way or overlooked the paperwork, the University researchers again remarked at how few losses there had been in comparison with other trials.

It is unknown whether any patients continued to have healing privately after their five sessions at the hospital. For those who experienced improvements, it would seem natural to seek additional healing but this appears not to have been the case. Certainly, the healers at our voluntary group were not aware of any of these patients making an appointment with them, and ours is the most local group to the hospital. In addition, subsequent feedback to Dr Singh has been that, although they benefited from the sessions and enjoyed them, they would not contemplate having healing outside of an NHS facility. Consequently, the Week 12 and Week 24 questionnaires are unlikely to have been enhanced by the effect of additional sessions to the requisite five. It amuses me to note that, if someone were to complain that this could have happened, they would be tacitly admitting that healing sessions are beneficial.

The Placebo Effect

Whatever the results of our healing trial, scientists and doctors are likely to point to the placebo effect as being the only cause of any

The Results

improvements. It is therefore worth taking a closer look at this remarkable phenomenon.

When trialling drugs or surgery, it is imperative to establish how much of any health benefit is due to the actual medical treatment and how much is down to the placebo effect. Otherwise, people could be prescribed medication or undergo surgery unnecessarily. Medication and surgery have risks and side effects that anyone would avoid if a non-invasive alternative were equally effective.

In a drugs trial, one group is given the actual drug while another takes a sugar pill, and a third group has no pill at all. The results of all three groups are compared to ascertain whether there are differences and, if so, by how much. Our trial could not include a placebo because it is not possible to provide one for healing. As pointed out earlier, everyone has the potential to be a healer so a sham practitioner can be as effective as a trained one. For this reason, our trial was simply focused on whether the health and wellbeing of IBS and IBD patients could be further improved by having healing sessions. It was not designed to ascertain by which mechanism any improvements were achieved.

All of our patients had exhausted whatever their own doctor could offer and were now working their way through the specialised treatments recommended by their consultant. Some had no more options. The question was whether adding healing to their provision of care could improve their lot in any way.

With no placebo group to compare with, scientists and the medical fraternity may contend that the placebo effect is the only means by which our patients improved. If they do, this would be the same as saying that healers have learned how to harness the power of the placebo effect over and above the level that best medical care and attention can achieve. In that case, surely all medical professionals should learn to do likewise or employ healers to provide this valuable aspect of healthcare. Patients would then be afforded the full spectrum of care to aid their recovery.

Looking back to my audit graphs, we can see the improvements gained by patients immediately after their consultation with Dr Singh. In each category, the grey columns all nudged towards the 'Excellent' end, suggesting that the placebo effect had been activated. Patients often remark upon Dr Singh's empathy and attentiveness, so it is difficult to imagine a more effective physician than he to stimulate this phenomenon. We can assume, then, that these patients achieved the maximum placebo gains that could be hoped for by receiving best medical attention. They then had a healing session. The towering white columns at the 'Excellent' ends reveal dramatic improvements in every graph. Can it be reasonable to say that this level of further benefit is attributable only to placebo?

It is tempting to think that the word 'placebo' could be redefined as being the patient's own self-healing ability that has been triggered into action. It probably is, in part, but this term could only apply to humans, since 'placebo' means that the treatment works solely because the patient has faith in it. The same word cannot apply to plants or animals, or to human tissue in Petri dishes, because none of these can have faith in a treatment. Abundant research gives clear evidence that something different from placebo must be causing non-human subjects to gain the improvements seen. Humans will benefit from whatever causes the changes in non-human subjects—but also from the placebo effect.

Scientists have sought to understand the placebo effect for many years. In 1946, the Cornell Conference in America brought together the pioneers of placebo research, who agreed that any future clinical trials should include a placebo group (136). The results of this placebo group could then be compared with those who received the real treatment, and also with those who had no treatment, for meaningful comparisons to be made.

In 1955, Henry Beecher, a Boston medical doctor, brought together the findings of those trials that included a placebo group and published his classic work *The Powerful Placebo* (137). During World War II, he had witnessed the placebo effect in action when morphine was in short supply. Injured soldiers, who believed that they were getting morphine but who had actually received a salt-water solution, still gained relief from pain. Intrigued, Beecher later researched the phenomenon and was the first author to attempt to quantify the effects of placebos across a range of ailments. Based on the results of over 1,000 patients, he calculated that around 35% of people gain a high degree of benefit from the use of a placebo in respect of pain, nausea, mood, anxiety, tension and symptoms of the common cold. He found that the most marked effects were where stress had been the greatest. For over 40 years, his publication was the most frequently cited placebo reference (138).

However, in 1997, two German scientists at the University of Witten/Herdecke reviewed Beecher's data and uncovered a range of flaws (138). They analysed a further 800 articles on placebo and found no reliable demonstration that the placebo effect existed at all. They stated that Beecher's work was no more than fiction.

Later, in 2001, two medical doctors at the National Hospital of Denmark conducted a systematic review that reached a different conclusion (139). They identified over 100 clinical trials that met their standards, involving a total of over 8,500 patients. They concluded that placebos had no significant effects on objective outcomes (physically measurable) and only small benefits for subjective outcomes (wellbeing and pain).

Fabrizio Benedetti—Professor of Physiology and Neuroscience at the University of Turin Medical School—has been studying placebos since the 1990s. His extensive research includes trials that demonstrate various physiological effects caused by placebos. One example involves Parkinson's disease where placebos are shown to reduce the firing of neurons, thereby enabling patients to move more easily (140). His research also confirms that people benefit even when they know that the treatment is fake.

In 2008, researchers at Harvard Medical School wanted to determine how effective the placebo effect might be. They designed a trial that involved 262 patients diagnosed with irritable bowel syndrome (141). They chose people suffering with IBS because they are thought to be more influenced by psychological therapies and therefore more prone to respond to placebos.

In this trial, the control group received no treatment while two other groups were both given sham acupuncture. To be convincing, devices that looked like acupuncture needles were used. They did not actually pierce the skin but created the illusion of doing so. The first of the acupuncture groups was given the fake treatment along with minimal interaction with the practitioner. The second group received the same bogus acupuncture, but the therapist conveyed care and compassion during the session. Nobody at all received real acupuncture. At three weeks, the difference between the three groups was dramatic. Scores for overall improvement were:

3% for the control group (no treatment, no interaction)

20% for the group given fake treatment, minimal interaction

37% for the group that received fake treatment plus compassionate care (p<0.001)

The proportion of patients reporting adequate relief from physical symptoms showed a similar pattern:

28% of the control group (no treatment, no interaction)

44% of the group given fake treatment, minimal interaction

62% of the group that received fake treatment plus compassionate care (p<0.001)

Remembering that the control group received no attention whatever, it is extraordinary that 28% reported gaining adequate relief. Stranger still, nearly 20% of all the patients complained of negative side effects of one sort or another, even though nobody at all had actually received a real treatment. Bizarrely, 10% of the 'treated' patients complained of pain, swelling or redness at the needle sites when, in reality, no needle had been used. Adverse side effects like these cannot be called placebo because they clearly did not please the patient. Instead, they are called 'nocebo' effects, from the Latin for 'I will harm'.

The results of this research leave little doubt that the placebo effect is real and powerful.

Every research trial has its own approach, and the results of one cannot therefore be directly compared to another. For instance, in this Harvard study, some of the participants were recruited by advertising in the media and by distributing fliers. These methods are liable to attract people who believe that acupuncture will help them, and who will therefore be biased in favour of the treatment. It is commonly known that acupuncture has been in use for thousands of years, which automatically creates an element of credibility. In addition, acupuncture was formally recognized in the USA as a

The Results

mainstream medicine 11 years before this trial took place (142). These facts add to the patients' belief that acupuncture is effective and thereby increases their expectancy of positive results. On top of all this, acupuncture is a physical procedure; people see that something tangible is being done to them, and they naturally anticipate a physical response. Not one of these reinforcing points applies to spiritual healing or to our trial:

1. All of our participants were recruited by their gastroenterology consultant.

2. All of the consultants involved, except for one, were probably highly sceptical that healing could benefit their patients. The one exception was Dr Singh because he had previously witnessed patients improve after one healing session. Indeed, it seems likely that Dr Singh would have had to encourage other consultants to invite their patients to partake in our trial.

3. Most of the patients had not heard of spiritual healing before.

4. Almost all of the patients were sceptical that healing could help them.

5. Healing has not been recognised by any medical authority.

6. Nothing physical is done to the patient during a healing session. Moreover, it is difficult for people to believe that having a healer's hands near to them, or lightly touching, could possibly have an effect on their health or wellbeing.

The Harvard study concluded, as predicted, that a positive patient-practitioner relationship can promote the placebo effect and achieve statistically and clinically significant outcomes. In like manner, the consultants concerned in our own trial will have elicited a certain amount of placebo effect when administering their conventional treatments. When those patients then embarked upon a series of healing sessions, any further improvements would have to be due to additional placebo effect or to healing energy.

In contrast to our trial, the participants in the Harvard study who responded to advertisements may not have been receiving treatment from a doctor or consultant immediately prior to the trial being conducted. For those people, the amount of placebo effect triggered by having medical attention and fake acupuncture should be expected to take a greater leap, since it would be from a standing start. This is an additional point that makes it impossible to compare the results of the Harvard study with ours. Equally, the results of any other placebo trials need closer inspection before attempting to make comparisons.

Professor Ted Kaptchuk, one of the researchers involved in the Harvard study, says that placebo treatments—interventions with no active drug ingredients—have been found to stimulate physical responses such as heart rate, blood pressure, chemical activity in the brain, pain, depression, anxiety, fatigue and some symptoms of Parkinson's disease (143). He believes that, alongside increasing the effectiveness of drugs, we should also be working to maximise the placebo effect. To dismiss the placebo effect, he says, ignores a huge chunk of healthcare that caregivers could be utilising.

Kaptchuk also refers to alternative therapies that produce a more positive outcome than a proven, specific, conventional treatment (144). In these cases, he questions what makes a particular therapy more legitimate than another. Should it be the one that gained positive clinical outcomes? Or should it be the one that is provided by a traditionally acceptable method? And who decides which?

The conclusions of the Harvard study are reflected in the House of Lords Report thus (41):

'Research...has shown that those therapists who exhibit greater interest in their patients, greater confidence in their treatments and higher professional status, whatever their...training, all appear to promote stronger placebo responses in their patients.'

And adds:

'More serious and/or invasive procedures seem to have greater placebo properties, with placebo surgery yielding highly positive response rates.'

'Treatments that employ sophisticated technical equipment also enhance the placebo effect.'

The Results

The more distinguished the physician and the more sophisticated the treatment and machinery, the more costly the fake procedure is likely to be. As demonstrated by the success of sham knee surgery, perhaps there are many other expensive medical treatments for which healing sessions would be a far cheaper and equally effective alternative. It would certainly be a more pleasant experience for the patient. And where surgery or medication is actually necessary, healing sessions would be an ideal adjunct to maximise efficacy and reduce anxiety.

Studies at the University of Colorado show that, in people who respond to placebos, brain activity drops in areas that process pain, and it increases in areas involved in emotion. Rather than blocking pain signals, it seems that the placebo may be changing how the brain interprets pain (145). And this trait is thought to be passed on in our genes (146). Picking up on the discovery that positive emotion cuts off pain, this may be part of the reason why so many people in my two audits reported pain relief. The audit results certainly reveal a link between pain relief and a heightened sense of wellbeing. Naturally, one would expect to feel happier if pain has reduced or gone. But the Colorado research turns the sequence on its head—it shows that upliftment occurs first, then pain reduction.

Other research shows that there is no particular type of person who is susceptible to placebos. Age, gender, intelligence, personality traits and religious beliefs have no relevance (41). In addition, a person who responds to a placebo on one occasion may not do so on the next.

That said, it is known that between 30% and 50% of people suffering with depression respond to placebo (147). When a new generation of antidepressants was licensed and brought into regular use, their worth was soon questioned. The results of a subsequent meta-analysis in 2008 found that these new drugs only gained significant effects for the most severely depressed patients (148). Even then, the difference between the placebo group and the treated group seemed to be due to decreased responsiveness to placebos, rather than to greater effectiveness of the medication.

Further, an analysis of children with major depression revealed that 48% of them improved in response to taking a placebo pill in comparison to 59% when taking active medication (149). With only

11% more children benefiting when given the real drug, it would seem more ethical to prescribe a placebo pill first. If that failed, another safe and effective alternative would be a series of healing sessions. For those who did not respond to a placebo or to healing, the active medication would remain an option.

The antidepressant Prozac continues to be widely prescribed, even though 80% of its power is now known to be placebo and its use increases the risk of suicide for young people (150). A study in The Lancet reported that when 14 antidepressant drugs—all used by youngsters—were investigated, only one was statistically significantly more effective than placebo (151). And growing numbers of children and adolescents are on these drugs (152).

For his television series *Enemies of Reason*, the well-known debunker and atheist Professor Richard Dawkins interviewed Nicholas Humphrey, Professor of Psychology at the London School of Economics. Humphrey—also an atheist—stated that, even when using traditional medicine, most of the cure is usually from within the patient's own body. He went on to say that, for some patients, alternative medicine can be more effective than traditional treatment and that, therefore, people should not be dissuaded from seeing a healer. The uncut footage reveals further insights, and can be viewed on *youtube* (150).

According to some studies, the placebo effect does not exist, in which case all of the benefit to our patients must be due to healing energy. Other studies conclude that the placebo effect accounts for 15% or more of any improvements, whether using conventional or complementary treatment. In our study, the patients who had been seen by their consultant immediately prior to joining the programme will have already gained the maximum placebo gains triggered by medical care and attention. Any further benefit after receiving healing sessions can only be due to additional placebo effect or to healing energy.

Scientific evidence shows that non-human subjects respond favourably to healing, and this could not be due to the placebo effect. Humans must benefit from the same externally-generated healing energy causing those improvements, but also from their own internally-generated healing energy—the placebo effect.

196

The Results

Whatever the discussions about placebos, our trial was only concerned about the benefits to patients. Whether the improvements were due to healing energy or to the placebo effect was not of interest. The important point was whether patients improved as a result of receiving healing sessions.

Quantitative Results

This section includes the official findings of the research trial along with my own supplementary comments and analysis. I have tried to make it clear when a statement is mine rather than taken from the published research paper (153). In the event of doubt, viewing the paper itself will clarify.

For ease of reading, the results of the trial are reported here without the technical jargon and fine detail needed to satisfy a medical researcher. The academic paper itself is the obvious source of such data, for those who wish to refer to it.

Any numerical scores quoted are taken from the tables that appear in the research paper. The tables themselves are far too complex to be worth reproducing here.

My interpretation of the score improvements expresses greater benefit to the patients than the research paper conveys. The researchers aimed to be cautious in how they reported the results, and perhaps this explains the difference. To substantiate my explanations and statements, I have taken care to underpin them by referencing a reliable source.

Where I have used the word 'significant' in this chapter, it means significant in research terms and mirrors a statement in the research paper. 'Statistical significance' conveys change in mathematical terms—the odds against the outcome happening by chance. 'Clinical significance' reports the meaning—the difference it makes to a patient's life.

In trials, it is important to distinguish between statistical and clinical significance because a treatment might be statistically significant but not improve the patient's quality of life. For example, there was a study that aimed to evaluate the difference in blood loss between using the standard method of resurfacing hip bones or a minimally invasive system. Even though the reported blood loss between the two patient groups was statistically significant—$p<0.001$—the actual difference in blood loss was only 52ml, an amount that made no clinical difference to the patients (154). Another study showed a statistically significant reduction in pain—$p<0.05$—for continuous nerve block compared to a single injection. But the actual difference measured on the Visual Analogue Scale was just 0.57, a level most unlikely to be clinically important (154).

In our study, the measurements used to establish whether the therapy was effective or not were provided by the patients themselves. The questions were focused on the patients' symptoms and their ability to lead a normal life. On the face of it, then, a significant statistical improvement in our trial ought to mean that there had been a corresponding clinically significant improvement.

Statisticians and researchers produce an array of different figures to convey results, and I have endeavoured to present their findings clearly and precisely. Should my additional interpretation of the findings raise queries, the paper itself is publicly available for clarification.

As each person gave their consent to be part of the programme, they were randomly assigned to either the 'intervention group' or to the 'waiting list control group'. Both groups completed their first set of questionnaires at Week 0 to gather baseline information about their current state of health and quality of life.

The intervention group then embarked upon five healing sessions, ideally every week. At Week 6 they completed a second set of the exact same questionnaires to see if any changes had occurred. At the time of completing the Week 6 questionnaires, 42% of the intervention group had not yet received all five sessions, perhaps because of their holiday arrangements or other commitments. Therefore, one or two sessions for almost half of the intervention group took place after they had completed their Week 6 questionnaires. The Week 6 figures would reveal whether healing had made a difference to their physical symptoms and to their lives, whether or not they had yet received all five sessions.

In total, 78% of the intervention group ultimately attended all five sessions well before Week 12. At Week 12, they completed another set of the same questionnaires to see whether the measures noted at Week 6 had changed.

The Results

The people allocated to the control group received no healing for the first 12 weeks while they completed their respective sets of Week 0, Week 6 and Week 12 questionnaires. This 'control' data would then be contrasted against that of the intervention group. After they had completed their Week 12 paperwork, they were able to start their series of five healing sessions, most likely beginning at Week 13.

Normally, a control group would not receive the treatment being investigated, but it would have been unfair to deny our patients the opportunity to have healing. They had certainly been willing to have sessions because they were prepared to be allocated to the intervention group when they first signed up. Indeed, when they were called for their healing appointments three months on, they followed the same pattern of high attendance and low drop-out as the intervention group. Once they had received their series of healing sessions, their Week 24 results could again be compared with those of the intervention group. To convey their dual role in the programme they were called the 'waiting list control' group in the research paper, instead of simply the 'control' group.

Both the intervention group and the waiting list control group completed their final set of questionnaires at Week 24. For the intervention group, this was 19 weeks after their final healing session and would reveal whether any benefits had been retained in the longer term. The waiting list control group did not begin their healing sessions until after Week 12, so their Week 24 was only seven weeks after their final session.

Figure 13 makes it easier to understand that the intervention group's Week 12 results and the waiting list control group's Week 24 results are both seven weeks after their final session. Thus, the results for these two questionnaire time points could be expected to be similar to each other.

One could also suppose that the Week 24 figure for the intervention group might be lower than any other figures because their Week 24 was 19 weeks after their final session and any gains might have reduced by then. Both of these suppositions will be discussed in detail later.

Table showing when each group received healing and when they completed questionnaires

H = Scheduled Healing Sessions. In practice, sessions for some patients were spread over a longer period. Others did not complete all five sessions.

Q = Questionnaires completed at Weeks 0, 6, 12 and 24.

Q = Questionnaire completed seven weeks after the final healing session for each group.

Week No	0	1	2	3	4	5	6	7	8	9	10	11	12	13	14	15	16	17	18	19	20	21	22	23	24
Intervention Group	Q	H	H	H	H	H	Q						**Q**												Q
Waiting List Group	Q						Q						Q	H	H	H	H	H							**Q**

Figure 13: Timetable of healing sessions & questionnaires

The Results

Having now set the parameters of the study and explained some of the terms and terminology, we can turn to the actual results.

Quality of Life (MYMOP)

The primary goal of the research trial was to see if healing improved lives, and the main tool chosen to measure this was the MYMOP questionnaire.

As described earlier, MYMOP is centred around the patient's experience of life, not whether they have recovered from specific ailments. It aims to discover what is troubling a patient the most and determine whether the treatment under investigation is bringing about improvements. Patients are asked to describe their two worst symptoms and then identify activities that are hindered by them. Using a seven-point scale, patients give a score for each symptom and for each activity so that any changes can be measured. In our trial, we might expect bowel problems to be identified as the worst problem, but it could be something else entirely.

All participants, whether they had IBS or IBD, completed this questionnaire. As one might guess, patients identified physical difficulties as being the most problematic for them. Pain was one of the two worst symptoms for 25% of the participants. 'Bowel habit' was one of the worst for 17% of cases, and other common problems were diarrhoea, cramps and bloating. Whatever their worst two symptoms were, these had been making it difficult for patients to go to work, exercise and socialise, in varying degrees. With these elements being the prime activities of a normal day, it is no surprise that their quality of life had been seriously impaired.

The group that received healing from the outset—the intervention group—gained a significant improvement for each of their two worst symptoms and also for activities at Week 6 (all at either $p<0.001$ or $p=0.001$). These significant gains were maintained to Week 12 (all at either $p<0.001$ or $p=0.001$) and to Week 24 (all at $p<0.001$ or $p=0.001$).

Recalling the meaning of probability figures—or 'p' values—the term '$p<0.001$' means that the odds against these improvements happening by chance is less than one in 1,000. In medical research, $p=0.05$ (one in 20) is usually accepted as being significant (155) but, at the planning stage, the University researchers had raised the bar for our trial. They specified that p<0.005 (less than one in 200) would denote significance in respect of 'sub-scales and domains', which translates to 'symptoms and activities' within the MYMOP questionnaire. With results of p<0.001, the statistical significance in our trial for symptoms and activities were five times better than the raised bar, and 50 times better than the level normally accepted for medical research.

As is often the case in clinical trials, the control group improved slightly even though they had not received the treatment. But even when compared against this slight improvement, the results for the intervention group still remained at the same level of significance for each of their two worst symptoms and for activities at Week 6, and at Week 12 (all at p<0.001).

Probability figures convey the 'statistical significance' of how unlikely it is that the results obtained are due to chance. In trials, they may give no indication of the magnitude—or clinical importance—of the difference. 'Clinical significance' is more meaningful to the patient, because it conveys the practical importance of a treatment—it reports a genuine, palpable and noticeable effect on daily life. Clinical effects are expressed by a change in score, the extent of which indicates the amount of change that took place.

Using MYMOP, a decrease in score denotes an improvement, with a drop of one unit meaning that an individual has probably improved by a noticeable degree (156). Thus, the larger the decrease in score the greater the positive clinical significance.

Taking the MYMOP figures for the IBS and IBD groups together as a whole, changes to their two main health problems had been scored along with the activities affected by them. As mentioned earlier, the scores referred to here are taken from the table that appears in the research paper.

At baseline, the two worst symptoms and the affected activities were each scored at four units by all participants, whether they were in the intervention group or the waiting list control group. By Week 6, the scores for the intervention group had each decreased by one unit (from four down to three), indicating a clinically determinable improvement. At Week 12, the score decreased again

The Results

by a further one unit, from three down to two. As a healer, it was exciting to have scientific confirmation that our work improves lives to such a tangible degree.

The additional decrease in score by Week 12 could only be due to one of two things, or a combination of both.

One possibility could be in respect of the 42% who had not received all five of their sessions before completing the Week 6 questionnaire. These people received their last one or two sessions after Week 6. The benefits gained from these later sessions could be the cause of the decreased score at Week 12. If so, then it would mean that additional benefits occurred through having those additional healing sessions. The other possibility is that people continued to improve after their final healing session. Either way, receiving healing sessions caused improvements to take place.

Given that Week 12 was at least one month after their final healing session, one might assume that some initial gains could have diminished by the time patients completed that questionnaire. Taking this into account, the Week 12 scores are even more impressive than they first seem.

One might also suppose that the Week 24 figures for the intervention group might be worse than earlier scores, because this questionnaire was completed 19 weeks after their final session, and gains could have reduced by then. Indeed, the two worst symptoms and also activities were each scored at three, one unit higher than they had gained by Week 12, signifying a worsening of their condition. Nevertheless, this is still one unit better than before they started the course of treatment, and indicates a noticeable improvement.

By comparison, the scores for the waiting list control group had all remained at four during Week 6 and Week 12, the period when they received no healing. The people in this group then began their series of healing sessions from Week 13. Seven weeks after their final session, at Week 24, they completed their last set of questionnaires. At this point, they scored three for each symptom (an improvement of one point) and only two for activities (an improvement of two points).

The fact that the waiting list control group followed a similar pattern of progress to that of the intervention group gives additional

203

reliability to each group's results. It thereby adds further credibility to the assertion that healing has a positive effect.

The physical improvements recorded by these MYMOP scores may not have been related to symptoms of IBS or IBD. The worst problem for a patient can be something quite different. Examples of this among Dr Singh's patients include the young woman mentioned earlier who had partially lost the use of her legs; another is the woman who had suffered addictions for 30 years. After one healing session, those problems had disappeared. Had they been on the trial, their MYMOP scores would have seen massive improvement. But if they had been given questionnaires regarding IBS or IBD symptoms, their results might have been inconclusive. A similar case would be my own situation, when I had sought healing for psoriasis. The psoriasis improved a little but the main benefit was something quite different, explained later. Had I been completing a similar clutch of questionnaires to the ones used in our trial, my score for the troublesome medical condition—psoriasis—would have been mediocre, but my MYMOP score would have been excellent.

Similarly, if there were to be a detailed inspection of the completed MYMOP questionnaires in our trial, the data may reveal that a range of additional issues had been alleviated that had nothing to do with IBS or IBD. Hence, the MYMOP results are the most important of any, because the main priority of our trial was to establish whether people's lives had improved.

In the MYMOP questionnaire, one aspect of life that is measured is termed as 'wellbeing'. Despite the considerable improvements to their symptoms and quality of life, the intervention group did not record an equivalent enhancement to their sense of wellbeing, which seems odd. One would imagine that wellbeing should improve in line with physical improvements, but this was not reflected in the scoring.

At Week 0 they gave a more positive score—that is, three—for wellbeing than their distressing symptoms and impaired quality of life would suggest. They gave this same score for wellbeing throughout the programme, even though their symptoms had been alleviated and they were able to be more active. The waiting list control group improved by one point for wellbeing at Week 24

The Results

(seven weeks after their final session), but the intervention group's deflated wellbeing score reduced the overall results.

Regarding the concept of 'wellbeing', it could be that the meaning of the word is too subjective and therefore unclear to some people. Perhaps it needs to be clearly defined before asking people to give a score for it, as I had done when I conducted my hospital audits. Alternatively, the MYMOP webpage (156) offers another explanation:

> '...treatment may change the symptoms and activity scores dramatically, and the wellbeing may change less because so many social and personal things affect it.'

If the intervention group's wellbeing figures were not included in the total, the overall improvement figures for our trial would be greater. But even with the wellbeing figures included, the intervention group still retained significant improvements by Week 24 ($p=0.002$), 19 weeks after their final healing session. The phrase '$p=0.002$' means two in 1,000 or, simplified, odds of one in 500 against the amount of improvement occurring by chance.

As mentioned before, our researchers had specified higher significance levels than usual for our trial. For 'sub-scales and domains' they had stipulated $p<0.005$ (less than one in 200) but for 'overall' scores, they set the threshold at $p<0.01$ (less than one in 100). The overall MYMOP result of $p=0.002$ is five times better than the pre-specified level and 25 times better than the medically accepted norm of $p=0.05$ (one in 20).

The information presented in Figure 14 illustrates the IBS and IBD results separately, giving the overall scores for each condition including wellbeing. If the wellbeing scores were omitted, the downward trend of the curve (denoting improvement) would be even more pronounced. Nevertheless, the graph clearly shows that the two groups followed the same pattern of gains because their respective lines are virtually parallel. The lower position of the IBD line indicates that the IBD group reported less suffering than the IBS people, but the percentage of improvement was almost identical. The research paper therefore states that both groups benefited.

Healing in a Hospital

These excellent MYMOP results demonstrate that the research trial achieved its primary goal. It had established that adding healing sessions to conventional treatment improves the lives of patients with IBS and also the lives of patients with IBD.

A reduced score denotes improvement.

These figures include 'Wellbeing' scores. If the graph included only Symptoms and Activities it would reveal more dramatic improvements than are indicated here.

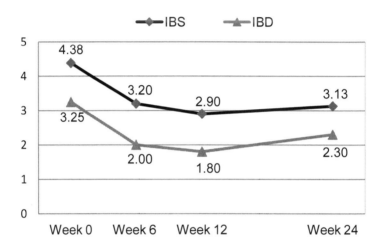

Figure 14: MYMOP Scores; IBS and IBD

Now we turn to the specialised questionnaires that were employed to ascertain whether patients had gained improvements to quality of life issues directly relating to their particular condition.

206

The Results

IBS Quality of Life

In the case of people with irritable bowel syndrome (IBS), they completed the IBS-QoL questionnaire described earlier. It focuses on the particular problems that commonly affect the day-to-day lives of people with IBS. It measures the effects of the symptoms rather than the symptoms themselves.

With 34 questions, each requiring a response on a five-point scale, the score can range from 34 to 170. An increase of between ten and 14 points reflects a meaningful clinical improvement (157). I have therefore used the mid-point of 12 for the calculation that follows.

For ease of analysis, our researchers had converted the scores to being out of 100. Mathematically, this conversion means that an increase of 12 points in the original scale—identifying clinical improvement—is equivalent to around nine points in our figures.

Incidentally, with the scores now being out of 100, one might presume that our results could be read as percentage improvements, but apparently not.

At Week 6, the intervention group (the group that received healing from the outset) gained an overall score improvement of 12.9 ($p<0.001$). At Week 12 the increase was 12.4 ($p<0.001$), and at Week 24 it was 13.8 ($p<0.001$). It is surprising to see a slight dip at Week 12 followed by an improvement at Week 24, which achieved a better score than Week 6.

With nine points in our figures indicating clinical improvement, the gains of 12.9, 12.4 and 13.8 must be impressive. And the 'p' figures in brackets reveal that the intervention group improved by a statistically significant degree at each time point throughout the trial.

The improvement at Week 24 shows that benefits continued to develop after their final healing session. Gains were therefore sustained for at least 19 weeks, and could have been longer but our study was limited to a total of six months.

The waiting list control group improved slightly during the 12 weeks that they waited for their healing sessions to begin. Nevertheless, even when compared to the control group, the intervention group's results remained statistically significant at Week 6 (p=0.001) and slightly less so at Week 12 (p=0.013).

Remembering that the University researchers had raised the bar for significance to p=0.01 (one in 100) for total scores, Week 6 outstripped this with p=0.001 (one in 1,000). Week 12 only just missed the elevated threshold with p=0.013 (13 in 1,000 or, simplified, 1.3 in 100).

Researchers also use 'effect sizes' to convey the magnitude of improvement, and 0.8 is considered a large enough change to be noticeable (158) (159). Effect sizes give a more clinically relevant picture of health status, and are a useful tool for interpreting changes in chronic illness (160).

The research paper explains that various adjustments were made to account for differences within the group such as age, gender and years since diagnosis. After making these adjustments, they arrived at effect sizes for the intervention group of 10.7 at Week 6, and 7.6 at Week 12, compared with the control group. I queried these seemingly outlandish figures, but they remained unchanged in the research paper so they must be correct.

An expert on the subject confirmed to me that 10.7 is indeed 'quite extreme', but he needed more details to be able to speak directly about the impact on patients. I felt unable to provide him with further information because the research paper had not yet been published. But whether or not these figures are a cause for celebration, they remain useful for a comparison that I wish to make shortly.

These effect sizes include the people who had not received all five sessions before completing their Week 6 questionnaires. As mentioned earlier, this represented 42% of the intervention group. I should point out that 42% actually refers to all of the participants as a whole, but I have assumed it would be near enough the same percentage for the IBS and IBD groups separately. If the IBS cohort had received their five sessions before completing the Week 6 questionnaires, there would have been better results for Week 6, Week 12 and Week 24. Let me explain how the scores substantiate this assertion.

Of the intervention group, 22% failed to attend all five sessions. As before, 22% refers to the whole intervention group but I have

The Results

assumed the same figure for the IBS and IBD groups separately. The researchers separated out the figures for those who had received all five and found that these people had gained greater improvements than those who had fewer. On the same basis as the various adjustments detailed before, the effect sizes for those who received all five were 12.6 at Week 6, and 10.4 at Week 12, compared with the control group. These figures reveal that, by having attended all five sessions, they had gained an additional 1.9 effect size points at Week 6 (12.6−10.7=1.9) and an additional 2.8 points at Week 12 (10.4−7.6=2.8).

Thus, we can see that the score for the whole intervention group was dragged down by 2.8 points at Week 12 by only 22% of the group—the ones who had fewer than five sessions. This means that the scores for the 22% must have been substantially lower than for the 78% who had all five.

These figures demonstrate that each session brings increased benefits. It therefore follows that the Week 6 figures would have been better if all participants had received their five sessions before completing the Week 6 questionnaires.

As well as this, the 78% who had all five sessions retained more of the benefits by Week 12 (12.6−10.4, giving a loss of 2.2 effect size points) than the intervention group as a whole (10.7−7.6, giving a loss of 3.1 effect size points). The people who had all five sessions therefore retained an additional 0.9 effect size over the intervention group as a whole (3.1−2.2=0.9). If 0.8 is considered a noticeable improvement, then it must be worth retaining this additional 0.9.

Again, the above comparison is between the 78% who had all five sessions and the whole (100%) intervention group. But the whole intervention group includes the 78% who had all five. If we compared the scores for the 78% (who had all five) against only the 22% (who had fewer) a greater difference would be revealed.

These calculations show that if all of the participants had received all five sessions, there would have been better results at Week 12 for IBS sufferers. And since more benefits were retained in the longer term by having all five, then the Week 24 figures would also have been enhanced.

Looking at the intervention group's Week 24, this was 19 weeks after their final session so one might assume that gains may have dissipated. However, the scores are better for every aspect, showing that benefits had not only been maintained but also continued to increase between Week 12 and Week 24. If everyone had received all five sessions before Week 6, there would have been a longer period for this trend to continue. Thus, the Week 24 scores could have been greater.

The majority of people had their final healing session seven weeks before Week 12 so it is intriguing to see improvements continuing to develop for so long afterwards. This positive trend could have continued beyond Week 24 but, as stated before, six months was the extent of our study.

The results of the IBS Quality of Life questionnaire (IBS-QoL) were found to be consistent with the findings of the MYMOP scores, thereby further confirming the reliability of both. With the questions being focused specifically on the issues associated with IBS, a greater insight was gained regarding the aspects of life that had improved. Almost all dimensions of quality of life within the intervention group exhibited at least a ten-point improvement at Week 12 and this was maintained to Week 24. Remembering that an increase of about nine points in our figures (by the reckoning explained earlier) conveys clinical significance, these are excellent results. Mood, outlook, activities, food issues, attitude, social life and sex life had all achieved a level of improvement that was noticeable to the patient.

The results of this questionnaire further confirmed that the research trial had achieved one of its primary goals. It had established that healing sessions improve quality of life issues that particularly affect patients with IBS.

IBD Quality of Life

Turning now to the people in the inflammatory bowel disease (IBD) group, they completed the IBDQ questionnaire described previously. It was designed specifically to measure the quality of life experienced by people with this particular condition. As opposed to the IBS-QoL, which does not ask about physical symptoms, the IBDQ devotes three-fifths of its questions to bowel problems and to general physical health.

The Results

Despite the difference in focus, the IBDQ results followed a similar pattern to the IBS-QoL, with the intervention group demonstrating a significant overall improvement at Week 6 (p=0.008) and even more so at Week 12 (p<0.001).

The questionnaire consists of 32 questions that are scored by the patient on a seven-point scale, giving a range of possible scores from 32 to 224. Higher scores indicate a better quality of life, with a 20-point improvement denoting clinical significance (161).

As with the IBS-QoL, our researchers had converted the actual IBDQ scores into being out of 100 for easier analysis. Mathematically, this must mean that an increase of about ten points in our trial's figures denotes a clinically significant improvement.

The two main problems regarding bowel function improved by 11.6 points (p=0.006) and 14.2 points (p=0.022) respectively by Week 12.

This shows that symptom improvements were retained and even increased over the seven weeks following their final healing session. There was a reduction over the following three months but they were still better off at Week 24 (p=0.044) than before joining the trial.

Again, we see that score improvements were greater at Week 12 than they had been at Week 6. The two dimensions that gained the most improvement were 'bowel function' (p <0.001) and 'social function' (p<0.001) at Week 12. Naturally, if a person's bowels are more predictable and less painful, social situations can be engaged in with more confidence and enjoyment.

After making the various adjustments referred to earlier regarding age etc, the intervention group achieved effect sizes of 5.8 at Week 6 and 10.1 at Week 12 (p=0.004) compared with the control group. Again, these seem surprisingly high figures if 0.8 is considered noticeable to a patient.

When the researchers separated out the results for people who had received all five sessions, they found that the scores were almost the same whether people had the full quota or less. There had been a notable difference between these figures for the IBS patients (IBS-QoL). But the IBD questionnaire had a stronger focus on physical symptoms, which could be an explanation. The researchers also thought the disparity may be due to IBS and IBD being different medical conditions.

The Week 24 figure for the intervention group could be expected to be worse than any other figure because this would be 19 weeks after their final session. Indeed, the figures are all slightly worse but most of the improvements had been retained. Again, these benefits may have lasted longer but our study was limited to a total of six months.

Overall, the researchers found that the IBDQ results were consistent with the findings of the MYMOP scores, which further confirms the reliability of both.

The results of this questionnaire again verified that the research trial had achieved one of its primary goals. It had established that adding healing sessions to conventional care improves the lives of patients with IBD.

On their own, these excellent quality of life enhancements for both IBS and IBD patients, reiterated across the three different questionnaires, would be highly meaningful for the patients involved. But the secondary aim of the trial was to ascertain whether the physical symptoms characteristic of IBS and of IBD had actually been alleviated. To measure changes in the severity of symptoms, each group completed a questionnaire designed for their particular diagnosis.

IBS Symptoms

The IBS group completed the Birmingham IBS questionnaire, described earlier. Its 11 questions are scored on a six-point scale, resulting in a minimum possible score of 11 and a maximum of 66.

Results revealed that the intervention group's physical symptoms had gained significant improvements especially at Week 6 ($p<0.001$) compared with the control group. The gains were slightly reduced at Week 12 ($p=0.018$) but the research paper nevertheless confirms that the retained improvements are likely to reflect a clinically determinable effect.

The scores were slightly lower at Week 24 but, even so, were still a substantial improvement over baseline in comparison to the control group. In other words, patients gained significant physical improvements during the period of time that they received healing and, despite the slight decline afterwards, were better off at Week 24 than before joining the programme. Positive effects of healing had therefore been retained for 19 weeks after their final healing session and could have lasted longer.

Now the researchers could see that the results of the Birmingham IBS questionnaire were consistent with the other two that had been completed by the IBS cohort (MYMOP and IBS-QoL), further confirming that the results across all three were reliable.

From these results, it was clear that a secondary aim of the trial had been achieved. Adding healing sessions to conventional treatment had alleviated the physical symptoms of IBS patients.

IBD Symptoms

Turning now to the inflammatory bowel disease (IBD) group, this was originally intended to only include patients with ulcerative colitis. Finding enough people with this condition proved more difficult than expected so the Steering Group had been prompted to include Crohn's disease. Crohn's is an IBD that is very similar to colitis but, in research terms, 'similar' is not 'the same'. With the IBD group split between these two different conditions, the results cannot be compared like-for-like within the group as a whole. Also, the number of people within each sub-group was too small to provide meaningful analysis for either condition, or for conclusions to be drawn. Nevertheless, the results make interesting reading and are presented here.

Ulcerative Colitis Symptoms

The ulcerative colitis group used the SCCAI questionnaire described earlier to measure changes in their physical symptoms. Total scores range from 0 to 19, with a decrease denoting improvement and a score of 2.5 correlating with remission (162).

The scores for the intervention group reveal an improvement from 4.3 at Week 0 to 3.8 at Week 6 (p=0.41). This was followed by a further gain at Week 12 with a score of 3.1 (p=0.046). There was a small slide back up to 3.4 by Week 24 but symptoms were still better at this point than before having healing.

The waiting list control group followed a similar pattern.

Crohn's Disease Symptoms

To establish whether symptoms improved for the Crohn's disease group, these patients used the H-B questionnaire described before. Again, a reduction of score signifies an improvement in symptoms, with 13 denoting extreme severity. A score of less than 5 is considered to represent clinical remission (163).

The intervention group's score began at 8.5 at Week 0, reducing to 7.9 at Week 6, and down again to 7.0 by Week 12. At Week 24 it was down to a remarkable 4.4, a score indicating clinical remission.

This signifies that outstanding improvements continued to develop between seven and 19 weeks after their final healing session. The natural question that arises is: How could the improvements during this latter period be due to the placebo effect if these patients were not receiving the care and attention that is deemed to activate it?

The waiting list control group followed a similar pattern, beginning with a Week 0 score of 6.7. They then waited for 12 weeks before beginning their healing sessions. Their Week 12 figure showed that nothing had particularly changed for them since Week 0. They then began to receive their series of healing sessions. Seven weeks later, at Week 24, their score had reduced to 4.3. They had improved by the same surprising degree as the intervention group, but more quickly.

These are astounding results, but the Crohn's group consisted of only 24 people. In research terms, this is too small a sample size to be statistically convincing. Consequently, although these scores appear in the table presented in the research paper, they are not mentioned within the text. But since both the intervention group and the waiting list control group improved by the same extraordinary degree, then surely further investigation is warranted. Added to this, the intervention group revealed increasing benefits for 19 weeks after their final session—and this trend could have lasted longer.

The Results

The waiting list control group may have fared equally well in the longer term, but this was well beyond the extent of our study.

Again, from the results of these two different IBD questionnaires, a secondary aim of the trial had been achieved. It had established that receiving healing sessions had alleviated the physical symptoms of IBD, though not convincingly in academic research terms.

A similar study with larger numbers in each IBD group would, of course, be more persuasive for scientists, but ulcerative colitis and Crohn's are not common diseases. Considering that a sufficient number of patients with ulcerative colitis could not be found for our trial in Birmingham—reputedly Britain's second biggest city—the results of our study may have to suffice for the time being. Clearly, a study of Crohn's disease would be even more challenging to populate.

Overall

There were 105 IBS patients in our study, a sufficient number from which to gain reliable statistical results in relation to IBS. The IBD group as a whole was also sizeable with 94 patients but it had to be split between 70 colitis and 24 Crohn's patients. The smaller the group is, the less dependable the statistical data analysis becomes. For the Crohn's group in particular, no conclusions have been drawn within the research paper.

Each of the three questionnaires completed by participants supported the findings of the other two. The questions were different in each one so the results naturally varied, but there remained substantial consistency across them all. For example, the MYMOP scores for the IBS people were compatible with the results of their IBS-QoL and Birmingham IBS questionnaires, and the same can be seen across the IBD cohort. This compatibility lends additional credibility to the findings of each one.

The researchers noted the difference in symptom benefits between the IBS and IBD groups and suggested that this could be because they are unrelated conditions, as outlined earlier.

With the IBS symptom improvements being more pronounced and lasting longer, the researchers suggest that people with functional disorders might be more disposed to benefiting from healing sessions than people with actual physical disease. The term 'functional disorder' refers to any medical condition that impairs the normal function of a bodily process, but where every part of the body looks completely normal under examination, dissection or under a microscope. Irritable bowel syndrome is not a disease, and there is no physical cause for the symptoms to occur, yet they are known to be exacerbated by emotional upset and stress (164).

Inflammatory bowel disease, on the other hand, does have physical causes for the symptoms to occur, though nobody knows what triggers the disease into existence in the first place.

But physical symptoms were the secondary focus of our investigation. Improving lives was the primary concern, and the MYMOP results confirm that this was achieved equally for both IBS and IBD patients.

In summation, from the quantitative data in front of them, the researchers were able to draw conclusions. Considering the controversial nature of the study, we could expect their statements to be cautious and fully considered. Each of the authors would no doubt wish to protect their professional and academic reputation. In addition, the University of Birmingham's executive is likely to have ensured that its internal peer review process was particularly rigorous.

The following statements appear in the research paper. First of all, regarding all participants, they confirmed that healing makes a positive difference:

> 'Results demonstrate that when used alongside standard medical care, healing therapy confers additional benefit.'

They pointed out that the patients who received all five sessions—referred to as 'per protocol'—benefited more than those who received fewer. This confirms that each additional session brought increased benefits:

> 'Per protocol analyses suggested that greater benefit was associated with compliance, further supporting the observed findings.'

The Results

In respect of the MYMOP scores measuring quality of life for all participants, whether they had IBS or IBD, they stated that:

'Changes in scores were of a size with the potential to result in notable improvements to the patient.'

'We have observed that healing therapy is beneficial, both in terms of improvement in patient perception of disease impact (determined by MYMOP), which was our pre-specified primary outcome.'

In respect of the MYMOP results for the intervention group, which included both IBS and IBD, the research paper confirms that benefits remained for many weeks after their final healing sessions and could have lasted longer:

'...all symptom and activity measures (except for wellbeing) showed improvements which were maintained up to Week 24, suggesting the possibility of longer-term benefits beyond the period of therapy.'

The anomalous scoring for wellbeing was discussed earlier on page 204.

In respect of IBS patients, they confirmed the substantial benefits gained:

'Benefits observed in our IBS cohort in terms of both symptom reduction and quality of life improvement were significant, consistent and of size likely to be associated with clinical benefit.'

The term 'clinical benefit' refers to noticeable improvements that are important to the patient.

A further statement reminds us that these patients had continued to be ill despite a range of orthodox treatment administered over a prolonged period of time:

'This study has demonstrated that clinically there is benefit to be gained from inclusion of healing in the management of IBS that has not responded to conventional management.'

Healing in a Hospital

Of course, it would be more useful to provide healing at a much earlier stage. Why wait until all conventional treatments have been tried?

Regarding the IBS group, the researchers confirmed that significant benefits had been gained, which had lasted for many weeks after their final healing session:

'Quality of life was considerably enhanced in the IBS intervention group with improvements in emotional states, socialization, and activity levels which were maintained up to Week 24 and were significantly different from controls.'

Continuing to talk about the IBS results, the research paper states that the waiting list control group improved similarly once they had received their series of healing sessions, and that this was commensurate with the MYMOP results:

'Parallel to observations made in the MYMOP data, there was a meaningful improvement in the quality of life scores for the control group once they also received the intervention.'

The researchers reached the conclusion that adding healing to conventional care increases benefits to IBS and IBD patients:

'The addition of healing therapy to conventional treatment was associated with improvement in symptoms and quality of life in IBS, and to a lesser extent in IBD.'

'This pragmatic trial demonstrates that patient benefit is accrued through the addition of healing therapy to conventional management of both IBS and IBD.'

A 'pragmatic trial' is a randomised controlled trial that is designed to inform medical practice.

In addition, they suggested that other conditions could benefit from healing:

'These findings may suggest that conditions linked to functional disorders could accrue greater benefit from healing therapy.'

Other functional disorders include fibromyalgia, chronic fatigue syndrome, migraine and tension headaches, chronic pelvic pain, interstitial cystitis and other conditions (165).

218

The Results

The placebo effect is invariably pointed to when a medical benefit has been gained without drugs or surgery. However, in our study, the effects were considered too great to be attributable to placebo alone:

'The benefit observed may at least be, in part, a placebo effect although the size of benefits observed suggests an alternative mechanism.'

In any case, the researchers advised that the benefit to patients should be the main concern, not whether the method can be understood:

'The value of any mechanism should not be discounted where it confers symptomatic relief.'

These are all particularly powerful statements, especially when set against the backdrop of extreme prudence described earlier. In addition, they confirmed that these findings are in keeping with previous research:

'Results from this study are analogous to the conclusions made by...previous studies which generally support the effectiveness of healing therapy to reduce pain, anxiety and improved QoL.'

They also made the observation that healing is safe and a positive experience for recipients:

'We found no evidence of harm from healing therapy.'

'Many patients found it to be an interesting and enjoyable experience.'

They positively recommended that healing be administered to patients:

'Patients with IBS and IBD seen in secondary care, who remain symptomatic despite the best medical care, should be considered for healing therapy, where this is available, with the understanding that benefit is likely to be greater in individuals with IBS.'

This statement points to potentially greater benefit for IBS symptoms than IBD. But the IBD group did gain benefits, and most especially the Crohn's sufferers. However, symptoms were a secondary focus of our research programme. The main concern was whether lives had improved, and this was confirmed by the MYMOP results, which showed that the IBS and IBD groups gained equally.

Almost all of these patients were receiving specialist medical attention immediately prior to joining the programme. Naturally, they would have already benefited from any placebo effect that is deemed to be triggered by professional care and attention. They had exhausted all of the treatments offered by their GP and were now at varying stages of receiving specialist care. The minimum time that any of these patients had suffered was eighteen months. Many had been receiving treatment for years.

It is worth reiterating that, since healing has been found to be effective, it would make sense to administer this therapy long before the patient reaches the stage of needing a consultant.

It was fantastic to have scientific confirmation from a top-rated university, known for high quality research, that our healing work was markedly beneficial to patients. Of course, the researchers made it clear that they did not know by which mechanism the benefits had occurred. The study was designed solely to establish whether healing sessions made a difference to people affected by chronic IBS or IBD. This was confirmed, and convincingly so.

Observations

The various questionnaires used in this trial scored in opposite ways to each other. Improvements were conveyed by an increase in score for some and by a decrease in others. It would be less confusing if there were a standardised method of presenting results. It would be seem appropriate to designate 0 as 'no symptoms', with increasing scores linked to escalating severity.

It was very difficult to track down the text of research papers that I wanted to reference throughout the book. Had I been affiliated to an academic or medical institution, I would have had the luxury of unlimited access. But being an ordinary member of the public, it took a great deal of time and effort to locate even the simplest information. One example was trying to find out how many points

The Results

of increase or decrease in score constitutes clinical significance in respect of each of the questionnaires. One would think that the public should be able to access medical research information if they wanted to but, in the main, it is not possible without paying multiple and expensive subscriptions.

The data for our trial were collected specifically to answer the research questions that were posed at the outset. But additional research is possible using the same raw data. Usually, the same researchers will develop a new research question that the existing data can answer. This is a time-efficient and cost-effective method of gaining further insights, and can lead to a number of research papers being published. Researchers from any other organisation ought to be allowed access to the data for our trial because it was funded by public money via the Lottery. It seems obvious that the next step would be to ascertain, using the same data, whether particular elements within the protocol helped to maximise or prolong the beneficial effects of receiving healing sessions.

For instance, a closer inspection might reveal whether patients who saw the same healer for all five sessions benefited more than those who saw multiple healers. Typically, each new patient is so impressed with their first healing session that they want to continue with the same healer. But when they do have to see someone else, they are almost always pleasantly surprised. Although patients might initially feel disconcerted, it would be useful to know if the healing outcome is affected. On our trial, all appointments for each participant were intended to be with the same healer, but it was not always possible. Consequently, there should be enough patients in each category to identify a difference.

Also, we know from the research paper that people gained more if they received all five sessions. In addition, I have explained how the scores reveal the degree to which these people benefited more, including in the longer term. But another potentially valuable point would be to know if the people who received all five healing sessions within five weeks gained better results than those whose appointments were spread over a longer period.

And did the people who had five in five weeks also benefit more in the longer term, as would be identified by their Week 24 figures? We know that 42% of participants had not received all five sessions when they completed their Week 6 questionnaire so there will be enough people in each category to make a comparison.

It would be useful to know whether the people with the worst symptoms gained the most improvements, as reported in other healing trials. A closer inspection of the data might show whether this to equally the case for IBS and IBD. If so, the obvious course of action would be to offer a series of regular healing sessions to all people suffering severe IBS or IBD symptoms.

And did patients benefit more if they were invited to join the programme by a consultant who imparted some confidence in the therapy? Dr Singh was in a position to convey, from firsthand knowledge, that many patients had been helped by healing sessions and that they had found it enjoyable. Other consultants, however—especially those external to Dr Singh's clinic—are unlikely to have been so encouraging, and this may have affected the outcome. Again, there should be enough patients in each category to make a comparison. If there were a difference between the two groups, this would highlight the value of a supportive recommendation given by a consultant, and would identify an element of the placebo effect in action. If there were no difference, this would be in keeping with my own observations where patients benefited despite their registrar's scepticism. If a future trial were to be conducted, additional questions could be incorporated to investigate this aspect. The patient could be asked to give a score for how confident and assuring the consultant seemed when offering healing, and also a score for how beneficial they themselves thought that healing might be.

An examination of the raw data might also reveal whether any participants made an instant and full recovery, like the teenager described in an earlier chapter (page 119). A future trial could aim to identify traits or attitudes that these people have in common, so that others have the opportunity to emulate them. Equally, it would be interesting to know whether anyone who attended all five sessions felt they had gained nothing. However, very few people could have fallen into these two extreme categories, because the results are expressed with 95% certainty that an identical trial would produce similar findings.

The Results

I mentioned earlier that the intervention group's Week 0 to Week 12 improvements could be expected to be similar to the waiting list control group's Week 12 to Week 24 results. Mentioned before, Figure 13 (page 200) makes it easier to understand that these two periods for the respective groups are equivalent to each other. Both periods begin one week before their healing sessions start, and finish about seven weeks after their final one. The only difference between the two is that the waiting list group had waited for 12 weeks before beginning their sessions. The waiting list control group generally gained slightly less than the intervention group in respect of physical symptoms. If this is actually the case, patients would clearly benefit more if they embarked on healing sessions right away, rather than having to wait for any length of time.

Regarding Week 12 and Week 24 figures, some of the results suggest that certain positive effects dissipated over time. However, a different explanation for lower scores could be provided by a well-known concept within social science that says, in essence, that today's perceptions become tomorrow's expectations (166). When people repeatedly experience a higher level of quality, this becomes the norm for them, and what used to be acceptable is now considered sub-standard.

A typical example refers to customer satisfaction when purchasing greengroceries. It used to be normal to buy fruit and vegetables that were of an uneven colour or shape, or with small blemishes. If we found a basketful of perfectly formed groceries, we would feel particularly pleased with our purchase. Nowadays, we have become so accustomed to perfect produce that we reject anything with the slightest flaw. Finding vegetables that are visually perfect no longer brings the pleasure that it once did, because it is what we now expect. If we were to be offered a slightly bruised apple, we would give it a low score for customer satisfaction even though it was acceptable before. This can be directly related to the dissipation effect seen in some of the results of our trial. A patient will give a particular score for their current health and a higher score later on if they improve. But if the improvement remains for several weeks, this new level of health becomes their normal expectation. It no longer has the 'wow' factor that it once had. As a result, the patient is likely to give this heightened level of health a lower score than they would have before, even though it is actually the same. Thus, the Week 12 and especially the Week 24 scores could have been marked lower than would reflect the actual health of the patient. If this is the case, then the positive effects may not have dissipated over time, even if the figures might suggest so in some of the results. Also, this would mean that the scores that did improve at Week 24 are particularly striking.

As explained, all clinical research results include comparisons between the control group (the group that had no treatment) and the group that did receive the treatment. The people in the control group often improve slightly despite having had no treatment or attention, and this occurred in some aspects of our trial. Accordingly, the benefits gained by our participants would be even more impressive if compared to patients who did not take part in the programme. And the difference must be greater than our study indicates.

By the time that our trial participants completed their Week 0 questionnaires, at least a few weeks had elapsed since they were originally invited to take part. It seems logical that the placebo effect would spring into action at the point of being asked to be part of a trial—the time at which they first received attention—not a few weeks later, after completing the Week 0 paperwork. If so, our Week 0 figures will actually be better than if the forms had been completed at the time these patients were first approached.

It follows that the Week 0 figures will also be better than for patients who did not take part at all. The real difference, then, between those who received healing and those who did not take part in the programme, will be greater than shown in our figures.

It would be intriguing to know if there is an even greater disparity in respect of people who flatly refused to take part because they thought that healing would be a waste of time.

Our trial confirmed that healing sessions are beneficial to patients. A future trial could aim to ascertain whether these positive effects could be maximised and/or prolonged by adjusting the protocol. The following ideas could provide a starting point.

People who received all five healing sessions gained greater improvements than those who had fewer. The next step would be to discover whether additional sessions bring about ever-increasing benefits. Perhaps there is an optimum number of weekly sessions at which improvements begin to plateau.

The Week 24 figures confirm that benefits were maintained over the longer term, but it would be useful to know how long they continued beyond this point. It had been a condition of the Lottery grant that the trial must be completed within two years. Although an extended trial would take a long time to gain the answer, the process would give more patients the opportunity to benefit from healing sessions while waiting to find out.

In addition, it would be worth investigating whether it is possible to actively prolong the beneficial effects. Perhaps ongoing monthly sessions would provide an effective maintenance level.

Qualitative Results

To gain a more comprehensive appreciation of how healing had affected actual lives, qualitative explanatory data was gained by interviewing 22 of the participants (167).

In research terms, these interviews add what is called triangulation. It means that more than one method has been used in a study to check the results. It gives more confidence in the results when different methods lead to the same findings. Triangulation has been defined as:

> '...an attempt to map out, or explain more fully, the richness and complexity of human behaviour by studying it from more than one standpoint' (168) .

To improve the uniformity of the interviewing process the participants were selected by one of the University researchers, and they were all interviewed by him. With only one researcher involved in this element of the study, the one-to-one sessions were more likely to be conducted in a consistent manner. Of the 22 people he interviewed, 13 had IBS, six had ulcerative colitis and three had Crohn's disease.

These interviews took place at the hospital immediately after their final healing session. The results of a healing session are not necessarily evident directly afterwards, so there may well have been more benefits to report if the interviews had been a few days later.

However, it was more convenient for people to be seen while they were already at the hospital, rather than asking them to make an additional trip.

The University researcher first asked if they had known of healing in any way before they were introduced to the programme. Of the 22 people interviewed:

Six had no prior knowledge of healing.

Two had friends who had benefited from healing.

Four had received some form of healing in the past.

I was surprised that as many as four people out of the 22 had received healing before. Barely any of the 267 people included in my hospital audits said that they had experienced healing before, when asked. Perhaps one explanation could be that some of the patients included in the trial had, at an earlier time, received healing at the hospital after an appointment with Dr Singh.

Having read all of the interview comments made by patients, there is not one who said that they believed that healing could help. Moreover, their statements underlined their prior scepticism. Nevertheless, they stated that they had entered into the sessions with an open mind and were curious as to what might happen. During the interviews, it transpired that:

Nine felt that they had benefited physically.

Eleven reported benefiting in other ways.

Ten said the sessions made them feel more relaxed or calm.

Six were not aware of any improvements or were unsure.

Regarding physical sensations while receiving healing, they reported the following impressions:

Seven felt localised warmth or heat.

Three identified a sense of energy.

Three felt involuntary muscle jumps.

The Results

Two reported feeling uplifted.

Two saw bright colours or light.

One had visions.

The interviewer then asked about their experience in more detail and found that the majority of their responses were in keeping with each other. Their verbatim statements are publicly available online within the research paper. For brevity, I have paraphrased them, but the unabridged text gives a richer picture. A number of the comments that follow were made by more than one patient.

First, the interviewer asked how they had felt during the sessions. They described an especially positive relationship with their respective healer that was based on trust and confidence.

1. The healer looks after you.

2. The healer is marvellous.

3. The healer seems to relax you immediately.

4. The healer has empathy with you.

5. The way the healer speaks is calming.

6. Extremely relaxing.

7. Your whole body sinks.

8. All the tension left.

9. I have learned how to relax.

10. Felt like 'me' time.

11. Felt nurturing.

12. Every session was a different experience.

Healing in a Hospital

He then asked for more details about any physical sensations experienced during the healing session.

1. Intense heat.

2. Heat from the healer's hands.

3. The healer's hands were cold yet felt heat in the body where the hands were.

4. Temperature of healer's hands alternated between hot and cold.

5. As though a bright light in the room.

6. Tingling.

7. Involuntary muscle spasms.

8. Sensation of being pulled.

9. Pain gone.

10. Felt heat where pain was. Now feels better.

All of the above observations are commonly reported by patients and serve to demonstrate that more must be happening than meets the eye. They are sensations that do not normally happen when simply relaxing.

The interviewer asked whether the healing sessions had made an ongoing difference to their lives. They mainly remarked upon how calm they generally felt, and that they were now far less likely to worry than before.

1. Can now get on with life.

2. Much calmer now.

3. Take things in my stride now.

4. No longer get worked up.

The Results

5. No longer tense.

6. Can relax now.

7. Less likely to agonise over things now.

8. Can switch off now.

9. Calm now, despite life's difficulties.

10. Can stop myself stressing now.

Regarding the difference to their physical symptoms, patients reported a range of improvements. The people who found that they had less dependency on bathrooms now enjoyed the freedom to go out and lead a more normal life. Any improvement of their symptoms must have been an enormous help to them.

1. Have not needed to take sick leave from work.

2. Sick less.

3. Less stomach cramps.

4. Less diarrhoea.

5. Less pain.

6. Able to be more active.

7. Bowels more normal.

8. Taking less medication.

9. No longer choking.

10. Less bloating.

11. Visiting the toilet less often.

12. Managed a full shift at work.

13. Didn't need the bathroom all day.

14. Swelling seems reduced.

15. Spring in my step now.

16. Feeling happier.

17. Feel full of life after a healing session.

As outlined in my two hospital audits, another commonly reported phenomenon regarding the effects of healing is that people often sleep better. Good quality sleep is a healer in itself, and patients said that they had noticed the following:

1. Sleeping better.

2. Sleeping is a big benefit.

3. More satisfying sleep.

4. Sleep brilliantly after a healing session.

5. Sleeping very well now.

Patients also reported coping better with their symptoms and generally had a more positive mental attitude. A better frame of mind is a great advantage and helps people to feel more in control, more confident and happier.

1. Improved perception.

2. Feeling positive about the illness now.

3. Positive outlook transfers to people around me.

4. Dealing with things better.

5. Now changing my thinking patterns for the better.

6. More clear-headed.

The Results

7. More open to situations now.

8. Feel able to do things for myself now.

9. Leading a more independent life now.

10. Happier because no longer dependent upon toilets.

11. Starting to get back on track.

12. Symptoms no longer depress me.

13. Handling situations in a more positive way.

14. Able to deal with things in a more relaxed way.

15. Feeling more confident.

16. No longer letting the illness control me.

17. Getting back to how I was before the illness.

18. Feeling cleansed.

19. More alert.

20. No longer feeling angry about being ill.

21. No longer take additional pills during a flare up.

22. No longer excessively worried about access to toilets.

In their totality, the above responses to the respective questions reiterate that healing can help physically, mentally and emotionally. Considering that these people had suffered for so long, they must have thoroughly appreciated the improvements they noticed. And so must their loved ones.

Healing in a Hospital

Observations

In addition to the significantly positive results, the research paper refers to the many patients who stated that they found the experience to be interesting and enjoyable. At one of the final Steering Group meetings, the University researchers commented that they themselves had enjoyed being involved in this particular trial. The healers enjoyed it, too, and the patients benefited, so it is true to say that this was a particularly successful clinical trial in all respects.

It is reassuring to note the similarities between what these patients told the researcher during their interviews and the comments made by my 267 audit patients. When speaking to me, it would be natural for people to be polite and positive about a session that I had just given them, and perhaps even more so if they knew that I was a volunteer. However, the wish to please the healer is removed if the patient is speaking to a third party, in this case the researcher. It was satisfying to see that the range of positive responses given to him echoed those provided to me by the audit patients. The results of our research trial had therefore further confirmed the validity of my two hospital audits.

One patient's experience within the research trial surprised me. I first heard of it at the dissemination event, during one of the presentations, and later read more details in the analysis of the interviews. One of the interviewed patients had found healing to be painful and highly emotional during and after every session. I had never heard of this happening to anyone before. However, despite what sounded like an ordeal, this person nevertheless maintained a very positive relationship with the healer, attended all five appointments and felt confident that every session had been highly beneficial.

Each time I greeted a patient on the research trial whom I had seen the week before, I would ask how they had fared in the meanwhile. Not one of them told me of an adverse reaction or of any concerns that they had about their experience. Only tiredness afterwards was mentioned, and this is often the case. Many healers believe that this is the body's way of encouraging the patient to rest so that it can focus all available energy on healing itself. When people allow themselves to respond to this weariness by having a nap, they usually notice how very much better they feel afterwards. One of Dr Singh's patients told me that she was so extremely tired after a healing session that her husband thought that she had been drugged. But after an abnormally long and deep sleep she felt renewed and full of vim.

By employing multiple healers, the positive results of this research trial demonstrate that a patient does not need to be dependent upon one particular healer. I was the only healer involved in my two hospital audits, and the impressive results might give people the notion that I am a particularly gifted healer. But the research trial employed three main healers plus a few others when needed and the patients nevertheless improved in very similar ways. Countless healers speak of comparable outcomes for their patients and, having used a variety of healers, our research trial shows that their claims are more than possible.

Since all the healers employed on the trial were members of The Healing Trust, the results indicate that any patient could expect to benefit in similar ways by using healers trained in the same method. My own opinion is that the precise system of healing is not so important. So long as the healer has been trained properly, I believe that it is the amount of passion behind the intent to heal that really matters.

Publication of the Research Paper

The quest to publish the research paper began towards the end of 2014. I had imagined that gaining publication would be reasonably straightforward. After all, the programme had been led by a university known for world-class research. Furthermore, its design and methodology had been given the seal of approval by a team of scientists appointed by the Lottery. There had been huge competition for limited funding; only the best must have been awarded.

There were hopes that a prestigious, mainstream medical journal might accept the paper. The editor of one of them offered the following explanation for rejection:

Healing in a Hospital

'Your paper is not suitable for [our] readers [as they] do not subscribe to complementary medicine.'

Considering that it was a scientific journal, the reason given for rejection seemed singularly unscientific. How can physicians make the decision to subscribe to a therapy if journals will not publish research papers about them? Nor did it seem likely that their readers' views had actually been gained.

A repeating objection was that there was no placebo group to compare results with. Our research paper had detailed why it is not possible to provide a simulation for healing, but this was disregarded. The same limitation applies to a number of medical interventions, so how are those dealt with?

Approaching each journal cost time and effort. Submission fees were another concern. But the pursuit continued, thanks to Dr Singh's determination.

A major drawback with publishing a paper in any of the main medical journals is that only medical people and academics ultimately have access to the full text. Universities and medical institutions pay subscription fees that allow their staff and students free access to research papers. For an ordinary member of the public, only the 'abstract' is usually available, which is merely a thumbnail sketch of what the paper is about. It took me a great deal of time to find the full text of papers that I wanted to reference in this book, and others were not available to non-academics at all, or they had to be paid for. The Steering Group wanted our two papers to be available free of charge to everyone–medics, researchers and the general public.

It was decided to submit to a journal specialising in complementary medicine that offered open access. The full text would then be permanently available online for anyone to inspect.

One would have expected the quantitative and the qualitative papers to be published together, since the main paper gives the secondary one more strength and meaning. But, in practice, this did not happen.

The secondary, qualitative study had no difficulty being published as it reports what the patients had to say about their experience. There could be little argument about that. From the date the paper was submitted, it took five months to publish, and this is not an unusual length of time for the process.

Within a few weeks of being available online it was labelled 'Highly Accessed', which points to the level of interest that it attracted. Had the two papers been published at the same time, more overall impact may have been gained, but it was encouraging to see that the secondary, qualitative paper was being noticed.

Surprisingly, the main, quantitative paper was rejected by two CAM journals. The editor of one of them sounded supportive, but then found that all of the reviewers he approached declined to review it. To get a green light for publication, three reviewers each need to give approval. The editor of another journal found enough reviewers but one of them rejected the paper, rendering it unacceptable.

It is possible that some scientists asked to review our paper were not willing to risk having their name—or perhaps their journal—associated with spiritual healing. After all, it must be a contentious subject in most scientific circles.

Nevertheless, the main, quantitative paper was ultimately published in the European Journal of Integrative Medicine.

The two journals that published our respective papers each offer easy, worldwide access to the full text. Enquirers do not need to pay subscription charges or meet any registration requirements.

On top of these advantages, online publication grants anyone the right to unrestricted dissemination and re-use of the information, so long as proper attribution is given to authors and to the journal concerned. This liberal licensing is best suited to allow the transfer and growth of scientific knowledge, facilitating maximum benefit and the widest possible use of new information.

Open access to the research paper, along with the freedom to reproduce and broadcast its contents, is entirely in keeping with the Lottery's intention. It also seems right and proper that anyone should be able to access and advertise research that was paid for by members of the public and designed for their benefit.

Despite limitless online access, a research paper is likely to attract fewer readers than a book. I therefore felt compelled to produce an easy-read version of the results, along with additional information that may inspire people to add healing to their healthcare provision.

Explained before, it was imperative that the research results remain confidential until after the main paper had been published. I therefore aimed to launch my book immediately afterwards.

Due to its controversial nature, our research paper ought to attract media attention. But, whatever happens, I shall be doing my utmost to make its findings known to the public and to NHS providers.

It is said that writers spend more time promoting their book than they do writing it, and it looks the same way for authors disseminating their research.

Key Points

The Placebo Effect

1. This is a powerful ally for any practitioner, medical or otherwise.

2. The hospital audit graphs reveal possible placebo improvements as a result of their consultation with Dr Singh. After a healing session, patients achieved further gains and to a substantial degree.

3. If the placebo effect is deemed to be the sole cause of our research results, then healers must have learned how to harness its power.

4. Healing studies on animals, plants and cells in vitro confirm that the placebo effect cannot be the cause of beneficial effects in these cases.

5. The mechanism that causes healing in animals, plants and cells in vitro must also benefit humans. In addition to this element, humans also gain from the placebo effect.

Quantitative Results

1. The high level of recruitment achieved in a short period of time suggests that patients are keen to have healing, if offered within an NHS setting.

2. The low level of drop-out suggests that patients enjoyed the sessions and felt that they benefited from them.

3. No patient reported an adverse effect.

4. Patients gained clinically significant improvements to their quality of life.

5. Symptoms were alleviated.

6. Five sessions incurred more benefit than fewer.

7. Those who had five sessions retained the benefits for longer.

8. Some benefits were maintained to Week 24 (19 weeks after their final healing session).

9. Some benefits continued to increase after their final healing session, as revealed by Week 24 figures.

10. Some benefits had reduced by Week 24. This could be due to the well-known phenomenon that improvements eventually become the accepted norm. If so, all of the Week 24 figures reflect less than the actual degree of gains.

11. The extent of improvement was deemed by our researchers to be greater than could be attributed to placebo.

Qualitative Results

Patients on this trial provided descriptions of their experience that were similar to those of the other cohorts of people described in previous chapters. Specifically, those groups were:

1. People who actively sought healing by visiting a healing centre, and were therefore likely to be optimistic regarding its efficacy.

2. People who were offered the opportunity to try healing when attending their support groups, such as MND or breast cancer. They did not seek healing but were likely to think they had nothing to lose.

3. Medical professionals who did not seek healing but accepted the opportunity while attending the Nursing in Practice exhibitions. Some were open-minded; most were sceptical.

The Results

4. The 267 hospital patients included in my two audits. They had no prior intention of having healing, and most were highly sceptical.

5. The 200 patients who agreed to take part in the research trial, many of whom were highly sceptical.

Added together, these five different groups represent a total of a few thousand people. The similarity of comments made by the individuals in each of the groups further confirms the validity of the statements across all five categories.

Conclusions

1. It would be logical to conduct trials that determine whether adding healing sessions to conventional care reduces NHS costs. It takes an inordinate length of time to secure funding, then conduct the trial and publish the research results. While waiting for such developments to occur, hospitals and doctors' surgeries could enlist healers (voluntary or paid) and conduct their own audits. They could then ascertain whether regular healing sessions help to reduce the number of appointments, medications and treatments required by their patients. A central register of such audits would facilitate sharing of the findings.

2. Healing is likely to be the least expensive complementary therapy to adopt because no equipment or supplies are required and it takes the least time to conduct a session.

3. Healing is the most universally usable therapy to adopt for the following reasons:

   a. The patient does not need to be touched or manipulated in any way.

   b. The patient can be in any physical condition, even unconscious or dying.

Healing in a Hospital

c. Healing can be administered in a private or public area, whether noisy or quiet.

d. Healing can be administered on hospital wards, in intensive care units, outpatient departments or doctors' surgeries.

A Case Study

One of the people on the research trial, whose five sessions were all with me, kindly provided a written statement about his experience. After months of severe bowel problems, he was finally diagnosed with inflammatory bowel disease, specifically ulcerative colitis.

When a patient develops ulcerative colitis, the medical prognosis is that it will remain for life. In addition, the medicines available to alleviate the distressing and debilitating symptoms are not always effective.

Against this hopeless and depressing outlook, the account provided by this particular patient makes surprising reading. His professional career had been science-based, but he was open-minded when Dr Singh invited him to join the research programme. He was not one of the 22 people selected for interview.

'Following bowel problems over the first six months of 2011, I underwent a colonoscopy at Good Hope Hospital and was diagnosed as having colitis. I was prescribed a specialist drug to help alleviate the symptoms and was then referred to Dr Singh's gastroenterology clinic at the hospital. The drug that I had been prescribed earlier made my symptoms worse, so it was changed to another. This second medication was no better than the first so it was changed again. The third medication was replaced with a fourth but still with no improvement. All of these drugs made my symptoms much worse and made me feel very ill. It became obvious that I was intolerant to all of the drugs that are normally used to help control colitis.

Healing in a Hospital

'As the problems persisted I had consultations with Dr Singh's registrar who explained to me that I may have to consider having my colon removed. During this distressing period I became depressed and irritable and my self-esteem was at an all time low. Normality had gone out of my life. I did not go out very often and, when I did, I did not venture far from home because of my need to make regular visits to the bathroom. I was worried about having an 'accident' if I went out, due to not getting to a toilet in time. I have never liked using public toilets and have always tried to avoid using them. This was a very difficult period for me and for my wife.

'During a further consultation with Dr Singh, who is someone I have great respect for, he suggested trying a different medication. He explained that it was not actually a drug, so I agreed to try it. He also asked me what I thought about alternative or complementary therapies. I told him that I was very open minded about it as I had tried acupuncture on an old knee injury a few years before and this had been successful. He went on to explain about the research project being carried out with the University of Birmingham and Freshwinds and suggested that I might be a suitable patient to take part in the study.

'I started to take the new medication with no ill effects. My condition gradually started to improve and I was able to get out of the house more often. After 12 weeks, in April and May 2012, I received the course of five healing sessions with Sandy Edwards at Good Hope Hospital. I had no preconceived ideas or expectations of what might or might not happen. Throughout my working life I had dealt in facts. In my professional career, I had to make decisions based on factual evidence that was in my possession. Opinions and hearsay could not be considered.

'I like to research anything that I am involved in, whether it be hobbies, holidays or anything else. I like to make use of the information that is now so readily available through the Internet.

242

A Case Study

However, to allow me to be objective about the healing sessions, I felt that I should not research anything to do with healing or the research project. I wanted a clear, open mind with nothing to prompt me into thinking that changes, good or bad, were happening.

'At my first session with Sandy, she explained what she would do and made me feel at ease. I could hear everything that was going on around me, as you would expect from a busy hospital. However, following what Sandy was telling me I became completely relaxed, and any noise or possible distraction drifted into the background.

'The first thing I noticed was that when Sandy touched my right shoulder I felt a very pleasant, warm feeling going right through my joint. [Unknown to Sandy] this joint had previously been injured, and it continued to be problematic and painful.

'As the session progressed, I had my eyes closed and started to see a purple flashing light which I can only describe as being like a beacon out at sea. This then gradually changed to a calming purple colour, just like purple silk. Throughout this time I was completely relaxed and pleasantly warm. It was like being in a calmer place. At the end of the session I felt completely different from when I had arrived. I was now warm and relaxed. A lot of my stress had gone.

'I continued with a further four sessions with Sandy and all were in a similar vein. I found them to be a pleasant experience, and my general demeanour and wellbeing improved enormously. I became less irritable and much calmer. My stress levels reduced considerably. I was beginning to cope with life better as my health improved. By this time I was going out more and able to cope better with the normalities of life. My wife told me that my whole demeanour had changed and that I was a lot easier to live with, a lot less grumpy. Certainly, we could go out socially more often.

'I had one major setback in July 2012 when we went away from home for the first time since being diagnosed with colitis [a year or so earlier]. We went to Southampton and stayed one night. I became very ill with sickness and diarrhoea, as bad as I have ever known. Later, at Dr Singh's clinic, it was thought that this was almost certainly food poisoning and not connected to colitis. However, this event made me lose all confidence in going away from home. Gradually, though, my confidence returned, and I have since had two small breaks away from home without problems.

'In October 2012 I underwent major surgery to have a replacement shoulder joint removed, and replaced with a 'reverse procedure'. This was a lengthy process that meant I took a lot of morphine and codeine to help with pain relief. Sleeping was quite difficult following the operation, but I found that, by using similar techniques to those during the healing sessions with Sandy, I was able to get myself into a calm and relaxed state, which helped me to sleep better.

'In conclusion, my life changed considerably in 2011 when I was diagnosed with colitis. I had only recently retired from work and I was suddenly restricted in what I was able to do and where I could go. I went through a dreadful period, which affected everything I did. My personality changed. I became very stressed and completely lacking in confidence.

'With the help and kindness of Dr Singh and Sandy Edwards I now have a great deal of normality back in my life. I am more confident, and my wellbeing has improved immensely. I am told that I am much easier to live with now, and I hope that I am able to continue like this into the future.'

This man's testimony brings to life the practical meaning of some of the 'statistically significant improvements' reported in the research paper. The figures suggest that a considerable proportion of the participants must have had similar experiences to these, which is heartening and uplifting. But, for this man, the story continued.

A Case Study

When he returned for a subsequent appointment with Dr Singh, the following year, he welcomed the offer of a further healing session. As he had been unable to find healing local to where he lived, I suggested that he turn up on any Wednesday mornings that he could manage and slot into a gap. This way, we managed to fit in five sessions during 2013. The following spring, he arrived full of smiles. This is what he had to say, confirmed by email:

'After having had consultations with Dr Singh and healing sessions with Sandy Edwards, my health continued to steadily improve. My symptoms have now become minor in comparison to what I had been suffering before. For instance, simply leaving my house was difficult during the second part of 2010. But now my life has returned to a degree of normality.

'In June 2012 I had a set-back when I became quite ill, but this was thought to be attributable to food poisoning. And in July 2013, I again had bowel problems that were quite bad. As I was about to go on holiday, my GP prescribed a course of steroid tablets, which helped to calm everything down and allowed me to travel. But other than these two episodes, my symptoms were generally improving.

'In September 2013 I was invited to take part in a routine bowel cancer screening programme for people my age. The results came back positive, meaning that something was wrong, including the possibility of cancer. I attended a consultation at University Hospital Coventry, where it was suggested that I consider having a colonoscopy to find out exactly what the problem was. I agreed that this would be the sensible course of action, but I was worried. Within a short period of time, the procedure was conducted, and I was verbally advised that there was no sign of ulcerative colitis in my bowel!

'I had been aware of continuous improvements to my symptoms, but to have this medical confirmation was totally unexpected and uplifting. I would have been ecstatic but for the possibility that cancer could not be ruled out until the polyps had been sent for examination. There were signs of diverticulosis, but this condition caused me hardly any problems in comparison to the dreadful time that I had gone through with ulcerative colitis.

'Some polyps were removed for further analysis, and it was a great relief to hear that these were free from cancer. The written report confirmed the verbal advice that I had been given: ulcerative colitis was not present in my bowel. This was, of course, very good news for me.

'I have continued to maintain stability with my bowels and colon, with only the occasional minor problem.'

It was amazing to have medical confirmation that ulcerative colitis had completely disappeared. This is not possible to achieve by any medical intervention. By this time, he had received a total of ten healing sessions—five on the research trial and, six months later, an additional five at Dr Singh's clinic. But the colitis may have disappeared before all ten sessions had been received.

Another unexpected benefit for this patient was regarding his replaced shoulder joint. A conventional shoulder replacement had proved unsuccessful so he then had a 'reverse' total shoulder replacement, in which the positions of the socket and metal ball are reversed. Despite this, the shoulder had remained very painful, with limited mobility and lack of power. Being right-handed, he found that his damaged right shoulder was making many normal activities very awkward, if not impossible. However, after the last healing session, he was delighted to tell me that he had recently washed the car using his right hand for the first time. This was two years after the surgery.

In his younger days, this man had enjoyed playing contact sports. As a result, his ankles had suffered repeated injuries and were now usually painful. He told me that his ankles in particular always felt warm and comfortable during healing sessions. Each time he left a session, he would comment on feeling an unusual warmth throughout his entire body, but particularly in the ankles, and that he could now walk more comfortably.

To recap the main story, this man's life was ruined by the debilitating and soul-destroying symptoms of ulcerative colitis.

A Case Study

There was no hope of recovery because colitis is fully expected to be a life-long condition. For some people, symptoms can be controlled by drugs, but he reacted badly to all of them. After a year of suffering, it was recommended that his colon be removed, but he declined the option. Then, after ten healing sessions, a thorough internal investigation showed no sign of ulcerative colitis. Three years later, he continues to be entirely free of the disease.

As a professional man with a science-based career, he was mystified but enthralled by the sensations he experienced while receiving healing. He would usually have vivid images of his childhood and relive happy times with people who loved him.

In his statement he describes observing a purple light, pulsating like a beacon and dominating every session. As is evident from the comments made by the many patients in my two hospital audits, the colour purple is often mentioned. Although I tell new patients that they might perceive colours, the only particular colour I mention is golden-white. To help people to relax, I suggest they imagine themselves filled with golden-white light, yet people often report afterwards that they saw purple instead. Purple has the shortest wavelength and the highest frequency of any colour that is visible to us. Hence, it is the last colour of the rainbow. Intriguingly, purple is the colour most associated with spiritual healing.

Despite the remarkable case study presented here, there is no guarantee that any number of healing sessions will eradicate colitis or any other condition. But there is nothing to lose by trying.

Cost/benefit issues are a primary factor for decision-making in the NHS. In today's money, the average medical expense of supporting each patient with ulcerative colitis has been estimated at £3,000 per year (169). Add to this the potential cost of sick pay and benefit payments. Considering the overheads of maintaining just one individual throughout the remainder of their life, it must be worth considering options that have produced results like this.

Key Points

1. Conventional treatments for this patient were ineffective. During a series of healing sessions, a complete and permanent recovery occurred despite the condition being considered incurable.

2. A senior consultant physician witnessed the recovery.

3. Individual cases like this will not convince the scientific and medical community that healing is beneficial, no matter how many there are.

What Next?

Before we began this project, Dr Singh warned me that even if the research trial were an outstanding success, the scientific community would merely add it to the body of evidence. It would not necessarily encourage the NHS to embrace or provide healing any more than it had done in the past. It was disappointing to think that the results of such a large and high quality trial might not make the slightest impact on healthcare provision. If more evidence is needed, who is likely to pay for it? This one project cost £205,000 plus countless hours of goodwill. And who would go to the effort of applying for a grant to research healing when the odds of success in securing funding are so low?

This particular trial concentrated specifically on people with IBS and IBD, and the scientific community must surely now concede that healing has been found to be beneficial for these two conditions. However, they would not agree that healing could be considered helpful for any other disorder. According to the scientific world, healing trials would need to be conducted for every illness and ailment before it could be deemed beneficial for all of them. This would be impossible to achieve. Financially, it is out of the question, and who would undertake all those projects? It would be unrealistic to expect funding for even one additional trial of healing, let alone a myriad of them.

Of course, it is vital that pharmaceutical drugs be trialled for each separate illness they are designed to remedy before they can be prescribed. All drugs have side effects, and doctors and patients alike need to be confident that a new medication is likely to be efficacious and safe to take. For those taking multiple drugs for a variety of illnesses, the combination of chemical ingredients also needs to be considered.

But healing is different. Healing energy is not manufactured using specific ingredients for a particular purpose. It is simply a natural, wholesome energy that seems to find its own way to where it is needed most, no matter what the trouble is. Nor has any healing trial provided evidence of an adverse impact. The concerns that apply to the approval of pharmaceutical drugs are therefore not relevant to healing.

An abundance of examples has already been given that support the view that healing is efficacious for all kinds of conditions. The following series of evaluations, funded by the North Cumbria Health Authority, also bear this out.

An evaluation in 2004 involved 300 patients who, between them, had a wide range of ailments (170). Each patient received four healing sessions within six weeks. The results showed that statistically and clinically significant improvements had been gained, both physically and psychologically. Gains included stress reduction, pain relief, increased ability to cope and increased general health. Results were $p<0.0004$ for all symptoms, which means odds of four in 10,000 against the changes being due to chance—very highly significant. The most substantial improvements were seen in those who had the worst symptoms to begin with.

Two further evaluations were funded jointly by the same health authority and Cumbria County Council. One involved 35 cancer patients (171), while the other studied 147 people with mental health disorders (172). As with the previous study, each patient received four healing sessions within six weeks and gained statistically significant results across a range of measures.

Added together, these three trials included 482 patients, none of whom reported an adverse effect.

As these three studies were preliminary evaluations, there was no control group. However, the positive outcomes illustrate the safety and effectiveness of healing. The results were significant enough to convince the researchers that controlled trials should be conducted. However, I was unable to find evidence that subsequent trials had actually been instigated.

What Next?

Additional studies have shown that healing helped patients with mental health issues. A group of randomly assigned patients each received six weekly sessions. Significant improvements were gained regarding depression and stress, and benefits continued to be present one year later (173).

Another trial involved 30 patients suffering from chronic pain, depression and sleep difficulties. They each received eight healing sessions, and gained significant improvements across all three aspects (174).

A review in 2004 (175) aimed to discover how effective healing was over a range of different conditions, including HIV, cancer and heart surgery. Over 30 trials were analysed that met the researchers' standards. Although it was found that many of these studies were either poorly designed or poorly reported, they did indicate positive results. Outcomes such as reduced stress, anxiety and pain were commonly reported, as were physical improvements. Data showed that patients benefited emotionally, their relationships improved and they gained a greater sense of wellbeing. With no adverse side effects reported, the researchers concluded that healing is a safe and non-invasive therapy that should be researched further. They suggested that, if other research found similarly positive results, healing could be introduced alongside conventional healthcare so that lower medical costs could be achieved in respect of reduced drugs, shorter hospital stays and less clinic time.

All of the above evaluations, along with the many other trials referenced, serve to support the healing community's assertion that healing can help any condition. As mentioned before, if an inspection were carried out of the MYMOP data in our trial, it might reveal that a range of maladies had been alleviated during the course of our study, not just those associated with IBS and IBD.

Also, although our trial focused on IBS and IBD patients, the positive results are relevant to patients with other medical issues. Hippocrates (460–370 BC), the father of modern medicine, stated that 'all disease begins in the gut'. Although he was not entirely correct, modern studies suggest that this is true for many conditions (176). For instance, diet-induced inflammation can lead to type 2 diabetes, obesity, liver disease and many of the world's most serious diseases (177) (178) (179). Due to the gut-brain axis, certain gut

251

disorders are also linked to schizophrenia, autism, anxiety and depression (180).

Regarding psychological problems, evidence has led researchers to conclude that most of the therapeutic change gained by counselling is due to the patient's own resources and their relationship with the practitioner (181). Their findings suggest that 15% of any improvement is attributable to the placebo effect and another 15% to the particular technique used. If only 15% of the improvement is down to the technique, it makes sense to use the cheapest and quickest option that works. Looking at the results of our research programme and the many other healing trials, plus my two hospital audits and hundreds of patients' comments, it is inevitable to conclude that healing helps the mind and the emotions. With sessions only taking 20 minutes, far more people can receive healing per hour than can be given counselling. This could speed up the time in which people improve, and reduce costs. In the event that there were patients who did not respond sufficiently to healing, they could then be referred to counselling.

Many of us know from our own personal experience that the mind and emotions play a part in the health of our physical body. In the Lords Report (41), Professor Patrick Bateson (Vice President of the Royal Society) states that psychological factors do affect physical health:

> 'When somebody suffers chronic stress, bereavement or loses a job...they are much more prone to disease and more likely to get cancer, and it is now believed that this is because of suppression of the immune system, which is constantly cleaning up bacteria and viruses and also cleaning up cells that are cancerous.'

Picking up on the Cumbrian studies involving people with mental health issues, the results of our trial confirmed their findings in that healing brought patients upliftment in the longer term. The general trend was that our patients worried less (IBS-QoL) or felt emotionally better (IBDQ) months after their final healing session, and to a substantial degree.

People tend to believe that their general level of happiness is set in stone because that is how they have always been. A number of people have labelled themselves as 'a born worrier' and say they could never change. But research shows that this notion is a fallacy.

Measuring brain activity on an fMRI scanner reveals that when people are in a positive mood, the left prefrontal cortex lights up more than the right. Each time this activity occurs, physical changes take place in the brain that reset the person's general emotional state to a more uplifted level (182). For many years, I have encouraged people to imagine that positive thoughts and feelings strengthen the part of the brain that delivers happiness—the stronger that part is, the more capacity it has. It made sense to me that the brain would be like the physical body. Exercise a particular part regularly and it can do more for you. Who has not heard of the adage 'use it or lose it'? It was wonderful to find that an element of this idea has been scientifically proven. These physical changes that occur in the brain could be the reason why the results of our trial revealed that benefits were sustained for months after the final healing session. And these improvements could be permanent for all we know, but our study was limited to six months.

As healers, we see evidence of this time and again because patients who have regular sessions usually become progressively more buoyant. Moreover, it would appear that a sufficiently intense burst of positive emotion must be able to make an immediate and permanent change, as demonstrated by the youngster featured in The Grand Round chapter.

I have also maintained that the more contented and happy we are, the more physically healthy our body will be. It transpires that scientific evidence exists to support this hypothesis, too.

In 2011, Ed Diener of the University of Illinois led a review of more than 160 studies of human and animal subjects and found compelling evidence that happy people and contented animals tend to be healthier and live longer (183). There were a few exceptions, but the overwhelming majority of the studies found that anxiety, depression, a lack of enjoyment of daily activities and pessimism were associated with higher rates of disease and a shorter lifespan.

One of the studies followed nearly 5,000 university students for more than 40 years and found that those who were most pessimistic as students tended to die younger than their peers.

Healing in a Hospital

Animal studies, too, reveal a strong link between stress and poor health. Stressed animals, such as those living in crowded conditions, are more susceptible to heart disease, have weaker immune systems and tend to die younger.

Laboratory experiments on humans have found that positive moods reduce the level of hormones related to stress, strengthen the immune system and speed the body's recovery after exertion. Other studies showed that marital hostilities are linked to slow recovery from wounds and a weaker immune system.

Diener was surprised that the data across such a range of studies were so consistent. He reached the conclusion that government health recommendations—which currently focus on obesity, diet, smoking and exercise—should also include happiness.

Our study, along with many others referenced in this book, shows that healing sessions engender a more uplifted mood. People can test whether this is true, and whether this does lead to improved health, by utilising MYMOP questionnaires. Measuring changes each week, over a course of regular healing sessions will answer the question. Naturally, if benefits were noted and were continuing, there would be no reason to stop the experiment.

Plotting progress on paper is highly valuable because people soon forget how acutely they previously suffered from a particular ailment and in how many ways it had affected their lives.

A completed set of forms would provide persuasive evidence to convey to a physician the ways in which healing had been beneficial. People normally only go to see their doctor when they are unwell. Hardly anyone makes an appointment to report that they have recovered. If it were inappropriate to speak to the doctor or consultant personally, a copy of the completed forms could be delivered to the surgery or hospital along with a covering letter.

As mentioned earlier, scientists would contend that the positive results of our healing trial are only relevant to people with IBS or IBD. However, there were some individuals within the trial who said that their symptoms did not improve yet the quality of their life was enhanced. After having healing sessions, they could cope with their illness better and had a more positive frame of mind. This uplift continued until at least Week 24. If an enhanced quality of life

What Next?

can be gained regardless of symptoms, then it follows that healing must be valuable for patients with any other condition.

People come along to our healing centre with all kinds of problems, and their feedback is in line with everything in this book. Those afflicted with disease, illness, skin conditions, insomnia and physical injuries have been helped. So, too, have people suffering from pain, fear, anxiety, bereavement, depression, stress, loneliness, anger and resentment. Some have been astonished at the change in themselves. Multitudes of healers across the country and around the world repeatedly receive similar feedback from their own patients.

Another effect of healing that people rarely notice, unless specifically asked, is that their eyesight has improved. This corresponds with the findings of Dr William H Bates (1860–1931) who asserted that relaxation is the key to better vision. Through his work as a well-respected eye surgeon and a tutor of ophthalmology at the New York Medical School, he came to question the prevailing theories and practices. It was accepted then—as it mostly is now—that prescription glasses were the only answer to long or short sightedness. Bates gave up his lucrative practice to conduct research at Columbia University and many of his papers were published by the New York Medical Journal. His findings indicated that eyesight varies tremendously according to someone's emotional state. This was consistent with previous trials showing that people tend to become short-sighted when they feel apprehensive. Bates himself was long-sighted but, by developing ways to avoid straining his eyes when reading, he regained normal vision. Nowadays, the Bates Method is often associated with doing eye exercises but, in reality, he recommended using relaxed natural vision habits all day long. He made it a life's work to bring this message to the masses, and his teachings are available to download free of charge from the Internet (184).

The most remarkable experience I have witnessed regarding vision improvement was with a woman who was virtually blind without her glasses. She took them off to have a healing session and relaxed for the next 20 minutes. When she opened her eyes afterwards, she looked around the room blinking with astonishment. Not only could she see everything clearly, but the colours were very much brighter. Having worn glasses since childhood, she could not contemplate being without them—not even for a short while to see how long this improvement might last. She slipped them back on and had to wait for a few minutes while her eyes adjusted to the strength of the spectacles.

Although I do not need glasses, I had a similar experience myself. While coming out of a deep meditation, I opened my eyes prematurely and discovered that I could read the text of an open book about 20 metres away. As I returned to normal consciousness, the far away text became increasingly blurred, as did the book, until my usual standard of vision returned.

These two cases identify that we each, temporarily, had the ability to see far better than we normally do. Both of us must therefore have the necessary anatomical equipment to do so. Something must be negatively affecting how those physical parts work when we are going about our normal day. Stress seems the likely culprit since it causes tension in the body's muscles, which probably includes the eye muscles. If so, either the relaxation techniques taught by Bates, or the stress relief brought about by healing, could be expected to have a positive effect on eyesight. People can test this hypothesis by using either of these two methods and plotting weekly progress by using an eyesight test chart.

As regards any side effects of healing, nothing detrimental was reported by any of the people in my two hospital audits or the research trial. Allowing for the few individuals in my audits whom I may have seen more than once, this makes a total of around 450 hospital patients who were not harmed in any way. We could add to this figure the hundreds of other hospital patients who received healing at Dr Singh's clinic, the medical professionals at the Nursing in Practice exhibitions and the people who have flowed through our voluntary healing centre.

In cases where conventional healthcare is unable to help patients, it has to be more cost-effective for the NHS to provide complementary therapies that have been shown to be beneficial (185). Additional treatment strategies that are effective would be highly desirable for these patients. Researchers on a different trial made the following statement:

What Next?

'Conventional drugs are aimed at suppressing symptoms, but we are now much more aware that symptom management is not limited only to the prescription of drugs (186).'

Our own researchers made the following recommendation in our paper:

'Further cost-effectiveness evaluation is required before determining the role healing therapy may play in resource-restricted health services, but patients with IBS and IBD seen in secondary care, who remain symptomatic despite best medical care, should be considered for healing therapy....'

The results of our trial will be especially welcomed by healers and healing organisations whose valuable work might now hope to receive greater acceptance by the medical world. Doctors are busy, time is short and resources are stretched, so it would seem ideal to have mainstream healthcare supported by healing and by other complementary therapies that have been similarly trialled and proven to be safe and effective.

The introduction of complementary therapies to standard healthcare provision would be a popular move, welcomed by many patients. As mentioned before, three quarters of the people asked were in favour of complementary therapies being made widely available on the NHS (187). In 2004, it was found that around 10% of the UK adult population had accessed a complementary therapy during the previous year (188) and, in the main, they did so to supplement their conventional care (189). This illustrates the fact that a great number of people are keen to find effective complementary remedies to assist their recovery and help them resume a normal life.

The term 'healing therapy' incorporates any one of an array of healing methods and practices, with training standards ranging from scant to professional. This is why the research paper and my book have underlined the importance of using properly trained healers who belong to a reputable organisation.

Also, when practitioners belong to a reputable association, they are bound by a professional code of conduct, which protects the public in two ways. First, individuals with unwholesome intentions are more likely to be deterred from joining an organisation with proper standards in place. Second, any unprofessional behaviour can be reported to the organisation so that an investigation can be instigated, and disciplinary procedures applied. The following example illustrates the point.

Angie Buxton-King describes in her book *The NHS Healer* a desolate time in her life when she sought healing. Her young son had died of cancer. After several uplifting and beneficial sessions with a private healer, he advised her that the only way to resolve her remaining problems was to have sex with him. Outraged that someone in a position of trust could attempt to groom and violate a vulnerable person, she sought to report him. But he did not belong to any organisation, and she was therefore powerless to stop him practising. It is important to check that a healer belongs to a reputable association, and any upstanding practitioner will gladly provide evidence of their membership.

Besides a strict code of conduct, The Healing Trust employs additional methods to ensure that applicants are genuine and upstanding. Personal references, tutors and mentors all play a part. At the same time, though, every effort is made to welcome sincere applicants and to support their development.

Although the research trial only included healers taught by The Healing Trust, similar results are achieved by equally well-trained healers from other organisations. Finding someone local should not be too difficult as there must be many thousands of healers across the UK. Voluntary healing groups and private healers can be found via the organisations listed on page 296. The level of fee charged bears no correlation to their ability as a healer. Many excellent healers are volunteers and, for various reasons, it suits some of them to work outside of their own home and as part of a voluntary group.

The prospect of going to a healing centre for the first time may feel unsettling, but healers are invariably warm and welcoming and soon put new visitors at their ease. One of the many benefits of going to a centre is that patients can try different healers to see if the experience varies. In the unlikely event that a patient feels uneasy with a particular healer they can simply ask to see someone else. Also, if a patient's preferred healer is absent there will probably be another available, and sessions need not be missed. When away from home, whether holidaying or working, it may be possible to find a healing centre nearby. And, financially, voluntary healing centres are very accessible as they usually suggest a minimum donation of a nominal amount, or nothing at all for those who cannot afford to contribute.

Sessions with a private healer might cost more but they are ideal for patients who do not want others to know that they are having healing. They are assured of having the same healer every time, and they may feel that they can relax better in a private treatment room.

Another avenue through which regular healing can be made available is at support groups, like the MND and breast cancer meetings mentioned earlier. One has to stand back and admire the indomitable spirit of the people who organise these groups and the people who attend them. Strange as it may seem, humour manages to survive, even within groups that support the most distressing and life-limiting diseases. One example is that of a bowel cancer group in Dorset that has named itself The SemiColons! The various self-help groups that our healers have attended have been fun as well as rewarding, and I would encourage anyone to take advantage of this form of support. On the financial side, when our volunteers attend such groups, attendees receive healing free of charge, and their organisation usually makes a donation to our healing group.

People sometimes need a course of regular sessions before they can detect a change and, even then, some are oblivious to their own improvements. It is only when their family and friends pass comment that they realise they have benefited. When I first had healing, long before I trained, it was only after six weekly sessions that I realised the profound difference that healing had made to me. I was sleeping better, laughing more and responding to situations in a much more positive way.

The physical problem for which I had sought healing—psoriasis—did improve, but not by much. The most incredible revelation was that a life-time fear had dissolved. I had always been afraid of being alone in a house at night. Strangely, I was fine outdoors in the dark at any time, but not inside a house. I have no idea why. Logic told me that over 14,000 nights of my life had passed without incident, so why should tonight be any different? But emotions are far more powerful than reason and, regardless of the sense of it, I hardly slept whenever my husband went away on occasional business trips. After a handful of healing sessions, I noticed the amazing difference within myself and began to revel in having the place to myself on those occasions. I did not wish my husband to be away but, when he had to be, it felt liberating to be able to do what I liked, when I liked. Of course, I still had the children to care for and a business to run, but this new sense of freedom and confidence was exhilarating. My husband continued to go away on business, but my response to his short absences was now entirely positive. Nothing had changed in my life, only my reaction to it.

This deeply held fear had been dissolved without my needing to realise it was there. I did not need to remember that it existed. Nor did I need to unearth what had caused it in the first place. These observations contribute towards why I think it is unnecessary for a healer to quiz patients about what is troubling them. My experience illustrates how hidden, underlying fears can melt away to make room for a more confident and buoyant mindset.

As with my own case, the patients involved in the research programme may have found that issues, unrelated to IBS or IBD, had been resolved. Perhaps health questionnaires should include a section that identifies and measures fears.

Whether people choose to have healing sessions or not, there is plenty that they can do for themselves. Quick and simple techniques have helped people to alleviate pain, gain peace of mind and improve their health. Some of the patients referred to earlier have been amazed at what they could do for themselves. The following account relates an experience of my own.

Out of the blue, I began having spasmodic stabbing pains in the abdomen that were so severe that they made me cry out each time they struck. There was no telling when an episode might start or subside but they were most often during the night. No amount of pain killers made a difference, and two courses of antibiotics were ineffective. Preliminary investigations revealed nothing, and the next step was to have a scan. If someone else had been in this predicament, I would have offered healing at the outset. For myself, the thought did not cross my mind. Not until I was doubled-up one night, in the thick of yet another bout, did it occur to me. The moment that I focused on healing the very core of the pain, it melted away within two seconds—literally—and never returned. Despite having seen this happen for many patients, I was incredulous when it worked for me. Now I could identify with the bewilderment and sense of disbelief that so many of my patients had expressed. My husband is witness to the months of recurring agony that instantly and permanently vanished. Thank goodness I had discovered healer training years ago. For those who are interested, the quick technique I used is outlined on page 294.

As my own example demonstrates, I readily reach for the medicine cabinet at the first sign of pain or discomfort. Like many others, I may try natural remedies first, but if that does not work quickly enough, my next stop is the chemist or the doctor's surgery. I have no intention of suffering if there is a pill or procedure that will bring swift relief and allow me to go about my normal day. We are extremely fortunate in the UK to have access to dedicated medical professionals free of charge and a plethora of pharmaceutical drugs at minimal cost. But, as our trial and many others confirm, this indispensible medical care can be further enhanced by the provision of healing, especially in situations where conventional treatment is ineffective or causes side effects. The next question is whether members of the public are likely to seek healing independently.

Since the completion of our trial, Dr Singh has seen a number of the participants at their follow-up appointments. They told him how much they enjoyed the sessions and that they had benefited from the experience, but they would not consider having healing outside of the NHS. It gave them confidence to know that the particular healer had been approved by the hospital and that the therapy had been recommended by the consultant. They felt protected by being treated in a medical setting. Clearly, many more people would be likely to take advantage of healing if it were made available in doctors' surgeries and hospitals.

It would also be more readily taken up if it were free, of course. Citizens of the UK are accustomed to receiving healthcare without being charged and there may be a psychological barrier against having to pay. Some people might baulk at the idea of even a nominal fee to receive healing at a hospital. Others simply could not afford the additional outlay.

Healing in a Hospital

To be made available on the National Health Service (NHS), each medicine and treatment has to be approved by The National Institute for Health and Care Excellence (NICE) (190). NICE looks to see how well a medicine or treatment works in relation to how much it costs, to ensure the NHS gets value for money. The NHS is legally obliged to fund any treatments recommended by NICE. The Medicines Act 1968 provides that a new medicine can receive a marketing authorisation from NICE if it is marginally more effective than a placebo (191). It does not have to be more effective than existing and well-established medicines. On the face of it, then, it should be a straightforward matter for healing to be made available on the NHS for a range of medical conditions.

Until that day comes, what can each of us do to encourage doctors and hospitals to make healing available?

The first thing is to make the results of our research trial known to people in key positions, both nationally and locally. This includes doctors and consultants, hospitals, primary care trusts, NHS chiefs, healthcare administrators, government officials, MPs and local councillors. If people in influential positions learn how patients have been helped by healing, they may take steps to make it available at NHS sites. Some surgeries might take the pragmatic view—as Cleveland Clinic did (page 9)—that it is worth implementing a cost-efficient therapy that has been shown to be safe and effective.

Second, people who have benefited from healing need to tell their doctor or specialist about their experience. A completed set of weekly questionnaires would give impressive evidence that may encourage a doctor to be more open-minded towards healing. As a result, a surgery or hospital might consider trialling a healer, either paid or unpaid. There is no reason why a voluntary healing group should not be based at an NHS venue, if space is available.

Third, and vitally important, is to broadcast to the public the fact that healing exists. Personal accounts convey the real difference that healing can make to an individual's life. It takes courage to offer one's own story to the media, but such articles are engaging, they instil hope, and they inspire others to take that first step. If different people's stories were regularly aired on television and radio programmes, and published in newspapers and magazines, it would help raise awareness and create interest. Healing could be mentioned within the dialogue of films, woven into the storyline of TV dramas, incorporated within the lyrics of songs, and could be a topic included in chat shows and interviews.

Take, for instance, the television show in which Piers Morgan interviewed Michael Flatley. Piers asked about a period of time when Michael was ill for three years with a mystery virus. Dozens of top specialists were unable to discover what was causing the problem. Michael became so badly affected that was unable to leave the house for nearly a year. Sometimes, he could not coordinate himself enough to answer a simple question, no matter how hard he tried. Eventually, a member of his staff suggested that he see a particular healer in Ireland, and he agreed without hesitation. After the first session he went for a mile-long walk. After ten sessions he was dancing again (192).

If stories like these were to be discussed more frequently within the public domain, healing would gain greater acceptance.

To help bring more case studies into the public arena, my website can be used as a hub. Members of the public are invited to send me their stories, and journalists are encouraged to register their interest. I can then attempt to put appropriate parties in touch with each other. For those wishing to remain anonymous, their accounts can be included in my next book. To facilitate making these books accessible to more people, readers can ask their local lending library to stock a copy.

Also, thanks to the miracle of today's technology, any one of us can spend just a few minutes tapping on a computer to circulate healing stories to friends and other contacts all around the world.

Some people are afraid to tell their own friends about their healing experience, never mind taking it into the public domain. Fear of ridicule and criticism causes them to keep any unusual knowledge to themselves. But with thousands of healers in the UK, there must be a myriad of uplifting and inspiring stories being kept secret. If everyone felt free to talk openly about their experiences, it would soon become clear just how prevalent healing really is.

I tried to find out how many healers there might currently be in the UK, but ran across a few obstacles. First, there are too many separate organisations to ask each one how many members they have. Second, the umbrella organisations to which these groups subscribe do not know how many healers belong to each of their member groups. I therefore asked Balens Insurance if they could help, since they seem to be market leaders in the field of complementary therapies, and all healers must be insured. They confirmed that they have 80,000 clients who are complementary therapy practitioners, but were unable to say how many of these are healers. However, they had an interesting healing story of their own to tell.

Balens was originally a general commercial brokerage but three generations later, David Balen became involved in the family business. As a young man, he had backpacked around India and contracted hepatitis A. He became gravely ill and, during the process of recovery, he learned of complementary therapies from fellow travellers. He benefited from this knowledge, and the experience broadened his view of health. A few years later, he had a serious accident, and his injuries were incorrectly treated by the NHS. As a result, he suffered long-term complications, causing trauma and pain for many years. He turned to natural therapies again, which he believes sustained him throughout the ordeal and led to his recovery.

In 1990, colleagues in the therapy world asked David to help develop professional insurance cover for therapists. Although Balens was the first company to offer this standard of cover, there are now several others to choose from. Consequently, their figure of 80,000 practitioners is only a starting point. Using this figure alone, coupled with the survey mentioned on page 38—which suggests that 40% of all CAM practitioners are healers—there may be around 32,000 healers on Balens' books, plus all those covered by other insurers.

This must mean that a tremendous number of people have received healing. If everyone talked openly about their experience, a growing number of others would be likely to seek healing. Of the many people who benefit from healing, some subsequently feel inspired to help others in the same way. If more people received healing, we would eventually have more healers. This can only be a good thing—so long as they are properly trained.

Various signs can indicate a natural ability, such as tingling in the hands when they think about healing. Some people have an obvious natural ability but cannot accept that it is real. Someone once told me about various occasions when she placed her hands on ailing friends who then improved instantly. Despite repeated evidence before her eyes, it was too unbelievable for her, and she continues to doubt her ability. Mixing with other healers would help her gain confidence and to acknowledge her gift. Proper training would ensure that she is not depleting herself when giving healing, and would also maximise the beneficial effects.

For those wishing to train, calling in at a voluntary healing centre is a good first step. Visitors can have a relaxed chat with the healers, view a session in progress and experience a healing session themselves.

Some people only ever intend to give healing quietly to family and friends, in which case the initial training courses gives sufficient knowledge. However, students find training to be so enriching that they are usually eager to enrol for the next level. Good quality training offers a firm foundation for dealing with one's own life challenges as well as for supporting loved ones through theirs. Life events will still occur, but our response to them is liable to be more constructive.

As additional people train to become healers and healing becomes more prevalent, the effects can only be increasingly better for the general health and wellbeing of society as a whole.

Most people are keen to have a long, happy and healthy life. Scores of studies carried out since the 1980s suggest that people who follow some sort of spiritual path fare better than those who do not. They seem to recover from major surgical procedures better and they have a lower incidence of nearly all the major diseases, including heart disease and cancer. According to some surveys, they live longer by seven to 13 years (193). With traditional church attendance is in steep decline, regular healing sessions could provide the spiritual element that is missing from so many people's lives.

Very often, people seek healing as a last resort when there seems no other option. They have either suffered for a long time or they have had a bolt out of the blue—like a heart attack—that has shaken them to their roots. We often do not realise how much our thoughts and actions affect our bodies until something suddenly goes wrong with it, and we have to re-evaluate our lifestyle and priorities. But there is no need to wait until something drastic develops. It is far better to recognise a small health issue as being a nudge to find healing. We shall have this same body until we die so it is in our own interest to make it last and wear well. And since it is our closest friend and lifetime companion, it makes sense to treat it as a precious gift and have a great relationship with it.

Healing has been shown to generate health, happiness and hope, with no adverse side effects. The next logical step is to take a slice of this action for ourselves. Now is the best time to make that happen. Delay simply sets back the moment when improvements can begin. The more we benefit physically and emotionally, the better it is for ourselves, for our loved ones and for everyone with whom we come into contact. No matter how well and happy we think we are, nobody is physically perfect and totally stress free. If such a person did actually exist, they would not be reading this book.

If the answer is 'no' to any of the following questions, healing sessions can improve your life.

1. Is your body in good shape and in perfect health?

2. Do you feel fulfilled and happy with life?

3. Do you have good relationships with everyone you know?

4. Do you sleep well?

5. Do you approve of yourself?

If the answer is 'yes' to any of the following questions, healing can help.

1. Do you have any fears or phobias?

2. Are you allergic to anything?

3. Do you take medication for anything?

4. Do you have any addictions?

5. Do you get stressed or annoyed?

6. Do you worry?

Honest answers to the above reveal that we all have something worthwhile to gain from healing. Healing sessions must be the easiest and most pleasant way to achieve improvements in all of these areas and more. If you still cannot believe that healing can help, be scientific and try it for yourself. Using your choice of questionnaires and following the simple guidance provided, you can plot your own progress over a series of six weekly sessions. If you notice any benefit from six treatments, it makes sense to carry on.

Fear, anxiety, worry, depression, stress and anger are just a few examples of the inward-looking emotions that weigh us down and hold us back. Left unchecked, they cause us physical harm, according to scientific evidence. The sooner we upcycle the energy of destructive thoughts and emotions, the more we can enjoy the remainder of our lives. Everyone around us benefits, especially our children and our grandchildren.

People repeatedly experience healing as a relaxing method of transforming physical pain and unhelpful emotions into that of calmness, vitality and improved health. You could be one of them.

Key Points

The Benefit of Healing Sessions

1. Clinical trials have shown healing to be beneficial for a wide range of conditions—physical, mental and emotional.

2. Many patients have reported the following improvements after receiving healing:

   a. Pain relief

   b. Reduced symptoms

   c. Increased mobility

   d. Reduced addictions

   e. Reduced anxiety and worry

   f. Reduced fears and phobias

   g. Reduced stress

   h. Increased confidence and motivation

   i. Improved sleep

   j. Improved relationships

3. Since gut disorders are the root cause of other physical and psychological problems, the results of our trial are relevant to a host of other patients.

4. Psychological factors are known to affect physical health. Happy people are healthier and live longer. Happiness causes physical changes in the brain that can be permanent. Healing sessions engender an uplifted state of mind, which is synonymous with happiness.

What Next?

5. People with a spiritual element in their lives are healthier and live longer. Healing sessions provide a spiritual element.

Healing Within the NHS

1. Healing sessions are as effective as some medical treatments and cost far less. For these cases, patients could first be given a series of healing sessions. If they continued to suffer, they could then have the medical treatment.

2. Healing sessions support conventional healthcare by reducing fear of treatment or surgery and other underlying worries.

3. Healing sessions support conventional treatments by alleviating distressing side effects.

4. Healing sessions can be beneficial for conditions where medical treatments are ineffective.

5. The majority of the population is in favour of having complementary therapies made available on the NHS.

6. Patients are more likely to accept healing when offered within an NHS setting.

7. Any therapy provided by the NHS must first be approved by NICE. All the research within this book would support an application to NICE.

8. Spiritual healing is likely to cost the least of any complementary therapies, because no equipment or supplies are needed and it takes the shortest time to conduct a session.

Benefits of Self-Help

1. Self-help techniques can trigger and/or support the healing process.

Healing in a Hospital

2. Basic healer training is valuable for self-healing and for treating loved ones.

3. Being equipped to help ourselves or others is empowering.

Promotion of Healing

More individuals are likely to seek healing if they know that it exists, are aware of the potential benefits and realise that it is natural and normal. The following actions would help achieve this:

1. Healing needs to be a regular topic featured by mass media channels.

2. The media needs to receive case studies to report on.

3. Individuals who have benefited from healing need to talk openly with others about their experience, including via social media.

4. Doctors and other medical professionals need to hear directly from their patients regarding how healing has helped them.

Frequently Asked Questions

Supporting evidence that underpins the statements made within this section is presented within the main body of the book.

What is spiritual healing?

Spiritual   from the Latin 'spiritus', means 'breath of life'

Healing   means 'making well'

Healing is experienced by many people as a relaxing method of transforming physical pain, unhelpful thoughts and negative emotions into constructive energy. This upcycling of energy then naturally brings about health, peace of mind and vitality.

When the mind experiences a deeply blissful state, the body returns to 'biological homeostasis', which is its natural state of balance and self-repair (194) (195). The deep sense of peace that many people experience during a healing session, coupled with the sensations they report, suggest that they experience this state.

The term 'spiritual healing' leads some people to assume that it must be connected to a religion, but this is not the case. Healers do usually believe in a 'great creator' or a 'universal mind' but not necessarily within an orthodox context.

To avoid being linked with religion, there are healers who prefer to use the term 'energy healing' instead. However, this can be misleading because some patients understand it to mean that healing will only help their energy levels, not their physical problems or emotional state.

A number of healers do belong to traditional religions but, whatever their creed, those who are members of a reputable organisation will not mention their own beliefs unless the patient specifically asks.

Some methods of healing have a long history in their country of origin, for example spiritual healing in the UK, and reiki in Japan. Others have been developed relatively recently, such as Therapeutic Touch in the USA.

The life force energy that is utilised in healing is referred to as 'prana' in Indian languages and 'chi' in Chinese culture.

How can healing help someone?

Healing is holistic, meaning that it addresses the person as a whole, not just the symptoms. The word 'holistic' is derived from the word 'whole'.

People often find that healing helps, no matter what the problem is. Physical problems, pain, mental anguish and emotional turmoil have all been alleviated to some degree. Occasionally, recovery has been remarkable by any standards, and several examples are offered in this book.

Any reduction of pain, fear, stress and worry is a benefit to our quality of life. A wealth of supporting research indicates that a reduction in these negative feelings improves our physical health and wellbeing.

What if I am already seeing my doctor?

Healing is complementary to any other treatment, medical or otherwise. It works well used alongside conventional medicine, procedures and surgery. Medical attention should always be sought for a health issue that is causing concern.

How does it work?

There are many ideas and theories, but probably nobody truly knows how healing works. Training courses often teach that energy flows through the healer into the patient, like water, and that the healer turns the flow on and off, like a tap. Just as the pipe gets wet bringing water to the tap, so the healer benefits from the healing energy passing through.

Using a different analogy, the healer attempts to generate a blissful vibration that stimulates the patient's energy into a similar state. This is called entrainment. An example of entrainment is where a tuning fork is struck and its sound waves activate an identical tuning fork nearby. Even though the second fork has not been touched, it picks up the vibration from the air and sounds its note. A less known fact is that heart cells in a Petri dish will start beating in rhythm even if they are not touching each other (196). Similarly, when the healer attunes to the healing vibration, the patient then entrains towards this level. ECGs visibly demonstrate this phenomenon in action. Consequently, I believe that patients heal themselves. Healers simply help them to reach that point.

No matter how healing might work, the fundamental point is that it does.

Is it just placebo?

The placebo effect is when the recipient's belief in a therapy causes a positive outcome. If someone believes that a pill will help them, it generally does. Placebo is a powerful ally to any form of healing, whether using conventional medicine or natural healing. Healthcare professionals and therapists alike would do well to maximise its potential for the benefit of their patients.

It is probably of no importance to the patient whether the positive results of a healing session are due to spiritual energy or to the placebo effect. The evidence is that, at the very least, healing helps unleash the patient's innate and powerful ability to self-heal.

However, as discussed later, healing on animals and plants removes the possibility of the placebo effect because animals and plants clearly cannot have an opinion. Animals and plants cannot have a belief that a therapy will work; nor can they be sceptical about it. Yet a range of research shows that healing remains effective for these non-human cases. Even giving healing to human tissue in Petri dishes, under laboratory conditions, registers a positive effect.

Does a patient need to believe in healing for it to work?

No. For example, the two hospital audits described in this book explain that the 267 patients involved did not seek healing and, except for a few, had never contemplated having healing. Some of them strongly believed that healing could not help them yet it did and, in some cases, remarkably so.

Spiritual healing is often confused with 'faith healing', where the patient is told that they must believe in a particular doctrine, deity or ritual for it to work.

As mentioned already, research studies reveal that animals and plants respond to healing and these serve to demonstrate that belief by the recipient is not necessary for healing to be effective.

Babies have no belief system yet they often respond well to healing. One example is a babe in arms who was brought to our voluntary healing centre. She was constantly crying and unable to sleep. No remedy could be found by either her mother or the doctor. After one healing session, the baby slept normally.

I am not aware of any healing research on babies, but I do know of a case where such a proposal was rejected on ethical grounds. First, parents and healers alike would be unhappy that some sick babies would have to be in the 'control' group. The 'control' group receives no healing, so that comparisons can be made between those who receive the treatment and those who do not. Parents of the control group babies would be additionally upset if they perceived that the babies having healing were improving while their own were being denied the therapy. Second, if a baby receiving treatment appeared to worsen for any reason, the distressed parents may blame the healing.

Does the healer need to know what the matter is?

No. In the same way that energy from the food we eat naturally goes to where it is most needed, healing energy finds its own way to the core of a problem. As the healer does not need to direct the energy, it is not necessary for the patient to explain what the problem is. This is a relief for people who would be embarrassed to divulge their personal information. They may have a medical problem that embarrasses them, or there may be something in their past or in their behaviour that they are ashamed of. Also, if a healer knows what the physical problem is, he might concentrate on that particular part and miss the root cause of the issue. For instance, a thumb that has lost its grip can be due to a trapped nerve in the neck, and pain in the lower back can be caused by stress. If the whole body is treated, nothing can be overlooked.

What happens in a healing session?

The patient simply sits or lies down with their eyes closed and there may be soft background music to encourage relaxation. If the person is more comfortable without their coat or shoes, that is fine, but otherwise they remain fully clothed. The healer may then offer a few words of guidance to help the patient unwind further.

If trained by The Healing Trust, the healer takes about 20 minutes to work around the person and complete the session. The healer usually works with their hands about ten inches (25cm) away from the body, except for a light touch on the shoulders and feet. The whole of the body is always treated, not just the part that is unwell.

If the healer chooses to work with touch, this is very light and only on the joints of the arms and legs. The healer will always ask permission before using touch of any sort. If the patient agrees to it, I prefer to use touch because the person then knows where I am, and the human touch can also be an added comfort. Some people are not touched by anyone, day after day, and others are only touched by medical professionals or by people who want something. A touch that demands nothing in return can be deeply supportive and reassuring.

During a healing session, a patient may feel heat, cold or tingling. They may have involuntary muscle jumps or see colours in their mind's eye. Their eyes may water or they may suddenly have a deep sigh or two. Sometimes a pain, a feeling of discomfort or an emotion might rise to the surface then quickly and gently dissipate. Equally, a patient may not sense anything at all. Every response is perfectly normal.

How many sessions are needed?

Just one session has made an astonishing difference to some patients. More typically, a series of five or six weekly sessions brings enough improvements for the patient to start noticing the difference. Some people who make a complete recovery nevertheless choose to continue with weekly sessions to maintain their health and wellbeing. A man with lifelong mental and emotional problems came to our voluntary healing group every week for many years, saying that it kept him from feeling suicidal. Others simply wish to free themselves of the week's stress and recharge their batteries, just as they might do by going to a gym or a yoga class.

Can healing help someone with a terminal condition?

Yes, but not necessarily to make them live longer. For many, the dread of dying melts away during a healing session, allowing the patient to live more contentedly during the limited time that they have left. People with a terminal condition are often fearful about how their worsening symptoms will affect them in the future. Others worry about leaving their loved ones behind or parting with their home and possessions. These concerns are often alleviated or brought into perspective as a result of healing.

What is distant healing?

The terms 'distant healing', 'distance healing' and 'absent healing' all refer to the same thing. They mean that the healer is not physically present with the patient, and 'sends' the healing.

As with prayer, there is no need for the recipient to know that they are being sent healing, and their permission is not required. Numerous groups arrange to send healing; some physically meet together, while others set a weekly time when anyone can add to the collective effort from the comfort of their own home.

Healing can be sent to individuals, companies, organisations, governments, to trouble spots and disaster areas around the world, to animals and plants, and to our beleaguered host planet, the Earth.

Do healers 'pick up' private information about the patient?

Let us assume, for a moment, that it is possible for personal details to be picked up by a psychic person who is attempting to do so. In every case, accessing private information without permission is wholly unethical. It does not occur if the healer has been trained properly and belongs to a reputable organisation that has a professional code of conduct. A list of healing organisations appears at the back of this book.

Where is healing available and can it be provided on the National Health Service (UK)?

Healing is available at voluntary healing centres throughout the country, as well as from private practitioners. Doctors can prescribe healing but might not pay for it. A few surgeries and hospitals have been offering healing at their premises for many years, some by salaried practitioners and others by volunteers. There are also doctors who make rooms available at their surgeries for patients to receive healing, where the patient pays a small fee directly to the healer.

Some religions offer healing and there is no need to belong to their creed to take advantage of this service. Spiritualist churches have always offered healing on a regular basis but some mainstream churches, such as Roman Catholic and Anglican, now offer laying-on of hands. In some churches, the healing is delivered only by the priest while others allow lay people to administer.

Can anyone become a healer?

Yes, everyone has the potential to become a healer. Some people are aware of their natural ability from a young age, while the rest of us have to learn from scratch to develop the skill. Healing is an art, and some people have a natural flair for it, as they might for any other creative pursuit. For instance, some people can cook or sew without effort and others learn languages with ease. The rest of us can manage these activities, but it takes more effort to learn and become proficient. Likewise with healing, everyone has the ability but some need to start with the basics and be determined to progress.

My view is that patients actually heal themselves; the healer simply provides the environment that activates the natural process. Therefore, I believe that those who respond especially well to healing would be particularly ideal candidates for training.

Medical professionals, carers and therapists are likely to be natural healers, having already been drawn to vocations that bring comfort to those in need.

Why train?

Healing is a natural and powerful energy and, like electricity, has simple rules for safe and effective use. With proper training, a healer cannot become drained as a result of giving healing or be negatively affected in any other way. Indeed, the act of giving healing benefits the healer by virtue of achieving an uplifted state, which in itself accrues health benefits.

People who have a career in tending to others, or who are caring for a loved one, would especially benefit from learning the basics.

278

Medical professionals, carers and complementary therapists are very often natural healers without realising it. Looking after the sick and needy can be draining, and learning to regain and maintain the integrity of one's own energies is essential. Also, by adding basic healing knowledge to their skillset, healthcare workers could enhance their patients' experience in the many ways described in this book.

Training to become a healer and putting into practice the philosophies that underpin healing lead to a happier, healthier and more enriched life.

For a list of reputable training organisations, see page 296. Additionally, many healers recommend the guidance given in Jack Angelo's book *Your Healing Power.*

Can people help themselves to heal without proper training?

Yes. This fascinating and empowering area of experiential learning is the subject of many books and workshops. People can be guided towards dissipating long-standing issues, and be introduced to constructive methods of dealing with life's inevitable challenges. Various ideas and resources are offered on page 46 and from page 291 onwards.

What does CAM mean?

Complementary and Alternative Medicine (CAM) includes two different groups.

Complementary therapies are those that complement any other form of healthcare and can be used alongside conventional treatment. They do not interfere with the beneficial aspects of medication or surgery. Healing falls into this category.

Alternative therapies, as the name suggests, are a substitute for conventional medical treatment and purport to provide diagnostic information.

In practice, the term 'complementary therapies' is often used to mean both categories, despite the important difference.

What is the difference between reiki and spiritual healing?

Reiki is a Japanese word meaning 'spiritual healing' or 'universal life energy', and there are a number of different types of reiki. Each healing method is probably slightly different from every other, but the essence is most likely the same. If there is variance in a patient's experience between different styles of healing, this could be due to the healer rather than to the method or modality.

Reiki is widespread because any practitioner who has completed the courses can teach others without approval or accreditation by a central organisation. There are no national standards to be adhered to regarding the course content or the tutor's credentials. Training is therefore abundantly available, and practitioners are easy to find. This ease of access has led to its huge popularity, which has been a tremendous boost for raising public awareness of healing.

Whether using a reiki practitioner or a spiritual healer, patients should ensure that the therapist belongs to a reputable organisation. A list is given on page 296.

What is The Healing Trust?

The National Federation of Spiritual Healers (NFSH) was established in 1954, soon after healing became legal in the UK. In recent years, it adopted the working title of 'The Healing Trust' to convey its purpose succinctly and to have a name that people can easily remember. It has no affiliation with any religion, its members hailing from all faiths and none. Over the decades, erstwhile members have spawned many of the other healing organisations in the UK and around the world. However, The Healing Trust is probably still the largest healer membership organisation. It is almost the only healing charity to own its office premises—made possible by a generous legacy from Clark Finlay—and to employ salaried staff.

Only trainers accredited by The Healing Trust provide training, and they teach to a national curriculum. Students are required to become members of the organisation before they can advance beyond the initial training course. Becoming a member involves providing personal references and finding qualified healers who are prepared to sponsor the applicant throughout their training. Members are subject to a minimum of two years' training period, final assessment, a professional code of conduct and disciplinary procedures. These standards are designed to give the public confidence that Healing Trust practitioners are respectable and have been trained well.

Experienced practitioners, often volunteers, run support groups for trainee healers throughout the UK and in some other countries. Volunteer members also provide a national network of healing centres to make healing accessible and affordable for members of the public.

The Healing Trust has developed a safe and effective method of giving healing that is delivered in a professional and dignified manner. For insurance purposes, and to comply with prevailing best practice requirements, the healer will ask for certain personal details. This information is treated as strictly confidential.

For ease of reading, NFSH/The Healing Trust is referred to throughout this book simply as The Healing Trust.

How much does it cost for a healing session?

Financially, voluntary healing centres are very accessible as they usually suggest a minimum donation of a nominal amount, or nothing at all for those who cannot afford to contribute.

Some private healers use a similar donation arrangement while others charge a professional fee. It is always advised to establish the cost before making a booking.

Comments Made by Medical Professionals

The following comments were made by delegates at the Nursing in Practice exhibition described on page 23.

When reading the following statements, it should be borne in mind that these people, mostly nurses, were at a busy conference with a tight schedule. As a result, their healing sessions were shorter than usual, the environment was noisy and there was no privacy. They were not unwell and they did not seek healing. Indeed, most were previously unaware of spiritual healing and were sceptical that it could be beneficial. However, they were intrigued enough to sample a session, and the following is a selection of their observations.

1. That was fantastic. Great warmth all over.

2. A most exhilarating experience. Felt wonderful and so relaxed.

3. Beautiful colours moving around. Very therapeutic.

4. A very pleasant experience. Felt some of my emotions coming to the surface.

5. A wonderful experience. Felt extremely calm and relaxed afterwards.

6. Very therapeutic.

7. A very powerful and pleasant experience. Would highly recommend.

Comments made by Medical Professionals

8.   Felt lighter.

9.   My bad arm and neck felt pins and needles.

10.   I was sceptical but found it relaxing.

11.   I felt a warm glow.

12.   Strange calming sensations in fingers.

13.   Strange spinning but calming.

14.   Left me with a tingling sensation all over. Feel very calm and relaxed.

15.   I went to a lovely place, unaware of my surroundings.

16.   Amazing! Very calming.

17.   Warm, relaxing, tilting feeling. Very peaceful.

18.   Warm, tingling sensation in neck and arm.

19.   Feel a lot calmer now and a lot brighter.

20.   Had a particularly bad night with pain and stress. Much calmer in mind and body now. Ready for the day.

21.   I felt so relaxed, felt as though I was asleep. Could do with this every night!

22.   What a lovely, peaceful time. I feel so much better.

23.   Excellent way to escape the rat race. Totally relaxing.

24.   Made my headache disappear.

25.   Very soothing. Felt electrical or spiritual current all over the body.

26. Very relaxing and warming. A tingling sensation. Felt lovely.

27. Excellent. Felt warmth, then tension in my neck released.

28. Wasn't sure at the start but by the end felt relaxed and soothed.

29. Felt very light and relaxed. Forgot where I was!

30. I found the healing process quite remarkable. Calming effect.

31. An amazing experience. I feel much more relaxed and focused.

32. I am hoping that this feeling lasts forever.

33. A very pleasurable experience. Thoroughly enjoyed and will be recommending.

34. Feeling of calm and serenity.

35. Lovely feeling of being here but not here.

36. Very relaxing and a feeling of being by the sea alone.

37. Very nice and relaxing. Felt some tingling.

38. Very relaxing. Felt cold at times.

39. Very nice and relaxing. Calm and tingling feeling.

40. Very exciting.

41. Very relaxing. I felt bad energies running out of my body.

42. Very calming. I feel chilled out and a feeling of lightness.

43. My colleague and I both felt that we had recharged our batteries.

Comments made by Medical Professionals

44. Tingly head; warm right hand. Really enjoyed it.

45. Fantastic and amazing feeling. Very relaxed and calm now.

46. Felt relaxed and confident.

47. Quite relaxing. I loved it.

48. Amazing. My pain has gone.

49. I'm stuck for words! Absolutely amazing.

50. Amazing. Absolutely fabulous.

51. Felt relaxed and sleepy, even with all the noise around.

52. Very relaxing. Felt light-headed immediately afterwards and then re-energised.

53. Reduced tension in shoulders. Very relaxing and calming.

54. Feel more relaxed. Felt a movement of energy in my knee.

55. What a fantastic feeling. A sense of calm was present.

56. I felt heat and warm relaxation instantly.

57. I feel strange but in a good way.

58. Have not experienced this before but would highly recommend it. Have suffered from a headache all morning. It has gone now.

59. Very tingly experience. Very relaxing and rewarding.

60. Very positive experience. Feel very relaxed. Tingling feeling in legs.

61. Did not know what to expect. Felt tingling sensation. Very relaxing.

62. Really felt tingling at areas where healer's hands were. Felt neck relax and pain relieved.

63. Very relaxing. Ended up with very warm feet.

64. Amazing experience. Want to find out more.

65. I cannot really believe how I felt. It was like a magnet that was pulling my negative energy. I was fully relaxed and will never forget the experience.

66. Felt very relaxed. Arm felt heavy—can't explain it. Feel refreshed.

67. Has eased my painful lower back area.

68. Not sure how to describe feeling. Very relaxing. Like an hour's sleep.

69. Absolutely fascinating. I am really surprised how I felt afterwards and will definitely be looking this up on the web.

70. Very relaxing. Feeling of internal 'denseness'. Very interesting.

71. Very relaxing and unique experience. Felt like somebody was touching my hair but they weren't.

72. Very relaxing and good experience. I felt heat and I enjoyed it.

73. At the beginning I felt as though pins and needles were travelling through my body. Also, I could feel warm spots on certain points of my joints. Relaxing.

74. The most relaxing few minutes in a long time. Felt a little like an Aero bar—bubbly.

75. Session was short but effective. Sent my hands very tingly. Felt very relaxed.

Comments made by Medical Professionals

76. I felt sleepy and nice.

77. Very calming. Strange sensation as if I were being pulled forward.

78. Very relaxed and slightly tingly.

79. Really felt rays on my head and tummy.

80. Could feel where the healer was as areas of my body became hot. Felt tired but rejuvenated at the same time.

81. Surprisingly relaxing. Will recommend.

82. Good experience. Definitely felt the problem area being healed.

83. Felt the heat from the healer. Wonderful work.

84. Felt really relaxed! One wonderful experience!

85. Felt clear minded, like I wasn't thinking. Felt energy around me, like a force.

86. Excellent. Very relaxed. Clears the mind.

87. Love, calmness and a feeling of pureness.

88. Could feel the tension/heat through my shoulders and top of head. Thank you.

89. Wonderful feeling of stress relief and very relaxing.

90. Heat felt on knees. Lovely and relaxing.

91. Felt heat around my head.

92. An excellent way to relieve stress. Feel energised and relaxed.

93. Felt tingling and engulfed in light.

94. Very relaxing and good experience. Felt a cool breeze, very gentle, around my face.

95. Excellent. Felt the stress leaving my arms in particular.

96. That was amazing. The energy that flows afterwards is wonderful.

97. Relaxing but strange. The energy felt very strong and at one stage a little uncomfortable, though not painful.

98. Best part of the day! The anxiety I came with has gone.

99. Absolutely lovely. I want to learn how to do it.

100. Interesting departure from my normal logical thinking. The world is full of mysteries and this made me tingle and relax. Will explore further. Keep up the good work.

101. Wonderful. A real uplifter. Would be great for our patients.

102. Healing felt warm and comforting. My shoulders feel less tense.

103. Great experience. Felt very relaxed and safe.

104. I felt as though all my troubles were leaving my body and all happy things entering.

105. A remarkable healing experience.

106. Floaty. Tingly down arms and legs. Relaxing. Very light.

107. Really good. Felt really light and floaty. My foot stopped itching—it had itched all day until now.

108. Got rid of headache.

109. Very interesting. A cynic now believes!

Comments made by Medical Professionals

110. Completely relaxed. Thank you so much. Amazing experience.

111. Very calming and relaxing. Felt heat throughout body. Will definitely recommend.

112. Absolutely lovely. Relaxing. Beautiful colours. Floating.

113. Cold tingling sensation. Feel stress-free.

114. Very relaxing. Could feel tingling in calves. Brilliant. Well worth having.

115. I found the experience very relaxing and comforting. Felt energised afterwards.

116. I was sceptical and didn't want to have a session but my friend recommended it and I'm glad I did. The experience was definitely calming and relaxing. I felt a presence. Instantly, my knee felt better.

117. The negative energy was moving from my body.

118. What a very happy, enriching experience. I nearly didn't come to the exhibition but so glad I did! What wonderful people.

119. I really enjoyed the healing session. Experienced heat and tingling.

120. I felt really relaxed and energised. It was really good.

121. I felt so relaxed it was unreal. It's like all negative energy left my body. It was physically felt.

122. Very pleasant, relaxing and rejuvenating.

123. Found the healing very relaxing. Saw some colours.

124. Thank you so much for giving me so much peace in this busy life of ours. It has been a truly special experience.

Healing in a Hospital

125. Thanks for the peaceful feeling of calmness that overtook me.

126. Amazing. Very relaxing. Firstly, I didn't think it would. Glad I've had the experience.

127. Extremely interesting experience. I would definitely recommend this to my friends and patients.

128. I feel a lot happier and relaxed.

129. Brilliant. Really felt good energy.

130. Brilliant. I didn't think it would work but it did. I was really impressed.

131. I could feel heat from the healer's hands.

132. Excellent! Felt like I was floating.

133. Excellent. Felt lovely and the pain in my right foot went away. I would recommend it to anyone.

134. Surprisingly good.

My Website

www.healinginahospital.com

To encourage others to seek healing, please send me your healing story for publication. If you are willing to be publicly identified, I shall strive to team you up with a media contact. Otherwise, you can choose to remain anonymous and be included in my next book.

Subscribe (free) for details of future talks, workshops and publications.

Simple Techniques that Support Healing

First of all, find a healer with whom you feel at ease and commit yourself to at least five weekly sessions. The following suggestions will help maximise the potential benefits.

During each healing session:

1. Surrender yourself completely to the healing energies.

2. Imagine breathing in brilliant light with each in-breath.

3. Imagine breathing out smoke with every out-breath.

4. Make your body limp and heavy; sink into the chair or couch.

5. If emotion rises, open the mouth and throat and breathe deeply, making no sound.

6. Relax any muscles that become tense or uncomfortable.

7. Every time your mind wanders, bring it back.

Between sessions:

1. Listen to the Sleep Easy & Be Well CD every night.

2. Do things that you enjoy.

3. Learn to enjoy the things that you cannot avoid.

4. Surround yourself with things that make you smile.

Simple Techniques that Support Healing

5. Weave the word 'yes' into your thoughts and language.

6. Avoid saying 'no' and 'not'. Instead, state what you do want.

7. Laugh as often as possible—watch comedies.

Quick Technique to Relieve Pain

Quick and simple does not mean less efficient. This technique has worked time and again in just a few minutes, and has been 100% effective for some people. I was as thunderstruck as my patients when this worked for me (see page 260). The key to success is in commandeering every shred of attention to the task and using vivid imagination.

1. Focus the entirety of your attention onto the core of the pain.

2. Totally relax that part of the body.

3. Imagine that part filled with brilliant golden-white light.

4. Imagine the word 'yes' reverberating throughout that part.

5. Repeatedly intensify all of the above.

6. Let no other thought enter your mind.

If a different colour light occurs, or is easier to imagine, focus on that colour and make it the brightest possible.

Sleep Easy & Be Well CD

This spoken word recording helps the listener to relax and drift into deep and nourishing sleep. The background sound has been designed to be intensely soothing with no beat and no chimes.

Page 89 offers a multitude of reasons to develop good quality sleep, and testimonials on page 91 demonstrate how this CD has helped particular individuals.

Hospital radio stations and prisons are invited to broadcast this recording at a suitable time each evening, free of charge.

The Natural Healing Group, Aldridge sells the CD for a nominal sum. All proceeds support their voluntary healing work. A copy can be downloaded from their website:

www.midlandshealing.org.uk

Find a Healer or Training

For protection of the public, all healers belonging to the following organisations are subject to a minimum of two years' training, a professional code of conduct and disciplinary procedures. They are also covered by professional insurance. Addresses have been given only if the organisation has its own premises with employed staff. These organisations are not connected to any particular religion.

NFSH/The Healing Trust

21 York Road, Northampton, NN1 5QG
Website : www.thehealingtrust.org.uk
Email : office@thehealingtrust.org.uk
Tel : 01604 603247

Besides being the oldest and probably the largest healer membership organisation in the world, no other owns its own premises (thanks to a generous legacy) with salaried staff plus the following:

1. Voluntary healing groups throughout the UK.

2. Find a healer service (online or by telephone).

3. Training to national standards by accredited tutors throughout the UK and overseas.

4. Support groups for trainees and healers throughout the UK.

Established in 1954, the National Federation of Spiritual Healers (NFSH) was originally an umbrella organisation for disparate healing groups throughout the UK. Its first President was Harry Edwards, a famous healer whose public demonstration at the Royal Albert Hall drew an audience of 6,000 people.

In 1976, the NFSH decided to only accept individuals as members, not groups, so that training standards etc could be introduced. Many groups preferred to remain as they were, so they set up a separate umbrella organisation for themselves (BAHA). The total number of healers that had originally belonged to NFSH was therefore split between the two organisations.

No longer a federation and no longer only national, the NFSH adopted the working title of 'The Healing Trust' in 2009. This name is much easier for people to remember, and immediately conveys the purpose of the organisation.

The particular voluntary healing centre that is referred to throughout this book was the first independent centre to be accredited by NFSH/The Healing Trust:

Natural Healing Group
Aldridge, Walsall, West Midlands
Website : www.midlandshealing.org.uk
Tel : 0793 8838 047 or 0793 8838 010

British Alliance of Healing Associations (BAHA)

Website : www.britishalliancehealingassociations.com

Established in 1977, BAHA is an umbrella organisation for healing groups that meet its standards.

College of Healing

Website : www.collegeofhealing.org

Established in 1983 by a group of doctors and healers, the College of Healing was set up as an educational charity. One of its founders, Diane O'Connell, had previously developed healer training courses with colleagues, which they ran from 1975/6. At that time, it was generally believed that healing was a gift and could not be taught but when their pioneering work became known to other healing organisations, they followed suit. Diane continues to be at the forefront of training standards in the UK.

Confederation of Healing Organisations (CHO)

Website : www.the-cho.org.uk
Email : admin @the-cho.org.uk
Tel : 0300 302 0021

The CHO is an umbrella organisation for healing groups that meet its standards. It was created in 1982 by Denis Haviland who was a prominent industrialist. When he retired due to ill health and arthritis, he was persuaded to receive healing from the wife of a major general (197). He was soon walking without sticks and, as a result, was inspired to make healing more available and accepted. He formed the CHO with a number of founding organisations, with the aim that healing be made available throughout the NHS.

Harry Edwards Healing Sanctuary

Burrows Lea Cottage, Hook Lane, Shere, Surrey GU5 9QG
Website : www.harryedwardshealingsanctuary.org.uk
Email : info@burrowslea.org.uk
Tel : 01483 202054

Burrows Lea was originally the private home of Harry Edwards, a successful businessman and famous healer. He converted part of the property into a healing sanctuary that continues to offer healing and training.

UK Healers

Website : www.ukhealers.info
Email : admin@ukhealers.info

UK Healers is an umbrella organisation for healer membership organisations that meet its standards. It is the largest voluntary, professional standards setting, accrediting body for the training and practice of spiritual healing.

Reiki Organisations

The Reiki Council

Website : www.reikicouncil.org.uk
Email : info@reikicouncil.org.uk

The Reiki Council is an umbrella organisation for reiki groups that meet its requirements. Its website states that the Council cannot take any liability for reiki practitioners sourced via its member associations.

UK Reiki Federation

Website: www.reikifed.co.uk
Email : enquiry@reikifed.co.uk

The UK Reiki Federation is a member of the Reiki Council and is one of the largest Reiki organisations in the UK. Its website states that it promotes best practice within the field of reiki and stipulates a minimum training period of nine months.

Healing offered by Religions

Although healing need not be connected to a religion, some readers may wish to consider this option.

Spiritualists National Union (SNU)

>   Stansted Hall, Stansted, Essex, CM24 8UD
>   Website : www.snu.org.uk
>   Tel: 01279 816363

The SNU has always had a strong tradition of healing. It has excellent standards of training, with a minimum period of two years. Healing is usually offered every week at hundreds of its churches scattered throughout the UK and overseas. People of any religion or none are welcomed.

Other churches

Healing is becoming more available at different Christian denominations, even the orthodox ones.

Other Religions

I could find no information to suggest that healing is offered to the public by any other religion.

Healing Research Sources

The Research Council for Complementary Medicine (RCCM)

c/o Professor N Robinson, Faculty of Health & Social Care
London South Bank University, London SE1 0AA
Website : www.rccm.org.uk
Email : info@rccm.org.uk

The RCCM was founded in 1983 to develop high quality research in Complementary and Alternative Medicine (CAM).

Wholistic Healing Research

Website : www.wholistsichealingresesarch.com

Dr Daniel J Benor is a American medical doctor who has devoted decades of his life to amassing a wealth of research evidence regarding healing. It is presented on this website and also in his books, particularly Healing Research Volumes I–IV.

Healing in Medical Settings

The Sam Buxton Sunflower Healing Trust

Website : www.cancertherapies.org.uk

In 2006, Angie Buxton-King and her husband set up a charity in memory of her young son, who had died of cancer. Since then, it has financed the first two years' salary of over 25 healers working in different NHS hospitals and hospices around the UK. At the end of the two years, the salary commitment for the majority of these healers has been taken over by the recruiting NHS centre.

Doctor Healer Network

Website : www.doctorhealer.org

The Doctor Healer Network (DHN) exists to encourage the acceptance and use of integrated medicine, incorporating healing as a major component. The DHN offers information, advice and a forum for discussion for healthcare professionals who wish to become involved in healing. It aims to promote understanding and awareness of healing as a recognised and viable form of complementary therapy and to form collaborative links with medical and healthcare professionals and researchers.

Members of the DHN include medical staff, academics and also complementary therapists who work alongside medical professionals. Approximately 25% of the membership comprises doctors.

Citations

1. **Harvey, D.** *The Power to Heal: An Investigation of Healing and the Healing Experience.* s.l. : The Aquarian Press, 1983. ISBN 978-0-850-30326-1.

2. **Armstrong, K.** *A History of God.* ISBN 0-9493-0692-0.

3. *Healing Across Cultures: Learning From Traditions.* **Pesek T, Helton L, Nair M.** s.l. : EcoHealth, 2006, Vol. 3.

4. **Collins, FS.** *The Language of God: A Scientist Presents Evidence for Belief.* s.l. : Pocket Books, 2007. 978-1-84739-092-9.

5. Biological Homeostasis. *The Encyclopedia of Earth.* [Online] [Cited: 21 May 2015.] http://www.eoearth.org/view/article/150655/.

6. Guided Imagery & Heart Surgery. *Cleveland Clinic.* [Online] [Cited: 8 June 2015.] http://my.clevelandclinic.org/services/heart/prevention/emotional-health/stress-relaxation/guided-imagery-heart-surgery.

7. **Malmivuo J, Plonsey R.** *Bioelectromagnetism; Principles and Applications of Bioelectric and Biomagnetic Fields.* s.l. : Oxford University Press, 1995. ISBN 978-0-195-05823-9.

8. Magnetoencephalography. *Wikipedia.* [Online] [Cited: 30 August 2015.]

9. *Effect of psychosocial treatment on survival of patients with metastatic breast cancer.* **Spiegel D, Bloom JR, Kraemer HC, Gottheil E.** s.l. : Lancet, 1989, Vol. 2.

10. *Effects of an early structured psychiatric intervention, coping and affective state on recurrence and survival six years later.* **Fawzy FI, Fawzy NW, Hyun CS, Elashoff R, Guthrie D, Fahey JL, Morton DL.** s.l. : Archives of General Psychiatry, 1993, Vol. 50.

Citations

11. *Clinicians' Attitudes and Usage of Complementary and Alternative Integrative Medicine.* **Song M-Y, John M, Dobs AS.** s.l. : The Journal of Alternative and Complementary Medicine, 2007, Vol. 13.

12. *Complementary and alternative therapies: survey of knowledge and attitudes of health professionals at a tertiary pediatric/women's care facility.* **Brown J, Cooper E, Frankton L, Steeves-Wall M, Gillis-Ring J, Barter W, McCabe A, Fernandez C.** s.l. : Complementary Therapies in Clinical Practice, 2007, Vol. 13.

13. *Personal and professional influences on practitioners' attitudes to traditional and complementary approaches to health in the UK.* **Lorenca A, Blairb M, Robinson N.** s.l. : Journal of Traditional Chinese Medical Sciences, 2014, Vol. 1.

14. *Does healing benefit patients with chronic symptoms? A quasi-controlled trial in general practice.* **Dixon, M.** s.l. : Journal of the Royal Society of Medecine, 1998, Vol. 91.

15. Parliamentary Business; Publications & Records. *Parliament UK.* [Online] [Cited: 12 May 2015.] http://www.parliament.the-stationery-office.co.uk/pa/ld199900/ldselect/ldsctech/123/12301.htm.

16. House of Lords Publications; Lords Hansard; Daily Hansard. *Parliament UK - Parliamentary Business; Publications & Records.* [Online] 29 May 2001. [Cited: 12 May 2015.] http://www.publications.parliament.uk/pa/ld200001/ldhansrd/vo010 329/text/10329-13.htm.

17. **Baldwin, E.** A Look at CAM. *Annie Apple Seed Project.* [Online] [Cited: 13 May 2015.] http://s406515300.onlinehome.us/lookatcambyl.html.

18. *Users and Practitioners of Complementary Medicine.* **Zollamn C, Vickers A.** s.l. : British Medical Journal, 1999, Vol. 319.

19. Complementary medicine: information pack for primary care groups. *The National Archives.* [Online] [Cited: 25 May 2015.] http://webarchive.nationalarchives.gov.uk/+/www.dh.gov.uk/en/Pub licationsandstatistics/Publications/PublicationsPolicyAndGuidance/ DH_4006869.

20. Neutron Stars. *NASA*. [Online] [Cited: 12 November 2015.] http://www.nasa.gov/mission_pages/GLAST/science/neutron_stars. html.

21. Dark Energy, Dark Matter. *NASA Science Astrophysics.* [Online] [Cited: 17 8 2015.] http://science.nasa.gov/astrophysics/focus-areas/what-is-dark-energy/.

22. *Anita Moorjani.* [Online] [Cited: 22 November 2014.] http://www.anitamoorjani.com.

23. About Dannion Brinkley. *Dannion.com.* [Online] [Cited: 24 October 2015.] http://www.dannion.com/about/.

24. Denise Linn. *About Denise.* [Online] [Cited: 23 May 2015.] http://www.deniselinn.com/.

25. *Martin Brofman.* [Online] [Cited: 22 November 2014.] http://www.healer.ch.

26. *Donna Eden.* [Online] [Cited: 22 November 2014.] http://www.theinnersourcestore.com.

27. *Byron Katie.* [Online] [Cited: 22 November 2014.] http://www.thework.com.

28. *Psychiatric Morbidity report.* s.l. : The Office for National Statistics , 2001 .

29. *Eckhart Tolle.* [Online] [Cited: 22 November 2014.] http://www.eckharttolle.com.

30. **Cousins, N.** *Anatomy of an Illness; as perceived by the patient.* s.l. : W W Norton & Co Inc, 2005. ISBN 978-0-393-32684-0.

31. Laughter Therapy. *CancerTreatment Centers of America.* [Online] [Cited: 27 May 2015.] http://www.cancercenter.com/treatments/laughter-therapy/.

32. *Louise Haye.* [Online] [Cited: 22 November 2014.] http://www.louisehay.com.

33. Spontaneous Remission Bibliography Project. *Institute of Noetic Sciences.* [Online] [Cited: 15 November 2015.] http://www.noetic.org/research/projects/spontaneous-remission.

34. **Mayo, E.** *Hawthorne and the Western Electric Company, The Social Problems of an Industrial Civilisation.* s.l. : Routledge, 1949.

Citations

35. The Sleep Council. [Online] [Cited: 10 December 2015.] http://www.sleepcouncil.org.uk/2014/05/why-we-need-to-take-sleep-seriously/.

36. *Selective REM sleep deprivation in humans: Effects on sleep and sleep EEG.* **Endo T, Roth C, Landolt HP, Werth E.** s.l. : The American journal of physiology, 1998, Vol. 274.

37. **Carey, J.** *The Faber Book of Science.* ISBN 0-571-16352-1.

38. *Touch the pain away: new research on therapeutic touch and persons with fibromyalgia syndrome.* **Denison, B.** s.l. : Holistic Nursing Practice, 2004, Vol. 18.

39. What is Stress? The Stress Management Society. [Online] [Cited: 10 December 2015.] http://www.stress.org.uk/What-is-stress.aspx.

40. **D, Bloom.** Instead of detention, these students get meditation. *CNN News.* [Online] 2016. [Cited: 7 Novmber 2016.] http://edition.cnn.com/2016/11/04/health/meditation-in-schools-baltimore/.

41. House of Lords - Science & Technology; Sixth Report. *Parliament UK - Parliamentary Business; Publications & Records.* [Online] 1999-2000. [Cited: 12 May 2015.] http://www.parliament.the-stationery-office.co.uk/pa/ld199900/ldselect/ldsctech/123/12301.htm.

42. *Use of complementary therapies by patients with IBD may indicate psychosocial distress.* **Langmead L, Chitinis M, Rampton DS.** s.l. : Inflammatory Bowel Disease, 2002, Vol. 8.

43. *The incidence of self-prescribed oral complementary and alternative medicine use by patients with gastrointestinal diseases.* **Kong SC, Hurlstone DP, Pocock CY, et al.** s.l. : Journal of Clinical Gastroenterology, 2005, Vol. 39.

44. Complementary and Alternative Medicine - Biotech, Pharma and Life Science Channel. *BioPortfolio Website.* [Online] [Cited: 27 October 2014.] http://www.bioportfolio.com/channels/complementary-and-alternative-medicine.

45. **Lewith GT, Jonas WB, Walach H.** *Clinical Research in Complementary Therapies: Principles, Problems and Solutions.* s.l. : Elsevier, 2011. ISBN 978-0-443-06956-7.

46. *Painful diabetic neuropathy: impact of an alternative approach.* **Gillespie EA, Gillespie BW, Stevens MJ.** s.l. : Diabetes Care, 2007, Vol. 30.

47. *Physiotherapy and the Placebo Effect.* **Mengshoel, AM.** s.l. : Physical Therapy Reviews, 2000, Vol. 5.

48. *The Placebo Is Powerful: Estimating Placebo Effects.* **Wampold BE, Minami T, Tierney SC, Baskin TW, Bhati KS.** 7, s.l. : Journal of Clinical Psychology, 2005, Vol. 61.

49. *Randomised trials in surgery: problems and possible solutions.* **McCulloch P, Taylor I, Sasako M, Lovett B, Griffin D.** s.l. : British Medical Journal, 2002, Vol. 324.

50. *Surgical Randomized-Controlled Trials.* **Farrokhyar F, Achilles T.** s.l. : Annals of Surgery, 2010, Vol. 251.

51. *A Controlled Trial of Arthroscopic Surgery for Osteoarthritis of the Knee.* **Moseley JB, O'Malley K, Petersen NJ, Menke TJ, Brody BA, Kuykendall DH, Hollingsworth JC, Ashton CM, Wray NP.** s.l. : New England Journal of Medicine, 2002, Vol. 347.

52. *Arthroscopic Partial Meniscectomy versus Sham Surgery for a Degenerative Meniscal Tear.* **Sihvonen R, Paavola M, Malmivaara A, MD, et al.** 26, s.l. : The New England Journal of Medicine, 2013, Vol. 369.

53. Where is the wisdom? *British Medical Journal.* [Online] 5 October 1991. [Cited: 14 May 2015.] http://www.bmj.com/content/303/6806/798.

54. **Carey, J.** Medical Guesswork. *Bloomberg Business.* [Online] 2006. [Cited: 26 May 2015.] http://www.bloomberg.com/bw/stories/2006-05-28/medical-guesswork.

55. *Prevalence of irritable bowel syndrome: a community survey.* **Wilson S, Roberts L, Roalfe A, et al.** 504, s.l. : British Journal of General Practice , 2004, Vol. 54.

56. *Health-related quality of life and cost impact of irritable bowel syndrome in a UK primary care setting.* **Akelhurst RL, Brazier JE, Mathers N, O'Keefe C, Kaltenthaler E, Morgan A, Platts M, Walters SJ.** s.l. : Pharmacoeconomics, 2002, Vol. 20.

57. *Health-related quality of life among persons with irritable bowel syndrome: a systematic review.* **El-Serag HB, Olden K,**

Citations

Bjorkman D. s.l. : Alimentary Pharmacology & Therapeutics, 2002, Vol. 16.

58. *The impact of irritable bowel syndrome on health-related quality of life.* **Gralnek IM, Hays RD, Kilbourne A, Naliboff B, Mayer EA.** s.l. : Gastroenterology , 2000, Vol. 119.

59. *The prevalence, patterns and impact of irritable bowel syndrome: an international survey of 40,000 subjects.* **Hungin AP, Whorwell PJ, Tack J, Mearin F.** s.l. : Aliment Pharmacol Ther, 2003, Vol. 17.

60. *Unemployment and disability in patients with moderately to severely active Crohn's disease.* **Feagan BG, Bala M, Yan S, Olson A, Hanauer S.** s.l. : Journal of Clinical Gastroenterology, 2005, Vol. 39.

61. *Impairment of health-related quality of life in patients with inflammatory bowel disease.* **Casellas F, Arenas JI, Baudet JS, Fábregas S, García N, Gelabert J, Medina C, Ochotorena I, Papo M, Rodrigo L, Malagelada JR.** s.l. : Inflammatory Bowel Disease, 2005, Vol. 11.

62. *Impact of ulcerative colitis from patients' and physicians' perspectives: Results from the UC: NORMAL survey.* **Rubin DT, Siegel CA, Kane SV, et al.** s.l. : Inflammatory Bowel Disease, 2009, Vol. 15.

63. *A review of the Clinical Economics of Irritable Bowel Syndrome.* **Hahn, BA.** s.l. : Annals of Gastroenterology, 2002, Vol. 15.

64. *Epidermiology and Natural History of Inflammatory Bowel Diseases.* **Cosnes J, Gower-Rousseau C, Seksik P, Cortot A.** s.l. : Gastroenterology , 2011, Vol. 140.

65. **National Institute for Health and Care Excellence (NICE).** Depression in Adults with a Chronic Physical Health Problem; Treatment and Management. [Online] 2009. [Cited: 15 November 2014.] http://www.nice.org.uk/CG91.

66. **NHS.** Depression. *NHS Choices.* [Online] [Cited: 15 November   2014.] http://www.nhs.uk/Conditions/Depression/Pages/Introduction.aspx.

67. *Mental health and long term conditions : Managing depression .* **Nash M, McDermott J.** s.l. : Nursing Times, 2011, Vols. Jun 28-Jul 4.

68. **Kendrick T, Chantal S.** Depression in Primary Care. *InnovAiT.* [Online] Sage Journals, 2008. [Cited: 15 November 2014.] http://rcgp-innovait.oxfordjournals.org/content/1/3/187.full.

69. *Recognition of depression in medical patients with heart failure.* **Koenig, HG.** s.l. : Psychosomatics, 2007, Vol. 48.

70. **Coalition.** Twice as Likely: Putting long term conditions and depression on the agenda. *British Heart Foundation.* [Online] [Cited: 15 November 2014.] http://www.bhf.org.uk/pdf/Twice%20as%20likely%2023.04.12.pdf.

71. *The management of patients with physical and psychological problems in primary care: a practical guide .* s.l. : The Royal College of Psychiatrists , 2009, CR152 .

72. *Healing in NHS Hospitals.* 2, s.l. : Journal of Holistic Healthcare, 2010, Vol. 7.

73. *Touch therapies for pain relief in adults.* **So PS, Jiang Y, Qin Y.** s.l. : Cochrane Database Systematic Review , 2008 , Vol. 4.

74. *The effects of therapeutic touch on patients with osteoarthritis of the knee.* **Gordon A, Merenstein JH, D'Amico F, Hudgens D.** s.l. : TheJournal of Family Practice, 1998, Vol. 47.

75. *The effect of therapeutic touch on pain and anxiety in burn patients.* **Turner JG, Clark AJ, Gauthier DK, Williams M.** 1, s.l. : Journal of Advanced Nursing, 1998, Vol. 28.

76. *Review of studies of healing touch.* **Wardell DW, Weymouth KF.** 2, s.l. : Journal of Nursing Scholarship, 2004, Vol. 36.

77. *The experience of spiritual healing for women with breast cancer.* **Barlow FV, Biley F, Walker J, Lewith G.** s.l. : Journal of Complementary Therapies in Medicine, 2010, Vol. 18.

78. **Hodges, RD.** A Review of the Scientific Evidence Supporting the Reality of Spiritual Healing. *The Healing Trust.* [Online] [Cited: 18 June 2015.] http://www.thehealingtrust.org.uk/node/134.

79. *A psychokinetic effect of neurotransmitter metabolism: Alterations in the degradative enzyme monoamine oxidase.* **Rein, G.** s.l. : Research in Parapsychology; Scarecrow, Metuchen, NJ, 1986.

80. *Experiments with Matthew Manning.* **Braud W, Davis G, Wood R.** s.l. : Journal of the Society for Psychical Research, 1979, Vol. 50.

Citations

81. *Psychokinetic effects on yeast: An exploratory experiment.* **Haraldsson E, Thorsteinsson T.** s.l. : Research in Parapsychology; Scarecrow Press, Metuchen, NJ, 1973.

82. *Exploration of long-distance PK: A conceptual replication of the influence on a biological system.* **Tedder WH, Monty ML.** s.l. : Research in Parapsychology; Scarecrow Press, Metuchen, NJ, 1981, Vols. 1980 (Roll WG et al, eds) pp 90-93.

83. *Demonstration of a healing effect in the laboratory using a simple plant model.* **Scofield AM, Hodges RD.** s.l. : Journal of the Society for Psychical Research, 1991, Vol. 57.

84. *Some biological effects of laying-on of hands: a review of experiments with animals and plants.* **Grad, BR.** s.l. : Journal of the American Society for Psychical Research, 1965, Vol. 59.

85. *The effect of alternative healing therapy on the regeneration rate of salamander forelimbs.* **Wirth DP, Johnson CA, Horvath JS, Macgregor JA.** s.l. : Journal of Scientific Exploration, 1992, Vol. 6.

86. *Psychokinesis in experimental tumorgenesis.* **Onetto B, Elguin GH.** s.l. : Journal of Parapsychology, 1966, Vol. 30.

87. *Possible PK influence on the resuscitation of anesthetized mice.* **Watkins GK, Watkins AM.** 4, s.l. : Journal of Parapsychology, 1971, Vol. 35.

88. *A replication of a "psychic healing" paradigm.* **Wells R, Klein J.** s.l. : Journal of Parapsychology, 1972, Vol. 36.

89. *Further studies on the resuscitation of anesthetized mice.* **Watkins GK, Watkins AM, Wells RA.** s.l. : Research in Parapsychology; Scarecrow Press, Metuchen, NJ, 1973, Vols. 1972 (Roll WG, Morris RL. Morris JD, eds.) pp 157-159.

90. *Linger effects in several PK experiments.* **Wells R, Watkins G.** s.l. : Research in Parapsychology; Scarecrow Press, Metuchen, NJ, 1975, Vols. 1974 (Morris JD, Roll WG, Morris RL, eds) pp 143-147.

91. *PK on living systems: Further studies with anesthetized mice.* **Schlitz, MJ.** s.l. : Presentation at Southeastern Regional Parapsychological Association, 1982. Reviewed in: Weiner DH (1982). Report of the 1982 SERPA Conference. Parapsychology, 1982.

Healing in a Hospital

92. *Therapeutic touch: The imprimatur of nursing.* **Krieger, D.** s.l. : American Journal of Nursing, 1975, Vol. 7.

93. *Reiki healing: A physiologic perspective.* **Wetzel, WS.** s.l. : Journal of Holistic Nursing, (1989)., Vol. 7.

94. *Unorthodox healing: the effect of non-contact therapeutic touch on the healing rate of full thickness dermal wounds.* **Wirth, DP.** s.l. : Research in Parapsychology, 1989, Vols. 1989 (Henkel L, Palmer J, eds) pp 47-52.

95. *Study on the effectiveness of remote mental healing.* **Miller, RN.** s.l. : Medical Hypotheses, 1982, Vol. 8.

96. *Effects of therapeutic touch on tension headache pain.* **Keller E, Bzdek VM.** s.l. : Nursing Research, 1986, Vol. 35.

97. *Effects of therapeutic touch on the anxiety level of hospitalized patients.* **Heidt, P.** s.l. : Nursing Research, 1981, Vol. 30.

98. *An Investigation of the Effect of Therapeutic Touch Without Physical Contact on State Anxiety of Hospitalized Cardiovascular Patients.* **Quinn, JF.** s.l. : Unpublished PhD thesis. New York University. Quoted by Benor (1993), 1982.

99. *The effect of complementary healing therapy on postoperative pain after surgical removal of impacted third molar teeth.* **Wirth DP, Brenlan DR, Levine RJ, Rodriguez CM.** s.l. : Complementary Therapies in Medicine, 1993, Vol. 1.

100. *Demonstration of a Healing Effect in the Laboratory using a Simple Plant Model.* **Scofield AM, PhD and Hodges RD, PhD.** s.l. : Journal of the Society for Psychical Research, 1991, Vols. Vol 57 (822), 321-343.

101. *Field Study of an Enhancement Effect on Lettuce Seeds: A Replication Study.* **Roney-Dougal SM, Solfvin J.** s.l. : Journal of Parapsychology, 2003, Vol. 67.

102. **Hodges RD, Scofield AM.** The Healing Effect: Complementary Medicine's Unifying Principle? *Positive Health Online.* [Online] [Cited: 15 May 2015.] http://www.positivehealth.com/article/healing/the-healing-effect-complementary-medicine-s-unifying-principle.

103. *Is Spiritual Healing a Valid and Effective Therapy?* **Hodges RD, Scofield AM.** s.l. : Journal of the Royal Society of Medicine, 1995, Vol. 88.

312

Citations

104. *Therapeutic Touch Stimulates the Proliferation of Human Cells in Culture.* **Gronowicz GA, Jhaveri A, Clarke LW, Aronow MS, Smith TH.** s.l. : The Journal of Alternative and Complementary Medicine, 2008, Vol. 14.

105. *Therapeutic Touch affects proliferation and bone formation of human osteoblasts in vitro.* **Jhaveri A, Wang Y, McCarthy MB, Gronowicz GA.** s.l. : Journal of Orthopaedic Research, 2008.

106. *The cell biology of energy medicine: a human osteoblast-based study on Therapeutic Touch.* **Gronowicz GA, Jhaveri A.** s.l. : Elements Magazine, 2006, Vol. 4.

107. *Therapeutic Touch affects osteoblast proliferation and bone formation in cell culture.* **Gronowicz, GA.** s.l. : Connection (Nurse Healers-Professional Associates International), 2007, Vol. 27.

108. *Hartford Courant.* [Online] [Cited: 16 November 2014.] http://articles.courant.com/2008-07-28/news/healingtouch0728.art_1_healing-touch-therapeutic-touch-therapies.

109. **Gronowicz, GA.** *University of Connecticut.* [Online] [Cited: 16 November 2014.] http://digitalcommons.uconn.edu/cgi/viewcontent.cgi?article=1166 &context=uchcgs_masters.

110. *A randomized controlled trial of spiritual healing in restricted neck movement.* **Gerard S, Smith BH, Simpson JA.** New York : Journal of Alternative & Complement Medecine, 2003, Vol. 9.

111. **Buxton-King, A.** *Wholistic Healing Research.* [Online] [Cited: 17 November 2014.] http://www.wholistichealingresearch.com.

112. *The efficacy of distant healing: a systematic review of randomised trials.* **Astin JA, Harkness E, Ernst E.** s.l. : Annals of Internal Medicine, 2000, Vol. 132.

113. *A methodology for the objective study of transpersonal imagery.* **Braud W, Schlitz M.** s.l. : Journal of Scientific Exploration, 1989, Vol. 3.

114. *Meta-analysis of the effects of therapeutic touch on anxiety symptoms.* **Warber SL, Gillespie BW, Kile GLM, Gorenflo D,**

Bolling SF. s.l.: Focus on Alternative and Complementary Therapies, 2000, Vol. 5.

115. *Evidence for Correlations Between Distant Intentionality and Brain Function in Recipients: A Functional Magnetic Resonance Imaging Analysis.* **Achterberg J, Cooke K, Richards T, Standish L, Kozak L, Lake J.** s.l.: The Journal of Alternative and Complementary Medicine, 2005, Vol. 11.

116. **Arom K, MacIntyre B.** *The Effect of Healing Touch on coronary artery bypass surgery patients.* Denver: Healing Touch International 6th Annual Conference, 2002.

117. *The effect of hands-on healing on enzyme activity.* **Bunnell, T.** s.l.: Research in Complementary Medicine, 1996, Vol. 3.

118. *The effect of healing on peak expiratory flow rates in asthmatics.* **Bunnell, T.** s.l.: Subtle Energies, 2002, Vol. 13.

119. *Extraordinary healing using Resonance Modulation distance energy healing in T6 spinal paraplegia.* **Connor M, et al.** Colorado Springs: Poster session, ISSSEEM meeting, 2004.

120. *Measuring effects of music, noise and healing energy using a seed germination bioassay.* **Creath K, Schwartz GE.** s.l.: The Journal of Alternative & Complementary Medicine, 2004, Vol. 10.

121. Uniqueness of the Mind Mirrors. *Mind Mirror EEG.* [Online] [Cited: 15 November 2015.] http://www.mindmirroreeg.com/w/equipment/mm3/unique.htm.

122. *Compassionate intention as a therapeutic intervention by partners of cancer patients: effects of distant intention on the patients' autonomic nervous system.* **Radin D, Stone J, Levine E, Eskandarnejad S, Schlitz M, Kozak L, Mandel D, Hayssen G.** New York: Explore, 2008, Vol. 4.

123. **Penman, D.** *Mail OnLine.* [Online] [Cited: 21 November 2014.] http://www.dailymail.co.uk/health/article-408280/Could-spiritual-healing-actually-work.html#ixzz3JhKBM1a7.

124. How Dr Hew Len healed a ward of mentally ill criminals with Ho'oponopono. *HubPages.* [Online] [Cited: 16 November 2015.] http://hubpages.com/religion-philosophy/How-Dr-Hew-Len-healed-a-ward-of-mentally-ill-criminals-with-Hooponopono.

125. How Quantum Entanglement Works (Infographic). *Live Science.* [Online] [Cited: 2 September 2015.]

Citations

http://www.livescience.com/28550-how-quantum-entanglement-works-infographic.html.

126. **Heisenberg, W.** *Physics and Beyond.* New York : Harper and Row, 1971.

127. **Feynman, RP.** *The Character of Physical Law.* s.l. : Penguin Press Science, 1992.

128. **Gribbin, J.** *In Search of Schrodinger's Cat: Quantum Physics and Reality.* 1984. ISBN 978-0553341034.

129. **Wright, Peter.** *Spy Catcher; The Candid Autobiography of a Senior Intelligence Officer.* s.l. : Viking Penguin Inc, 1987. ISBN 0-670-82055-5.

130. *Electro-membrane microcurrent therapy reduces signs and symptoms of muscle damage.* **Lambert MI, Marcus P, Burgess T.** s.l. : Medicine & Science in Sports & Exercise, 2002, Vol. 34.

131. *Accelerated healing of skin ulcer by electrotherapy: preliminary clinical results.* **Wolcott LE, Wheeler PC, Hardwicke HM and Rowley BA.** s.l. : Southern Medical Journal, 1969, Vol. 62 (7).

132. *Two Meta-Analyses of Non-Contact Healing Studies.* **Roe CA, Sonnex C, Roxburgh EC.** s.l. : EXPLORE: The Journal of Science and Healing, 2015, Vol. 11.

133. *Why we need a new model for 21st century healthcare.* **Peters, D.** s.l. : The Journal of Holistic Healthcare, 2005, Vol. 2.

134. **Patton, M.** *Qualitative evaluation and research method.* Newbury Park, CA : Sage Publications, 1990.

135. Centre for Academic Primary Care. *University of Bristol.* [Online] [Cited: 2 December 2014.] http://www.bris.ac.uk/primaryhealthcare/resources/mymop/general-information/.

136. **Miller FG, Colloca L, Crouh RA, Kaptchuk TJ.** *The Placebo; A Reader.* s.l. : The Johns Hopkins University Press, 2013. ISBN 987-1-4214-0866-8.

137. *The Powerful Placebo.* **Beecher, HK.** s.l. : The Journal of the American Medical Association, 1955.

138. *The powerful placebo effect: fact or fiction?* **Kienle GS, Kiene H.** s.l. : Journal of Clinical Epidemiology, 1997, Vol. 50.

Healing in a Hospital

139. *Is the Placebo Powerless? An Analysis of Clinical Trials Comparing Placebo with No Treatment.* **Hróbjartsson A, Gøtzsche PC.** s.l. : The New England Journal of Medicine, 2001, Vol. 344.

140. Fabrizio Benedetti. [Online] [Cited: 12 October 2016.] https://en.wikipedia.org/wiki/Fabrizio_Benedetti.

141. *Components of placebo effect: randomised controlled trial in patients with irritable bowel syndrome.* **Kaptchuk TJ, Kelley JM, Conboy LA, et al.** s.l. : British Medical Journal, 2008, Vol. 336.

142. Acupuncture. *University of Maryland Medical Center.* [Online] [Cited: 2 June 2015.] http://umm.edu/health/medical/altmed/treatment/acupuncture.

143. **Feinberg, C.** The Placebo Phenomenon. *The Harvard Magazine.* [Online] [Cited: 22 June 2015.] http://harvardmagazine.com/2013/01/the-placebo-phenomenon.

144. *The Placebo Effect in Alternative Medicine: Can the Performance of a Healing Ritual Have Clinical Significance?* **Kaptchuk, TJ.** s.l. : Annals of Internal Medicine, 2002, Vol. 136.

145. *Predicting Individual Differences in Placebo Analgesia: Contributions of Brain Activity during Anticipation and Pain Experience.* **Wager TD, Atlas LY, Leotti LA, Rilling JK.** s.l. : The Journal of Neuroscience, 2011, Vol. 31(2).

146. **Prescott, B.** The Placebome? *Harvard Medical School.* [Online] [Cited: 15 June 2015.] http://hms.harvard.edu/news/placebome.

147. **Brownstein, J.** 11 Surprising Facts About Placebos. *LiveScience.* [Online] [Cited: 22 June 2015.] http://www.livescience.com/37073-surprising-facts-placebo-effect.html.

148. *Initial Severity and Antidepressant Benefits: A Meta-Analysis of Data Submitted to the Food and Drug Administration.* **Kirsch I, Deacon BJ, Huedo-Medina TB, Scoboria A, Moore TJ, Johnson BT.** s.l. : PLOS Medicine, 2008, Vol. 5.

149. *Placebo response in randomized controlled trials of antidepressants for pediatric major depressive disorder.* **Bridge JA, Birmaher B, Iyengar S, Barbe RP, Brent DA.** s.l. : American Journal of Psychiatry, 2009, Vol. 166.

Citations

150. Richard Dawkins interviews Prof. Nicholas Humphrey (Enemies of Reason Uncut Interviews). *YouTube.* [Online] 4 May 2013. [Cited: 12 October 2016.] https://www.youtube.com/watch?v=t3Z1SodN42o.

151. *Comparative efficacy and tolerability of antidepressants for major depressive disorder in children and adolescents: a network meta-analysis.* **Ciprianin A, Zhou X, et al.** 10047, s.l. : The Lancet, 2016, Vol. 338.

152. *Trends and patterns of antidepressant use in children and adolescents from five western countries, 2005–2012.* **Bachmann CJ, Aagaard L, Burcu M, et al.** 3, s.l. : European Neuropsychopharmacology, 2016, Vol. 26.

153. *A pragmatic randomised controlled trial of healing therapy in a gastroenterology outpatient setting.* **Lee RT, Kingstone T, Roberts L, Edwards S, Soundy A, Shah PR, Haque MS, Singh S.** s.l. : European Journal of Integrative Medicine, 2016, Vol. 11.017.

154. **Jevsevar, DS.** The Importance of Clinical Significance in AAOS CPGs. *American Academy of Orthopaedic Surgeons.* [Online] [Cited: 26 July 2015.] http://www.aaos.org/news/aaosnow/may13/research2.asp.

155. **Altman, DG.** *Practical Statistics for Medical Research.* s.l. : Chapman & Hall, 1991, p. 168.

156. MYMOP Frequently Asked Questions. *University of Bristol.* [Online] [Cited: 30 June 2015.] http://www.bristol.ac.uk/primaryhealthcare/resources/mymop/faq/.

157. *Characterization of health related quality of life (HRQOL) for patients with functional bowel disorder (FBD) and its response to treatment.* **Drossman D, Morris CB, Hu Y, Toner BB, Diamant N, Whitehead WE, Dalton CB, Leserman J, Patrick DL, Bangdiwala SI.** s.l. : American Journal of Gastroenterology, 2007, Vol. 102.

158. *What is an effect size? University of Oxford; Centre for Evidence Based Intervention.* [Online] [Cited: 24 June 2015.] http://www.cebi.ox.ac.uk/for-practitioners/what-is-good-evidence/what-is-an-effect-size.html.

159. *Measuring Clinically Meaningful Change Following Mental Health Treatment.* **Eisen SV, Ranganathan G, Seal P,**

Spiro A. s.l. : The Journal of Behavioral Health Services & Research, 2007, Vol. 34.

160. *Effect sizes for interpreting changes in health status.* **Kazis, LE, Anderson, JJ and Meenan, RF.** s.l. : Medical Care, 1989, Vol. 27.

161. *Patient defined dichotomous end points for remission and clinical improvement in ulcerative colitis.* **Higgins PDR, Schwartz M, Mapili J, Krokos I, Leung J, Zimmermann EM.** s.l. : BMJ Gut, 2005, Vol. 54.

162. **Targan, SR, Shanahan, F and Karp, LC.** *Inflammatory Bowel Disease: Translating Basic Science into Clinical Practice.* s.l. : Wiley-Blackwell, 2011. ISBN 978-1-4443-5911-4.

163. Crohn's Disease Activity Index. *Wikipedia.* [Online] [Cited: 7 November 2015.] https://en.wikipedia.org/wiki/Crohn%27s_Disease_Activity_Index.

164. Irritable bowel syndrome (IBS) - Causes. *NHS Choices.* [Online] [Cited: 29 October 2014.] http://www.nhs.uk/Conditions/Irritable-bowel-syndrome/Pages/Causes.aspx.

165. IBS and Non-GI Functional Disorders. *International Foundation for Gastro Intestinal Disorders.* [Online] [Cited: 26 January 2016.] http://www.aboutibs.org/site/what-is-ibs/other-disorders/non-gi-functional-disorders#table1.

166. *SERVQUAL: A Multiple-Item Scale for Measuring Consumer Perceptions of Service Quality.* **Parasuraman A, Zeithaml VA, Berry LL.** s.l. : Journal of Retailing, 1988, Vol. 64.

167. *Experiences of healing therapy in patients with irritable bowel syndrome and inflammatory bowel disease.* **Soundy A, Lee R, Kingstone T, Singh S, Shah PR, Edwards S, Roberts L.** s.l. : BioMed Central, 2015, Vol. 15.

168. **Cohen L, Manion L.** *Research Methods in Education.* s.l. : Routledge, 2000.

169. *Cost of illness of inflammatory bowel disease in the UK: a single centre retrospective study.* **Bassi A, Dodd S, Williamson P, Bodger K.** 10, s.l. : Gut, 2004, Vol. 53.

170. *Evaluation of healing by gentle touch.* **Weze C, Leathard HL, Grange J, Tiplady P, Stevens G.** s.l. : Journal of the Royal Institute of Public Health, 2004.

Citations

171. *Evaluation of healing by gentle touch in 35 clients with cancer.* **Weze C, Leathard HL, Grange J, Tiplady P, Stevens G.** s.l. : European Journal of Oncology Nursing, 2003.

172. *Healing by Gentle Touch Ameliorates Stress and Other Symptoms in People Suffering with Mental Health Disorders or Psychological Stress.* **Weze C, Leathard HL, Grange J, Tiplady P, Stevens G.** s.l. : Evidence-Based Complementary and Alternative Medicine, 2006.

173. *Long-term effects of energetic healing on symptoms of psychological depression and self-perceived stress.* **Shore, AG.** 4, s.l. : Alternative Therapies in Health and Medicine, 2004, Vol. 10.

174. *The effectiveness of therapeutic touch on pain, depression and sleep in patients with chronic pain: clinical trial.* **Marta IE, Baldan SS, Berton AF, Pavam M, da Silva MJ.** s.l. : Journal of the Nursing School of the University of Sao Paulo, 2010, Vol. 44.

175. *Review of Studies of Healing Touch.* **Wardell DW, Weymouth KF.** 2, s.l. : Journal of Nursing Scholarship, 2004, Vol. 36.

176. Does All Disease Really Begin in The Gut? The Surprising Truth. *Authority Nutrition: An Evidence-Based Approach.* [Online] [Cited: 24 October 2015.] http://authoritynutrition.com/does-all-disease-begin-in-the-gut/.

177. *Involvement of gut microbiota in the development of low-grade inflammation and type 2 diabetes associated with obesity.* **Cani PD, Osto M, Geurts L, Everard A.** s.l. : Gut Microbes, 2012, Vol. 3.

178. *Gut Microbiota, Intestinal Permeability, Obesity-Induced Inflammation, and Liver Injury.* **Frazier TH, DiBaise JK, McClain CJ.** s.l. : Journal of Parenteral and Enteral Nutrition, 2011, Vol. 35.

179. *Chronic exposure to Low dose bacterial lipopolysaccharide inhibits leptin signaling in vagal afferent neurons.* **de la Serre CB, de Lartigue G, Raybould HE.** s.l. : Physiology & Behavior, 2015, Vol. 139.

180. *The Gut-Brain Axis: The Missing Link in Depression.* **Evrensel, A and Ceylan, ME.** 3, s.l. : Clinical Psychopharmacology and Neuroscience, 2015, Vol. 13.

181. **Lambert, MJ.** Books and Articles on General and Comparative Counselling and Psychotherapy Research. *Counselling*

Books. [Online] 1992. [Cited: 19 June 2015.] http://counsellingbooks.com/bibliography/theory-and-research/general-and-comparative.html#Lambert_1992.

182. *Meditation experience is associated with increased cortical thickness.* **Lazara SW, Kerr CE, Wasserman RH, Gray JR, Greve DN, Treadway MT, McGarvey M, Quinn BT, Dusek JA, Benson H, Rauch SL, Moore CI, Fischl B.** s.l. : NeuroReport, 2005, Vol. 16.

183. *Happy People Live Longer: Subjective Wellbeing Contributes to Health and Longevity.* **Diener E, Chan MY.** s.l. : Applied Psychology: Health and Wellbeing, 2011, Vol. 3.

184. About Dr W H Bates. *Visions of Joy.* [Online] [Cited: 13 October 2015.] http://www.visionsofjoy.org/AboutBates.htm.

185. **Smallwood, C.** The role of complementary and alternative medicine in the NHS: An investigation into the potential contribution of mainstream complementary therapies to healthcare in the UK. *Get Well UK.* [Online] (2005). [Cited: 29 October 2014.] http://www.getwelluk.com/uploadedFiles/Publications/Smallwood.

186. *Does therapeutic touch help reduce pain and anxiety in patient's with cancer?* **Jackson E, McNeil P, Schlegel L.** s.l. : Clinical Journal of Oncology Nursing, 2008, Vol. 12.

187. *MORI Poll.* s.l. : The Times, 13 November 1989.

188. **Thomas K, Coleman P.** Use of complementary or alternative medicine in a general population in Great Britain: Results from the National Omnibus survey. s.l. : Journal of Public Health (Oxf) , 2004. Vol. 26, 2.

189. *Use of non-orthodox and conventional health care in Great Britain.* **Thomas KJ, Carr J, Westlake L, Williams BT.** s.l. : British Medical Journal, 1991, Vol. 302(6770).

190. NICE technology appraisal guidance. *National Institute for Health and Care Excellence.* [Online] [Cited: 4 June 2015.] https://www.nice.org.uk/about/what-we-do/our-programmes/nice-guidance/nice-technology-appraisal-guidance.

191. **Jackson, E.** *Law and the Regulation of Medicines.* s.l. : Bloomsbury, 2012. ISBN: 9781849461795.

192. YouTube. *Michael Flatley speaks about Bio-Energy on Piers Morgan's Life Stories.* [Online] [Cited: 31 August 2015.] https://www.youtube.com/watch?v=McoSiK3T9hs.

Citations

193. **Levin, J.** *God, Faith & Health.* s.l. : http://religionandhealth.com/books/god-faith-and-health/.

194. *Clinical applications of the relaxation response and mind-body interventions.* **Jacobs, GD.** s.l. : Journal of Alternative & Complementary Medecine, 2001, Vol. 7.

195. **Lovallo, WR.** *Stress & Health; Biological and Psychological Interactions.* s.l. : Sage Publications, 2005. ISBN 1412904781.

196. **Landau, MD.** Energy Healed Me — Over the Phone! A Scientist Explains How. *Huffington Post.* [Online] 19 October 2011. [Cited: 9 October 2016.] http:www.huffingtonpost.com/meryl-davids-landau/healing-over-the-phone_b_1011510.html.

197. The Telegraph. [Online] [Cited: 25 November 2014.] http://www.telegraph.co.uk/news/obituaries/1346621/Denis-Haviland.html.

198. *Demonstration of a Healing Effect in the Laboratory using a Simple Plant Model.* **Scofield AM, Hodges RD.** s.l. : Journal of the Society for Psychical Research, 1991, Vol. 57.

199. **Lipton, BH.** *The Biology of Belief.* 2011. ISBN 9781781805473.

200. **Buchanan, S.** *The Portable Plato.* s.l. : Penguin, 1977. ISBN 978-1-101-12749-0.

Healing in a Hospital